HOUGHTON BOOKS IN LITERATURE

KENNETH S. LYNN · ADVISORY EDITOR

DESIGNS FOR READING

- ○ Plays
- ○ Poems
- ● Short Stories
- ○ Nonfiction Prose

THE RANGE OF LITERATURE

- ○ Drama
- ○ Poetry
- ○ Fiction
- ○ Nonfiction Prose

DESIGNS FOR READING:

Short Stories

JANE EKLUND BALL

HOUGHTON MIFFLIN COMPANY · BOSTON

ATLANTA DALLAS GENEVA, ILLINOIS HOPEWELL, NEW JERSEY PALO ALTO

ABOUT THE AUTHOR AND EDITOR

Jane Eklund Ball, novelist and teacher of English at William Howard Taft High School in Los Angeles, has participated in NDEA and Los Angeles City Schools workshops on materials developed by the Project English curriculum centers.

Kenneth S. Lynn, advisory editor for the Houghton Books in Literature, is an authority in American literature. The author of *Mark Twain and Southwestern Humor* and *The Dream of Success: A Study of the Modern American Imagination,* he is also preëminent for his editing of classic American writers. Dr. Lynn is now a professor at the Johns Hopkins University.

Printed in the U.S.A.

CONTENTS

1 What is required to survive hardship and danger?

Early Marriage

CONRAD RICHTER

For two days the leathery face of Asa Putman had been a document in cipher to anyone who could read the code. Since Saturday but one traveler had passed his solitary post, a speck of adobe and picket corrals lost on the vast, sandy stretch of the Santa Ana plain. Far as the eye could see from his doorway, the rutted El Paso trail, unfenced, gutterless, innocent of grading, gravel, culverts, or telephone poles, imprinted only by iron tires, the hoofs of horses and oxen, sheep and cattle, and the paw of the loping lobo wolf, lay with dust unraised.

Ordinarily, there were freighters with cracking whips and trailers rumbling on behind. Army trains to and from the forts set up their tents for the night beyond the springs. The private coaches of Santa Fe and Colorado merchants, of cattle kings and Government officials, stopped long enough for the Putman children to admire the ladies, the magnificent woodwork, and the luxurious cushions inside. Trail herds of gaunt red steers bawled for the water in the earthen tank, and pairs and companies of horsemen rode up and down.

But since Saturday not even a solitary buckboard from the far settlements in the Cedar country had called for supplies or letters. Only a girl from the Blue Mesa had ridden in for her and her neighbors' mail. She had eaten dinner with the Putmans, refused to stay overnight and started her long ride home.

A stranger from the East would have spoken about the stillness, the deadly waiting, and asked uneasily why Uncle Gideon hadn't come as promised. But in the Putman household it was not mentioned.

Asa deliberately busied himself about the post, filling the bin beneath the counter with navy beans and green coffee, leafing through the packet of letters in the drawer, and making a long rite out of feeding the occupants of the picket corrals — four horses of which were fresh for the next stage.

Rife, just turned fifteen, carried water and gathered cow chips[1] in an old hide dragged by a rope to his saddle horn. Ignacita, the Mexican housekeeper, spat sharply on her heavy irons in the torrid kitchen and kept glancing over her shoulder and out of the open door and windows.

And Nancy Belle, going on seventeen, packed and repacked the high, iron-bound trunk that her father had bought for her at Santa Fe and sang softly to herself in the way that women sang fifty and sixty years ago.

Saturday she was being married at Gunstock, two hundred miles away — five days' journey in a wagon, four in a saddle or buckboard.

For six months she had thought of little else. The almanac fell apart at June as naturally as her mother's Bible did at the Twenty-third Psalm. So often had she run her finger down that page that anyone might tell from the worn line of type the very day she and Stephen Dewee would be man and wife. The Dewees lived four hundred miles west across the territory in the Beaverhead country. She and Stephen were taking a mountain ranch near his people, and for the wedding they had compromised on Gunstock, nearly equidistant from both families and convenient to friends scattered up and down the Rio Grande.

She had lighted a candle in the dusk, when a figure appeared reluctantly in her doorway. Asa Putman had never been at ease in his daughter's bedroom. A tall, rawhide man in an unbuttoned, sagging vest, he was visibly embarrassed by any furnishings that suggested refinement. Invariably he kept his hat on in the house. He had it on now, a flat top and a flat brim, not so much like the Western hats you see now. Nancy Belle knew that her mother's people had never forgiven him for bringing his young wife and

[1] **cow chips:** dried dung, used as fuel.

their two small children to this lonely post, at the mercy of outlaws and the worse Apaches.

Tonight she could see that something bothered him. He gave her a sidewise glance, so sharp and characteristic.

"I don't expect, Nancy Belle, you could put off your weddin'?"

The girl stood quietly gazing at him with a face like the tintype[2] of her mother. But under her sedate gray dress, with tight waist and full skirts to the instep, she had frozen. She looked much older than her years. Her air of gentlefolk and her wide-apart gray eyes came from her mother. But the chin, tipped up with resolute fearlessness, was her father's.

"No, papa!" Her two clear words held all the steady insistence of the desert.

"I figured how you'd feel," he nodded, avoiding her eyes. "I just wanted to put it up to you. I'd 'a' covered the *jornada*[3] on foot to be on time at my own weddin', but I didn't have to count on Gideon to hold me up."

"Are you telling me, papa, that you can't go to Gunstock tomorrow?" Her voice remained quiet, but a coldness had seized her. Of all the people she had visualized at her wedding, the one next to Stephen she could least spare was the tall, grave figure of her father.

"I reckon I kind of can't, Nancy Belle," he said soberly. "Rife could tend to the stage all right and do the feedin'. But they's men come to this post no boy can handle." He shifted his position. "I figured once on closin' up the post till I got back. But the stage is comin' and the mail. And the freighters count on me for feed and grub. Then I got to protect my own property and the mail and freight for the Cedar country that's in the storage room."

"I know," Nancy Belle said steadily. "I can get to Gunstock all right."

Far back in her father's assaying eyes, she fancied she saw a glint of pride.

"You're pretty nigh a woman now, Nancy Belle. And Rife's a good slice of a man. It's a straight trail to the Rio Grande, once you turn at the old post. Both you and Rife's been over it

[2] **tintype:** photograph taken on an iron plate.

[3] ***jornada:*** a long expanse of desert, as might be covered in a journey of one or more days.

before. Of course, I'd like to be at the weddin', but the boy can tell me about it." He went to the window. "Rife!" he called.

Nancy Belle's brother came in presently. A slight boy, with his father's blue eyes, he seldom made a fuss over anything, even when he shot a stray duck on the tank or when they braked down the last cedar hill into Santa Fe with all the open doors of the plaza shops in sight. And when his father told him now, he showed neither enthusiasm nor regret — merely straightened.

"Sure. I can take you, Nancy Belle," he said.

Something pulled under his sister's tight basque.[4] She remembered the long miles they would have in the wagon, the camps at lonely places, the ugly shadow ever hovering over the outposts of this frontier country, and the blight that, since Saturday, seemed to have fallen on the trail. Her eyes swam. Now, at the last minute, she yielded.

"If you'll let me ride, papa, I'll wait another day for Uncle Gideon," she promised.

Her father's eyes moved to the ruffled red calico curtains at the shadeless windows.

"I don't hardly count on Gideon comin' any more, Nancy Belle. Besides, it's too long in the saddle to Gunstock — especially for a girl to get married. You'd be plumb wore out, and you wouldn't have your trunk. You couldn't get dressed for your weddin'."

He turned thoughtfully and went out, Rife close behind. Nancy Belle could hear her father's tones, slow and grave, coming from near one of the picket corrals.

It was too far to catch the words; but when they came in, she saw that her brother's features looked a little pale under the tan.

"You better get some sleep, Nancy Belle," her father said. "You and Rife are startin' before daylight. If Gideon comes, I'll ride after."

They had scarcely gone from the room when Ignacita came in from the kitchen, her black eyes glittering over a pile of freshly starched white in her arms.

"Nancy Belle, *chinita!*"[5] she whispered, plucking at the girl's sleeve. "You don't say to your *papacito*[6] I talk to you! I have

[4] **basque:** bodice.
[5] ***chinita:*** dear.
[6] ***papacito:*** daddy.

promise I don't scare you. But I can't see you go so far in the wildness alone, *pobrecita!*[7] Sometimes people go safe from one place to the other, oh, *sí!* But sometimes, *chinita,* they don't come back. You have not the oldness like Ignacita. Ay, I tell you these old eyes have seen men and women quartered from a tree like sheep or maybe tied over a stove like I don't have the words to say to you."

Nancy Belle did not answer except to lay, one by one, the ironed pieces in her trunk — a bride's muslin underwear trimmed with red and blue feather stitching; long petticoats stiffly flounced with ruffles, and nightgowns long in the sleeve and high in the neck, with ruffles at wrist and throat. The Mexican woman went on hoarsely. The girl folded away her winter's cashmere dress, buttoned up the front and with a white fichu.[8] She unwrapped and wrapped again in crumpled white tissue the red slippers the old gentleman on the stage had sent her as a wedding present from Philadelphia.

When Ignacita had left, she opened her keepsake box covered with colored shells. The mirror on the inside lid turned back a face as calm as the little golden clouds that hung of an evening over the east to catch the desert sunset. But after she had undressed and put on her nightdress, for a long time she was aware of the soft pound of her heart faintly swaying the bed on its rawhide springs.

At the first sound of Ignacita's hand on the kitchen stove, Nancy Belle sprang out of bed. She dressed on the brown pool of burro skin, the only carpet on her adobe floor. Through the west window she could see the morning star burning like a brilliant candle. It hung, she told herself, over Gunstock and the Beaverhead, where Stephen, at this moment, in their new log ranch house, lay thinking about her.

They ate in the kitchen by lamplight. She had never been so conscious of every detail — the great white cups and saucers, the familiar steel knives, the homey smell of the scorched paper lamp-shade, the unreadable eyes of her father, Rife, and Ignacita.

Asa Putman himself carried out the trunk. There was already hay in the wagon, a gunny sack of oats, food in a canned-tomato box and utensils in another, a water-keg, bed roll tied in a wagon sheet, an ax, a bridle, and her own side-saddle, made to order

[7] ***pobrecita:*** poor little thing.
[8] **fichu:** scarf worn around the shoulders and fastened in front.

over a man's tree.[9] Her eyes caught the gleam of a rifle leaning up against the seat in the lantern-light. Tethered to the rear of the wagon stood her saddle mare, Fancy, with pricked-up ears. She was going along to their new ranch home. Nancy Belle felt that she was still among intimate things, but outside the little circle of light lay darkness and the unknown.

When she said good-by to her father, he kissed her — something he had not done for years.

"You haven't changed your mind, Nancy Belle?" he asked.

She climbed quickly up over the wheel to the spring seat of the wagon before he might see that she was crying. Rife swung up like a monkey on the other side and pushed the rifle into the crevice behind the seat cushion. The lines tautened and the wagon lurched.

"*Dios*[10] go with you safe to your husband, Nancy Belle!" she heard Ignacita cry after her.

The morning star had set. They moved into a world of silent blackness. Nancy Belle could not see how the horses remained on the trail. When she looked back, the only light in all these square miles of black, unfriendly earth was the yellow window of her father's post.

It was almost a vision, golden and far away, like all beautiful things. She didn't trust herself to look again.

Two hours later the wagon was a lonely speck of boat rocking in an illimitable sage-green sea beneath the sun. The canvas wagon sheet fastened over the bows was a kind of sail, and eastward the sandy water did not stop rolling till it washed up at the foot of the faintly blue ramparts of the distant Espiritu Range.

Just before they turned west on the cross trail to the Rio Grande, a heavy wagon with a yoke of oxen in front and a cow behind toiled round the crumbling adobe walls of the old, abandoned post house. A bearded man and a thin woman with a white face sat on the seat. She held a baby in her arms, and three black-eyed children peered from under the wagon sheet.

The bearded man saluted and stopped his willing team. Rife did likewise. The woman spoke first. Her tongue was swift and slightly acid.

[9] **man's tree:** frame for making a man's saddle.
[10] ***Dios:*** God.

"You better turn around and follow us if you want to save your hair!" she called. "Yesterday a sheep-herder told us he saw — "

A sharp word from the bearded man caused her to relapse into sullen silence. He asked Rife where he might be going, then climbed down to the trail and said he wanted to talk to him a little. The boy followed reluctantly behind his wagon. Nancy Belle could hear the bearded man's tones coming slow and grave like her father's, while the woman made silent and horribly expressive lip language.

Rife came back, walking stiffly. The bearded man climbed up beside the woman.

"They got to go on," he told her in a low tone, then saluted with his whip. "Good luck, boy! And you, miss!"

Rife raised his whip in stiff acknowledgment. The wagons creaked apart. Nancy Belle saw in front of her the trail to the Rio Grande, little more than a pair of wheel tracks, that lost itself on the lonely plain. Rife seemed relieved that she did not ask what the bearded man had said. But it was enough for her not to be able to forget the woman's fearful signs and mouthings and the horror in the curious eyes of the staring children.

Sister and brother talked very little. Nancy Belle saw her brother's eyes keep sweeping the country, scanning the horizons. Bunches of bear grass that might have been feathers pinioned his blue gaze, and clumps of cane cactus that seemed to hold pointing gun barrels. At arroyos[11] thick with chamiso and Apache plume[12] she could see his feet tighten on the footboard. Once he pulled out the rifle, but it was only a herd of antelopes moving across the desert page.

They camped for the night when the sun was still high. Nancy Belle asked no questions as the boy drove far off the trail into a grassy cañada.[13] She sang softly to herself as she fried the salt side bacon and put the black coffee-pot to boil.

Rife hobbled Anton Chico and the Bar X horse and staked out Fancy close to the wagon.

She pretended not to notice when, before dark, he poured earth on the fire till not a spark or wisp of smoke remained.

[11] **arroyos:** gullies formed by running water.
[12] **chamiso and Apache plume:** shrubs growing together to form thickets.
[13] **cañada:** small canyon.

Out of one eye she watched him climb the side of the cañada and stand long minutes sweeping the country from the ridge, a slight, tense figure against the sullen glow of the sunset.

"It's all right," he said when he came down. "You can go to bed."

"What's all right?" she asked him.

"The horses," he said, turning away, and Nancy Belle felt a stab of pain that so soon this boy must bear a man's responsibilities and tell a man's lies.

She prayed silently on her blankets spread on the hay in the wagon box, and lay down with her head on the side-saddle, her unread Testament in her hand. She heard Rife unroll his camp bed on the ground beneath the wagon. It was all very strange and hushed without her father. Just to feel the Testament in her hand helped to calm her and to remember the day at the post when she had first met Stephen.

Her father had never let her come in contact with the men of the trail. Always, at the first sign of dust cloud on the horizon, he would tell both children to heap up the chip-box, fill the water-buckets and carry saddles and bridles into the house. But this day Asa Putman and Rife had gone to Fort Sumner. And to Nancy Belle, Uncle Gideon could seldom say no.

It had been a very hot day. She had been sitting in the shade of the earthen bank of the tank, moving her bare feet in the cool water, watching the ripples in the hot south wind. The leaves of the cottonwoods clashed overhead, and she heard nothing until she looked up, and there was a young man on a blue-gray horse with dust clinging to his hat brim and mustache. His eyes were direct as an eagle's. Firm lines modeled his lean face. But what she noticed most at the time was the little bow tie on his dark shirt.

Instantly she had tucked her bare, wet legs under her red dress. Her face burned with shame, but the young stranger talked to her about her father coolly, as if she, a girl of fifteen, had not been caught bare-footed. Then he did what in her mind was a noble thing. When Uncle Gideon came out, he magnificently turned his back for her to run into the house and pull on shoes and stockings.

She thought of Stephen constantly next day and the next. She had grown a little used to the journey without her father now — the still, uncertain nights under the wagon sheet, sitting, lying, listening, waiting; the less uncertain days with the sun on the endless spaces; her never-quiet perch on the high spring seat under the slanted bow; the bumps, creaks, and lumberings of the wagon; the sand sifting softly over the red, turning wheels; all afternoon the sun in their faces; ahead the far haze and heat waves in which were still lost Gunstock and the Rio Grande. Almost she had forgotten the bearded man with the oxen and the curious, detached horror in the eyes of his children.

Since morning of the third day their progress had been slower. The trail seemed level, except for the heavy breathing of the horses. But when Nancy Belle glanced back she could see the steady grade they had been climbing. Abruptly, in mid-afternoon, she found that the long, blue Espiritu Range had disappeared, vanished behind a high pine-clad hill which was its southernmost beginning. It was like the lizard that swallowed itself, a very real lizard. At this moment they were climbing over the lizard's tail.

"Cedars!" Rife said briefly, pointing with the whip to dark sprawling growths ahead.

"You breathe deep up here!" Nancy Belle drank in the light air.

Rife took a sniff, but his blue eyes never ceased to scan the high, black-thatched hill under whose frowning cliff they must pass.

"Soon we can see the Gunstock Mountains," Nancy Belle said.

"And Martin Cross's cabin," Rife nodded. "It's the last water to the Rio Grande."

"He's a nice old man," Nancy Belle ventured casually. "It would be nice to camp by his cabin tonight and talk."

The boy inclined his head. After a few moments he started to whistle softly. At the first cedar Nancy Belle leaped off the moving wagon and climbed back with an evergreen branch. The twig, crushed in her hand, smelled like some store in Santa Fe.

They gained the summit. A breeze was sweeping here from the southwest, and the horses freshened. But Rife had suddenly stopped whistling and Nancy Belle's sprig of cedar lay on her lap. The frowning cliff of the pine-clad hill was still there. But

Martin Cross's cabin had turned to a desolate mound of ashes. As they stared, a gust of wind sent wisps of smoke scurrying from the mound, and a red eye opened to watch them from the embers. Nancy Belle felt an uncontrollable twitching in the hair roots at the base of her scalp.

Where Martin Cross's eastbound wheel tracks met the trail, Rife reluctantly halted the horses and wet his air-dried lips.

"The water keg's dry, and the horses. If papa was here, he'd drive over."

"I'm the oldest." Nancy Belle found her voice steady. "I'll ride over. There might be something we can do."

The boy rose quickly. His eyes seemed to remember something his father had said.

"You can drive the wagon over if I wave."

He had thrown her the lines and slipped back through the canvas-covered tunnel of wagon box, picking up Fancy's bridle and the rifle. Barebacked he rode toward the smoldering ashes at the foot of that frowning hill. The chestnut mare's tail and mane streamed like something gold in the wind.

When she looked back to the trail, her eyes were pinioned by a light object in the wheel track ahead of the Bar X horse. It was a long gray feather. Instantly she told herself that it had come from some wild turkey Martin Cross had shot, and yet never had air anywhere become so suddenly horrible and choking as in this canyon.

Rife did not signal her to drive over. She saw him come riding back at full speed. The mare was snorting. As he stopped her at the wagon, her chestnut head kept turning back toward what had once been a cabin. Rife slipped the lead rope about her neck and climbed into the seat with the rifle in his hands.

"The water — you wouldn't want it!" he said thickly. His cheeks, she noticed, were the color of *yeso*.[14]

"Rife" — Nancy Belle touched his arm when she had driven down the canyon — "what did you see at the cabin?"

The boy sat deaf and rigid beside her, eyes staring straight ahead. She saw that his young hands were still tortured around the barrel of his rifle.

Far down on the pitch-dark mesa she stopped the horses in the trail and listened. There were no stars, not a sound but the flapping of the wagon sheet in the wind and the clank of coffee-

[14] ***yeso:*** plaster.

pot and water-bucket under the wagon. Half standing on the footboard, she guided the team off the trail in the intense blackness. Her swift hands helped the trembling boy stake out the mare and hobble the team. They did not light a lantern. Rife declined to eat. Nancy Belle chewed a few dry mouthfuls.

The wind came drawing out of the blackness with a great draft. It hissed through the grass, sucked and tore at the wagon sheet, and whistled through the spokes and brake rigging. Rife did not take his bed roll under the wagon tonight. He drew the ends of the wagon sheet together and lay down in the wagon box near his sister. For a long time they were silent. When she heard his heavy breathing, she lifted the rifle from his chest.

The storm grew. Sand began pelting against the canvas and sifted into the wagon box. An invisible cloud of choking dust found its way into eyes, mouth, ears, and lungs. Nancy Belle laid down the rifle a moment to pull a blanket over the face of the boy. He tossed and muttered pitifully, but he slept on.

Magically the rain, when it came, stopped the sand and dust. The girl drank in the clean-washed air. At daylight she slipped out to the ground. The mesa, stretching away in the early light, touched here and there with feathers of mist, would have been beautiful except for a sharp new loneliness. The horses were gone!

At her exclamation, Rife appeared from the wagon box. His shame at having slept through the night was quickly overshadowed by their misfortune.

Together they found where Fancy's stake had been pulled out and dragged. Yards farther on they could tell by Anton Chico's tracks that his hobbles had parted.

Nancy Belle made her brother come back to the wagon and stuff his pockets with cold biscuits and antelope jerky.[15] She said she would have a hot breakfast ready when he returned. The horses, perhaps, were just down in some draw where they had drifted with the wind.

When he had gone with the rifle, she filled the coffee-pot from a clearing waterhole in the nearest arroyo. She fried potatoes and onions in the long-handled skillet. And when he did not come, she set fresh biscuits in the Dutch oven. Each biscuit held a square of salt side bacon in its top, and as it baked, the fat oozed down and incased it in a kind of glazed tastiness.

[15] **jerky:** sun-dried strips of meat.

At noon she thought she heard a shot. Nowhere could she see him on the endless sweep of mesa. By late afternoon she was still alone. She read her Testament and wondered how many women over the world had read it in hours like this. Sitting in the shadow of the wagon, facing the direction in which he had gone, she looked up every few minutes. But all her eyes could find were cloud shadows racing across the lonely face of the mesa. All she could hear were the desolate cries from the unseen lark sparrows.

Darkness, stillness settled down on the empty land. She climbed back into the wagon and sat on the chuck-box, hands rigid on her knees. Again and again she convinced herself that the horses could not have been driven off or she would have seen the drivers' tracks. When wild, sharp barks shattered the stillness and set wires jerking in her limbs, she talked to herself steadily, but a little meaninglessly, of the post — on and on as the darkness was filled with the ringing and counter-ringing of shrill, cracked yappings — not long tones like a dog's, but incredibly short syllables rising, rising in a mad eternal scale and discord.

"I wish papa had given me two of the chairs," she repeated. "Mamma said they were post oak from Texas. She said they had got white from scrubbing. I liked the laced rawhide seats with the hair left on. It made them soft to sit on. The seats in the parlor were black. And the ones in the kitchen were red. But I liked the brockle[16] one in my room best."

The insane din around the wagon had become terrific. There were only two or three of the animals, Nancy Belle guessed, but they threw their voices and echoes together to make a score.

"When I was little I liked to go in the storage room," her voice went on, scarcely intelligible to her own ears. "It was dark and cool, and smelled of burlap and kerosene and whisky, and sweetish with brown sugar. I can see the fat sacks of green coffee. And the round tins of kerosene had boards on the side. The flour-sacks were printed: 'Rough and Ready' in red letters. Mamma once used to make our underwear out of the sacking. I can smell the salt side bacon in the gunny sacks."

She could tell from the sounds that one of the animals was running insanely back and forth near the wagon tongue. She had never noticed before that they yelped both when breathing

[16] **brockle:** black and white.

in and out. Suddenly came silence. It warned her. Instinctively she felt for the ax.

"Nancy Belle!" a boy's far, anxious voice called from the darkness.

She hallooed and leaned out over the tailboard. Three shadowy forms were coming across the mesa in the starlight. Never had horses looked so good.

"Were you scared?" Rife greeted. "Anything bother you?"

"Nothing," Nancy Belle said. "Just coyotes."

"I had to give Fancy her head after it got dark." He slid wearily to the ground. "She brought us straight back to the wagon."

Nancy Belle had wanted to put her arms around her brother. Now she hugged the mare instead. Rife ate fresh biscuits and a tin plate of cold potatoes. He drank several tin cups of coffee. Nancy Belle had slipped the oats-laden gunny-sack *morrals*[17] over the horses' heads.

"I had to walk halfway to the mountain," Rife said.

"Just help hitch up; then you can sleep all night," she promised.

It rained again heavily toward midnight. Flashes of lightning lit the drenched plain. For minutes at a time, quivering fingers of blue phosphorescence stood on the ears of the toiling horses. At dawn Nancy Belle still held the reins as the mud-splashed wagon crawled through a world bathed in early purple splendor.

Four days they had been crossing a hundred and seventy miles of desolate plain. Now the end waited in sight. To the west lay a land broken and tumbled by a mighty hand. Hill shouldered hill and range peered over range, all indescribably violet except where peaks tipped by the unseen sun were far-off flaming towers of copper.

It was a new land, her promised land, Stephen's land, Nancy Belle told herself, where nobody burned cow chips, but snapping cedar and pine, where cold water ran in the wooded canyons, and the eye, weary of one flat circle the horizon round, had endless geometric designs to refresh the retina.

She sang softly as the wagon lumbered to the edge of a long, shallow valley, brown and uninhabited, running north and south, and desolate except for a winding ribbon that was white with sky and narrowly bordered with green.

"Rife!" Nancy Belle cried. "The Rio Grande!"

[17] ***morrals:*** feed bags.

An hour afterwards they pulled out of the sun into the shade of the long cottonwood *bosque*.[18] Nancy Belle wasn't singing now. Where she remembered wide sandbars glistening with sky and tracked by waterfowl, a chocolate-red flood rolled. Where had been the island, tops of tule[19] and scrub willow swung to and fro with the current.

Anton Chico and the Bar X horse stopped of their own accord in the trail, ears pricked forward at the swirling brown wash. While Rife turned the three horses loose to graze, Nancy Belle silently fried bacon and made coffee. When she had washed skillet and tin dishes in the river, the boy had wired the wagon box to the brake rigging. Now he was tying securely one end of his rope to the center of the coupling pole under the wagon. The other end she knew he would fasten to the inadequate upper horn of the side-saddle.

"I wouldn't mind the river if I just had my own saddle," he mourned.

They hitched up the team silently. Rife cinched the side-saddle on Fancy and straddled it, the single stirrup useless to a man. Nancy Belle climbed into the wagon and picked up the lines. The other bank looked as far away as the Espiritu Range from the post. She wanted to say something to her brother — some last word, in case they didn't make it. But all she did was cluck her tongue to the horses.

Gingerly, one slow foot at a time, the team moved down the trail into the water.

"Give 'em their heads!" Rife called from the right rear.

Nancy Belle held a rein in each hand. The red channel water came to the wagon tongue, covered it, reached the horses' bellies. The team wanted to stop. Nancy Belle swung her whip, a stick tipped with a long rawhide lash. The wagon went on. The collars of both horses kept dipping, but never entirely out of sight. Still barely wading, the slow team reached the firmer footing of the island.

Two thirds of the river still rolled in front of the wagon. The west bank did not seem to have grown much closer, but the east bank behind them had moved far away. The team had to be whipped into the violent current. The water churned white

[18] ***bosque:*** grove.
[19] **tule:** bulrushes.

through the wagon wheels. Suddenly both horses appeared to stumble and drop out of sight. Their heads came up wildly, spray blowing from their nostrils. The muddy water hid their legs, but by their bobbing motions Nancy Belle knew that they were swimming.

"Keep 'em pointed up the river!" Rife shouted.

Already she felt the wagon floating. It swung downstream with the current; then Rife's rope from Fancy's saddle snubbed it. The team was snorting with every breath. The Bar X horse swam high in the water, his withers and part of his back out of the chocolate current. But all she could see of Anton Chico were his nose and ears.

Down between her ankles she saw water in the wagon box. She thought of the hem-stitched sheets at the bottom of her trunk, the towels and pillow-cases crocheted with shell lace. Her blue velvet corduroy dress was probably wet already, and all the cunning print aprons with dust caps to match. River water couldn't hurt the little yellow creamer, sugar bowl, and covered butter dish that had been her mother's. And the gingham dresses could be washed. What worried her were her wedding dress and the keepsake box, especially the tintypes, one of which was Rife in a child's suit edged with black braid, his brand-new hat on his knee.

An older Rife was shouting something behind her now. She couldn't catch the words. Then she found what it was. The neck and withers of Anton Chico raised suddenly out of the water and both horses were scrambling up the steep bank below the ford. Only quick work with the lines saved the wagon from turning over. Safe and blowing on the high bank, the dripping horses shook themselves like puppies.

Nancy Belle couldn't go on until she had opened the trunk and appraised the damage. Rife unsaddled Fancy and drove on with the refreshed team. Behind his slight back in the wagon box, the girl changed to her blue velvet corduroy, which was hardly wet at all. Then she combed her hair and rolled into a cranny of her trunk the old felt hat that had been too large for her father.

A half-dozen riders met the wagon some miles down the Gunstock Canyon. All of them, Nancy Belle noticed, carried guns. Stephen wore a new white shirt and a gray hat with curled brim she had not seen before. He stood in his stirrups and swung her down in front of him on the saddle, where he kissed her. She had never felt his lips press into such a straight line.

"Papa couldn't come," she said. "So Rife brought me."

She felt Stephen's rigid arm around her.

"We just got in from Beaverhead ourselves."

"He means they never get any news out in the Beaverhead or he'd 'a' come further east to meet you!" Uncle Billy Williams put in. He had a lovable, squeaky voice. "The Apaches been breakin' loose again. Funny you didn't hear anything over in your country."

Nancy Belle gave him an inscrutable look with her gray eyes. Uncle Billy pulled out his bandanna and blew his nose.

"They got my old friend Judge Hower and his wife and kid in a buggy on the Upper Espiritu. The man that found what they did to 'em, they say, cried like a baby."

"That's all right, Uncle Billy," Stephen said in a gentle voice.

Nancy Belle glanced at Rife. Her brother's face looked gray, the eyes staring as when he had ridden in the late afternoon sunlight from the smoking ashes of Martin Cross's cabin.

Nearly fifty people, gathered in the big parlor upstairs at the hotel, greeted Nancy Belle. An old man whose young black eyes twinkled out of a bearded face said he was glad to see she had her "hair on straight." Rife stopped with the trunk before driving to the livery, and Stephen's mother showed Nancy Belle to a room to dress.

The guests stopped talking when she came into the parlor in her white wedding dress. Her basque came to a point in the front and back. It fitted like a glove. The silk underskirt came to her instep, and the ruffled overskirt to her knees. She had parted her hair from side to side and brushed the bangs down on her forehead. She felt very light-headed. The wagon still seemed to be jerking under her.

She glimpsed Rife gazing at her, a rapt expression in his reticent blue eyes. She was glad to see that he had brushed his hair. The brass swinging lamp had been lighted and the dark woodwork of the parlor festooned with evergreen branches. White streamers from the wall met in a papier-mâché bell in one corner. She noticed two children peering eagerly from the dark hall.

Stephen came to her, very straight in a long coat and stand-up collar with a black tie. He led her up beneath the papier-mâché bell. In a sibilant, churchlike whisper, the Gunstock preacher made sure of her full name. Then he coughed and began the ceremony. He had a deep voice, but Nancy Belle didn't hear all of the service. Her mind kept going back to a tall, grave man in a lonely adobe post on the wide Santa Ana plain. And after she had said: "I do," her lips moved, but she was not praying for Stephen, her husband.

* * *

EXAMINING THE STORY

1. What was the "blight" that had fallen on the trail? Why wasn't the danger ever mentioned by the Putmans? Asa decides he cannot go to Gunstock; Nancy Belle that she will go without him: why? Do this father and daughter understand each other? this father and son? How does Asa feel about his children's journey? For whom is Nancy Belle praying at her wedding?
2. How does the meeting with the bearded man's wagon emphasize the danger already suggested? Do you think the news he brings is a surprise to Rife? Why doesn't Rife discuss it with Nancy Belle? Nancy Belle pretends not to notice, the first night, when Rife covers the fire before dark and leaves their sheltered canyon to survey the horizon. Why? Describe the code of conduct they are both practicing.
3. Why is the third day slower? Are Rife and Nancy Belle more exposed to danger then? In what ways does the storm lessen their peril? increase it? At times, Nancy Belle finds herself reliving the past — her meeting with Stephen, moments from her childhood. What purpose do these recollections serve for Nancy Belle? (Do they also serve another purpose in the story?)
4. On the fifth day they enter "her promised land, Stephen's land." In what ways is this land different? Why must the horses be kept pointing upriver? What fact of pioneer life is shown by Stephen's not coming further out from Gunstock to meet his bride?
5. **A Broader Perspective •** Rife and Nancy Belle, at fifteen and seventeen, exhibit the pioneer character that risked life to make a dream come true. What vision of a better future held Nancy Belle to her course? What qualities and skills do she and Rife show in meeting

hardships? in sustaining each other in the face of danger? How do these qualities and skills help them to survive? Does this story suggest to you ways in which the pioneering experience helped to give Americans a sense of oneness and identity? Explain.

The Most Dangerous Game

RICHARD CONNELL

"Off there to the right — somewhere — is a large island," said Whitney. "It's rather a mystery — "

"What island is it?" Rainsford asked.

"The old charts call it 'Ship-Trap Island,'" Whitney replied. "A suggestive name, isn't it? Sailors have a curious dread of the place. I don't know why. Some superstition — "

"Can't see it," remarked Rainsford, trying to peer through the dank tropical night that was palpable as it pressed its thick warm blackness in upon the yacht.

"You've good eyes," said Whitney, with a laugh, "and I've seen you pick off a moose moving in the brown fall bush at four hundred yards, but even you can't see four miles or so through a moonless Caribbean night."

"Nor four yards," admitted Rainsford. "Ugh! It's like moist black velvet."

"It will be light enough in Rio," promised Whitney. "We should make it in a few days. I hope the jaguar guns have come from Purdey's. We should have some good hunting up the Amazon. Great sport, hunting."

"The best sport in the world," agreed Rainsford.

"For the hunter," amended Whitney. "Not for the jaguar."

"Don't talk rot, Whitney," said Rainsford. "You're a big-game hunter, not a philosopher. Who cares how a jaguar feels?"

"Perhaps the jaguar does," observed Whitney.

"Bah! They've no understanding."

"Even so, I rather think they understand one thing — fear. The fear of pain and the fear of death."

"Nonsense," laughed Rainsford. "This hot weather is making you soft, Whitney. Be a realist. The world is made up of two classes — the hunters and the huntees. Luckily, you and I are hunters. Do you think we've passed that island yet?"

"I can't tell in the dark. I hope so."

"Why?" asked Rainsford.

"The place has a reputation — a bad one."

"Cannibals?" suggested Rainsford.

"Hardly. Even cannibals wouldn't live in such a God-forsaken place. But it's gotten into sailor lore, somehow. Didn't you notice that the crew's nerves seemed a bit jumpy today?"

"They were a bit strange, now you mention it. Even Captain Nielsen — "

"Yes, even that tough-minded old Swede, who'd go up to the devil himself and ask him for a light. Those fishy blue eyes held a look I never saw there before. All I could get out of him was: 'This place has an evil name among seafaring men, sir.' Then he said to me, very gravely: 'Don't you feel anything?' — as if the air about us was actually poisonous. Now, you mustn't laugh when I tell you this — I did feel something like a sudden chill.

"There was no breeze. The sea was as flat as a plate-glass window. We were drawing near the island then. What I felt was a — a mental chill; a sort of sudden dread."

"Pure imagination," said Rainsford. "One superstitious sailor can taint the whole ship's company with his fear."

"Maybe. But sometimes I think sailors have an extra sense that tells them when they are in danger. Sometimes I think evil is a tangible thing — with wave lengths, just as sound and light have. An evil place can, so to speak, broadcast vibrations of evil. Anyhow, I'm glad we're getting out of this zone. Well, I think I'll turn in now, Rainsford."

"I'm not sleepy," said Rainsford. "I'm going to smoke another pipe up on the after deck."

"Good night, then, Rainsford. See you at breakfast."

"Right. Good night, Whitney."

There was no sound in the night as Rainsford sat there but the muffled throb of the engine that drove the yacht swiftly through the darkness, and the swish and ripple of the wash of the propeller.

Rainsford, reclining in a steamer chair, indolently puffed on his favorite brier. The sensuous drowsiness of the night was on him. "It's so dark," he thought, "that I could sleep without closing my eyes; the night would be my eyelids — "

An abrupt sound startled him. Off to the right he heard it, and his ears, expert in such matters, could not be mistaken. Again he heard the sound, and again. Somewhere, off in the blackness, someone had fired a gun three times.

Rainsford sprang up and moved quickly to the rail, mystified. He strained his eyes in the direction from which the reports had come, but it was like trying to see through a blanket. He leaped upon the rail and balanced himself there, to get greater elevation; his pipe, striking a rope, was knocked from his mouth. He lunged for it; a short, hoarse cry came from his lips as he realized he had reached too far and had lost his balance. The cry was pinched off short as the blood-warm waters of the Caribbean Sea closed over his head.

He struggled up to the surface and tried to cry out, but the wash from the speeding yacht slapped him in the face and the salt water in his open mouth made him gag and strangle. Desperately he struck out with strong strokes after the receding lights of the yacht, but he stopped before he had swum fifty feet. A certain coolheadedness had come to him; it was not the first time he had been in a tight place. There was a chance that his cries could be heard by someone aboard the yacht, but that chance was slender, and grew more slender as the yacht raced on. He wrestled himself out of his clothes, and shouted with all his power. The lights of the yacht became faint and ever-vanishing fireflies; then they were blotted out entirely by the night.

Rainsford remembered the shots. They had come from the right, and doggedly he swam in that direction, swimming with slow, deliberate strokes, conserving his strength. For a seemingly endless time he fought the sea. He began to count his strokes; he could do possibly a hundred more and then —

Rainsford heard a sound. It came out of the darkness, a high screaming sound, the sound of an animal in an extremity of anguish and terror.

He did not recognize the animal that made the sound; he did not try to; with fresh vitality he swam toward the sound. He heard it again; then it was cut short by another noise, crisp, staccato.

"Pistol shot," muttered Rainsford, swimming on.

Ten minutes of determined effort brought another sound to his ears — the most welcome he had ever heard — the muttering and growling of the sea breaking on a rocky shore. He was almost on the rocks before he saw them; on a night less calm he would have been shattered against them. With his remaining strength he dragged himself from the swirling waters. Jagged crags appeared to jut up into the opaqueness; he forced himself upward, hand over hand. Gasping, his hands raw, he reached a flat place at the top. Dense jungle came down to the very edge of the cliffs. What perils that tangle of trees and underbrush might hold for him did not concern Rainsford just then. All he knew was that he was safe from his enemy, the sea, and that utter weariness was on him. He flung himself down at the jungle edge and tumbled headlong into the deepest sleep of his life.

When he opened his eyes he knew from the position of the sun that it was late in the afternoon. Sleep had given him new vigor; a sharp hunger was picking at him. He looked about him, almost cheerfully.

"Where there are pistol shots, there are men. Where there are men, there is food," he thought. But what kind of men, he wondered, in so forbidding a place? An unbroken front of snarled and ragged jungle fringed the shore.

He saw no sign of a trail through the closely knit web of weeds and trees; it was easier to go along the shore, and Rainsford floundered along by the water. Not far from where he had landed, he stopped.

Some wounded thing, by the evidence, a large animal, had thrashed about in the underbrush; the jungle weeds were crushed down and the moss was lacerated; one patch of weeds was stained crimson. A small, glittering object not far away caught Rainsford's eye and he picked it up. It was an empty cartridge.

"A twenty-two," he remarked. "That's odd. It must have been a fairly large animal too. The hunter had his nerve with him to tackle it with a light gun. It's clear that the brute put up a fight. I suppose the first three shots I heard was when the hunter flushed his quarry and wounded it. The last shot was when he trailed it here and finished it."

He examined the ground closely and found what he had hoped to find — the print of hunting boots. They pointed along the cliff in the direction he had been going. Eagerly he hurried along, now slipping on a rotten log or a loose stone, but making headway; night was beginning to settle down on the island.

Bleak darkness was blacking out the sea and jungle when Rainsford sighted the lights. He came upon them as he turned a crook in the coast line, and his first thought was that he had come upon a village, for there were many lights. But as he forged along he saw to his great astonishment that all the lights were in one enormous building — a lofty structure with pointed towers plunging upward into the gloom. His eyes made out the shadowy outlines of a palatial château; it was set on a high bluff, and on three sides of it cliffs dived down to where the sea licked greedy lips in the shadows.

"Mirage," thought Rainsford. But it was no mirage, he found, when he opened the tall spiked iron gate. The stone steps were real enough; the massive door with a leering gargoyle for a knocker was real enough; yet above it all hung an air of unreality.

He lifted the knocker, and it creaked up stiffly, as if it had never before been used. He let it fall, and it startled him with its booming loudness. He thought he heard steps within; the door remained closed. Again Rainsford lifted the heavy knocker, and let it fall. The door opened then, opened as suddenly as if it were on a spring, and Rainsford stood blinking in the river of glaring gold light that poured out. The first thing Rainsford's eyes discerned was the largest man Rainsford had ever seen — a gigantic creature, solidly made and black-bearded to the waist. In his hand the man held a long-barreled revolver, and he was pointing it straight at Rainsford's heart.

Out of the snarl of beard two small eyes regarded Rainsford.

"Don't be alarmed," said Rainsford, with a smile which he hoped was disarming. "I'm no robber. I fell off a yacht. My name is Sanger Rainsford of New York City."

The menacing look in the eyes did not change. The revolver pointed as rigidly as if the giant were a statue. He gave no sign that he understood Rainsford's words, or that he had even heard them. He was dressed in uniform, a black uniform trimmed with gray astrakhan.[1]

"I'm Sanger Rainsford of New York," Rainsford began again. "I fell off a yacht. I am hungry."

The man's only answer was to raise with his thumb the hammer of his revolver. Then Rainsford saw the man's free hand go to his forehead in a military salute, and he saw him click his heels together and stand at attention. Another man was coming down the broad marble steps, an erect, slender man in evening clothes. He advanced to Rainsford and held out his hand.

In a cultivated voice marked by a slight accent that gave it added precision and deliberateness, he said: "It is a very great pleasure and honor to welcome Mr. Sanger Rainsford, the celebrated hunter, to my home."

Automatically Rainsford shook the man's hand.

"I've read your book about hunting snow leopards in Tibet, you see," explained the man. "I am General Zaroff."

Rainsford's first impression was that the man was singularly handsome; his second was that there was an original, almost bizarre quality about the general's face. He was a tall man past middle age, for his hair was a vivid white; but his thick eyebrows and pointed military mustache were as black as the night from which Rainsford had come. His eyes, too, were black and very bright. He had high cheek bones, a sharp-cut nose, a spare, dark face, the face of a man used to giving orders, the face of an aristocrat. Turning to the giant in uniform, the general made a sign. The giant put away his pistol, saluted, withdrew.

"Ivan is an incredibly strong fellow," remarked the general, "but he has the misfortune to be deaf and dumb. A simple fellow, but, I'm afraid, like all his race, a bit of a savage."

"Is he Russian?"

"He is a Cossack," said the general, and his smile showed red lips and pointed teeth. "So am I.

[1] **astrakhan:** Russian lamb's fur.

"Come," he said, "we shouldn't be chatting here. We can talk later. Now you want clothes, food, rest. You shall have them. This is a most restful spot."

Ivan had reappeared, and the general spoke to him with lips that moved but gave forth no sound.

"Follow Ivan, if you please, Mr. Rainsford," said the general. "I was about to have my dinner when you came. I'll wait for you. You'll find that my clothes will fit you, I think."

It was to a huge, beam-ceilinged bedroom with a canopied bed big enough for six men that Rainsford followed the silent giant. Ivan laid out an evening suit, and Rainsford, as he put it on, noticed that it came from a London tailor who ordinarily cut and sewed for none below the rank of duke.

The dining room to which Ivan conducted him was in many ways remarkable. There was a medieval magnificence about it; it suggested a baronial hall of feudal times with its oaken panels, its high ceiling, its vast refectory tables where twoscore men could sit down to eat. About the hall were the mounted heads of many animals — lions, tigers, elephants, moose, bears; larger or more perfect specimens Rainsford had never seen. At the great table the general was sitting, alone.

"You'll have a cocktail, Mr. Rainsford," he suggested. The cocktail was surpassingly good; and, Rainsford noted, the table appointments were of the finest — the linen, the crystal, the silver, the china.

They were eating *borsch,*[2] the rich, red soup with whipped cream so dear to Russian palates. Half apologetically General Zaroff said: "We do our best to preserve the amenities of civilization here. Please forgive any lapses. We are well off the beaten track, you know. Do you think the champagne has suffered from its long ocean trip?"

"Not in the least," declared Rainsford. He was finding the general a most thoughtful and affable host, a true cosmopolite. But there was one small trait of the general's that made Rainsford uncomfortable. Whenever he looked up from his plate he found the general studying him, appraising him narrowly.

"Perhaps," said General Zaroff, "you were surprised that I recognized your name. You see, I read all books on hunting published in English, French, and Russian. I have but one passion in my life, Mr. Rainsford, and it is the hunt."

[2] ***borsch:*** Russian soup made of beets.

"You have some wonderful heads here," said Rainsford as he ate a particularly well cooked *filet mignon*.[3] "That Cape buffalo is the largest I ever saw."

"Oh, that fellow. Yes, he was a monster."

"Did he charge you?"

"Hurled me against a tree," said the general. "Fractured my skull. But I got the brute."

"I've always thought," said Rainsford, "that the Cape buffalo is the most dangerous of all big game."

For a moment the general did not reply; he was smiling his curious red-lipped smile. Then he said slowly: "No. You are wrong, sir. The Cape buffalo is not the most dangerous big game." He sipped his wine. "Here in my preserve on this island," he said in the same slow tone, "I hunt more dangerous game."

Rainsford expressed his surprise. "Is there big game on this island?"

The general nodded. "The biggest."

"Really?"

"Oh, it isn't here naturally, of course. I have to stock the island."

"What have you imported, general?" Rainsford asked. "Tigers?"

The general smiled. "No," he said. "Hunting tigers ceased to interest me some years ago. I exhausted their possibilities, you see. No thrill left in tigers, no real danger. I live for danger, Mr. Rainsford."

The general took from his pocket a gold cigarette case and offered his guest a long black cigarette with a silver tip; it was perfumed and gave off a smell like incense.

"We will have some capital hunting, you and I," said the general. "I shall be most glad to have your society."

"But what game —" began Rainsford.

"I'll tell you," said the general. "You will be amused, I know. I think I may say, in all modesty, that I have done a rare thing. I have invented a new sensation. May I pour you another glass of port?"

"Thank you, general."

The general filled both glasses, and said: "God makes some men poets. Some He makes kings, some beggars. Me He made

[3] ***filet mignon:*** a round cut of tenderloin steak.

a hunter. My hand was made for the trigger, my father said. He was a very rich man with a quarter of a million acres in the Crimea, and he was an ardent sportsman. When I was only five years old he gave me a little gun, specially made in Moscow for me, to shoot sparrows with. When I shot some of his prize turkeys with it, he did not punish me; he complimented me on my marksmanship. I killed my first bear in the Caucasus when I was ten. My whole life has been one prolonged hunt. I went into the army — it was expected of noblemen's sons — and for a time commanded a division of Cossack cavalry, but my real interest was always the hunt. I have hunted every kind of game in every land. It would be impossible for me to tell you how many animals I have killed."

The general puffed at his cigarette.

"After the debacle in Russia[4] I left the country, for it was imprudent for an officer of the Czar to stay there. Many noble Russians lost everything. I, luckily, had invested heavily in American securities, so I shall never have to open a tea room in Monte Carlo or drive a taxi in Paris. Naturally, I continued to hunt — grizzlies in your Rockies, crocodile in the Ganges, rhinoceroses in East Africa. It was in Africa that the Cape buffalo hit me and laid me up for six months. As soon as I recovered I started for the Amazon to hunt jaguars, for I had heard they were unusually cunning. They weren't." The Cossack sighed. "They were no match at all for a hunter with his wits about him, and a high-powered rifle. I was bitterly disappointed. I was lying in my tent with a splitting headache one night when a terrible thought pushed its way into my mind. Hunting was beginning to bore me! And hunting, remember, had been my life. I have heard that in America business men often go to pieces when they give up the business that has been their life."

"Yes, that's so," said Rainsford.

The general smiled. "I had no wish to go to pieces," he said. "I must do something. Now, mine is an analytical mind, Mr. Rainsford. Doubtless that is why I enjoy the problems of the chase."

"No doubt, General Zaroff."

"So," continued the general, "I asked myself why the hunt no

[4] **the debacle in Russia:** the revolution of 1917, in which the Czar was overthrown.

longer fascinated me. You are much younger than I am, Mr. Rainsford, and have not hunted as much, but you perhaps can guess the answer."

"What was it?"

"Simply this: hunting had ceased to be what you call 'a sporting proposition.' It had become too easy. I always got my quarry. Always. There is no greater bore than perfection."

The general lit a fresh cigarette.

"No animal had a chance with me any more. That is no boast; it is a mathematical certainty. The animal had nothing but his legs and his instinct. Instinct is no match for reason. When I thought of this it was a tragic moment for me, I can tell you."

Rainsford leaned across the table, absorbed in what his host was saying.

"It came to me as an inspiration what I must do," the general went on.

"And that was?"

The general smiled the quiet smile of one who has faced an obstacle and surmounted it with success. "I had to invent a new animal to hunt," he said.

"A new animal? You're joking."

"Not at all," said the general. "I never joke about hunting. I needed a new animal. I found one. So I bought this island, built this house, and here I do my hunting. The island is perfect for my purposes — there are jungles with a maze of trails in them, hills, swamps —"

"But the animal, General Zaroff?"

"Oh," said the general, "it supplies me with the most exciting hunting in the world. No other hunting compares with it for an instant. Every day I hunt, and I never grow bored now, for I have a quarry with which I can match my wits."

Rainsford's bewilderment showed in his face.

"I wanted the ideal animal to hunt," explained the general. "So I said: 'What are the attributes of an ideal quarry?' And the answer was, of course: 'It must have courage, cunning, and, above all, it must be able to reason.'"

"But no animal can reason," objected Rainsford.

"My dear fellow," said the general, "there is one that can."

"But you can't mean —" gasped Rainsford.

"And why not?"

"I can't believe you are serious, General Zaroff. This is a grisly joke."

"Why should I not be serious? I am speaking of hunting."

"Hunting? Good God, General Zaroff, what you speak of is murder."

The general laughed with entire good nature. He regarded Rainsford quizzically. "I refuse to believe that so modern and civilized a young man as you seem to be harbors romantic ideas about the value of human life. Surely your experiences in the war —"

"Did not make me condone cold-blooded murder," finished Rainsford stiffly.

Laughter shook the general. "How extraordinarily droll you are!" he said. "One does not expect nowadays to find a young man of the educated class, even in America, with such a naive, and, if I may say so, mid-Victorian point of view. It's like finding a snuffbox in a limousine. Ah, well, doubtless you had Puritan ancestors. So many Americans appear to have had. I'll wager you'll forget your notions when you go hunting with me. You've a genuine new thrill in store for you, Mr. Rainsford."

"Thank you, I'm a hunter, not a murderer."

"Dear me," said the general, quite unruffled, "again that unpleasant word. But I think I can show you that your scruples are quite ill founded."

"Yes?"

"Life is for the strong, to be lived by the strong, and, if need be, taken by the strong. The weak of the world were put here to give the strong pleasure. I am strong. Why should I not use my gift? If I wish to hunt, why should I not? I hunt the scum of the earth — sailors from tramp ships — lascars,[5] blacks, Chinese, whites, mongrels — a thoroughbred horse or hound is worth more than a score of them."

"But they are men," said Rainsford hotly.

"Precisely," said the general. "That is why I use them. It gives me pleasure. They can reason, after a fashion. So they are dangerous."

"But where do you get them?"

The general's left eyelid fluttered down in a wink. "This island is called Ship-Trap," he answered. "Sometimes an angry god of

[5] **lascars:** East Indian sailors.

the high seas sends them to me. Sometimes, when Providence is not so kind, I help Providence a bit. Come to the window with me."

Rainsford went to the window and looked out toward the sea.

"Watch! Out there!" exclaimed the general, pointing into the night. Rainsford's eyes saw only blackness, and then, as the general pressed a button, far out to sea Rainsford saw the flash of lights.

The general chuckled. "They indicate a channel," he said, "where there's none; giant rocks with razor edges crouch like a sea monster with wide-open jaws. They can crush a ship as easily as I crush this nut." He dropped a walnut on the hardwood floor and brought his heel grinding down on it. "Oh, yes," he said, casually, as if in answer to a question, "I have electricity. We try to be civilized here."

"Civilized? And you shoot down men?"

A trace of anger was in the general's black eyes, but it was there for a second, and he said, in his most pleasant manner: "Dear me, what a righteous young man you are! I assure you I do not do the thing you suggest. That would be barbarous. I treat these visitors with every consideration. They get plenty of good food and exercise. They get into splendid physical condition. You shall see for yourself tomorrow."

"What do you mean?"

"We'll visit my training school," smiled the general. "It's in the cellar. I have about a dozen pupils down there now. They're from the Spanish bark *San Lucar* that had the bad luck to go on the rocks out there. A very inferior lot, I regret to say. Poor specimens and more accustomed to the deck than to the jungle."

He raised his hand, and Ivan, who served as waiter, brought thick Turkish coffee. Rainsford, with an effort, held his tongue in check.

"It's a game, you see," pursued the general blandly. "I suggest to one of them that we go hunting. I give him a supply of food and an excellent hunting knife. I give him three hours' start. I am to follow, armed only with a pistol of the smallest caliber and range. If my quarry eludes me for three whole days, he wins the game. If I find him" — the general smiled — "he loses."

"Suppose he refuses to be hunted?"

"Oh," said the general, "I give him his option, of course. He need not play that game if he doesn't wish to. If he does not wish to hunt, I turn him over to Ivan. Ivan once had the honor of serving as official knouter[6] to the Great White Czar, and he has his own ideas of sport. Invariably, Mr. Rainsford, invariably they choose the hunt."

"And if they win?"

The smile on the general's face widened. "To date I have not lost," he said. Then he added, hastily: "I don't wish you to think me a braggart, Mr. Rainsford. Many of them afford only the most elementary sort of problem. Occasionally I strike a tartar.[7] One almost did win. I eventually had to use the dogs."

"The dogs?"

"This way, please. I'll show you."

The general steered Rainsford to a window. The lights from the windows sent a flickering illumination that made grotesque patterns on the courtyard below, and Rainsford could see moving about there a dozen or so huge black shapes; as they turned toward him, their eyes glittered greenly.

"A rather good lot, I think," observed the general. "They are let out at seven every night. If anyone should try to get into my house — or out of it — something extremely regrettable would occur to him." He hummed a snatch of song from the *Folies Bergère*.

"And now," said the general, "I want to show you my new collection of heads. Will you come with me to the library?"

"I hope," said Rainsford, "that you will excuse me tonight, General Zaroff. I'm really not feeling well."

"Ah, indeed?" the general inquired solicitously. "Well, I suppose that's only natural, after your long swim. You need a good, restful night's sleep. Tomorrow you'll feel like a new man, I'll wager. Then we'll hunt, eh? I've one rather promising prospect —" Rainsford was hurrying from the room.

"Sorry you can't go with me tonight," called the general. "I expect rather fair sport — a big, strong chap. He looks resourceful — Well, good night, Mr. Rainsford; I hope you have a good night's rest."

The bed was good, and the pajamas of the softest silk, and he was tired in every fiber of his being, but nevertheless Rainsford

[6] **knouter:** whipper. (A knout, or whip, was used to punish criminals in Russia.)
[7] **tartar:** one who is unexpectedly troublesome.

could not quiet his brain with the opiate of sleep. He lay, eyes wide open. Once he thought he heard stealthy steps in the corridor outside his room. He sought to throw open the door; it would not open. He went to the window and looked out. His room was high up in one of the towers. The lights of the château were out now, and it was dark and silent, but there was a fragment of sallow moon, and by its wan light he could see, dimly, the courtyard; there, weaving in and out in the pattern of shadow, were black, noiseless forms; the hounds heard him at the window and looked up, expectantly, with their green eyes. Rainsford went back to the bed and lay down. By many methods he tried to put himself to sleep. He had achieved a doze when, just as morning began to come, he heard, far off in the jungle, the faint report of a pistol.

General Zaroff did not appear until luncheon. He was dressed faultlessly in the tweeds of a country squire. He was solicitous about the state of Rainsford's health.

"As for me," sighed the general, "I do not feel so well. I am worried, Mr. Rainsford. Last night I detected traces of my old complaint."

To Rainsford's questioning glance the general said: "Ennui. Boredom."

Then, taking a second helping of *Crêpes Suzette,* the general explained: "The hunting was not good last night. The fellow lost his head. He made a straight trail that offered no problems at all. That's the trouble with these sailors; they have dull brains to begin with, and they do not know how to get about in the woods. They do excessively stupid and obvious things. It's most annoying. Will you have another glass of *Chablis,* Mr. Rainsford?"

"General," said Rainsford firmly, "I wish to leave this island at once."

The general raised his thickets of eyebrows; he seemed hurt. "But, my dear fellow," the general protested, "you've only just come. You've had no hunting —"

"I wish to go today," said Rainsford. He saw the dead black eyes of the general on him, studying him. General Zaroff's face suddenly brightened.

He filled Rainsford's glass with venerable *Chablis* from a dusty bottle.

"Tonight," said the general, "we will hunt — you and I."

Rainsford shook his head. "No, general," he said. "I will not hunt."

The general shrugged his shoulders and delicately ate a hot-house grape. "As you wish, my friend," he said. "The choice rests entirely with you. But may I not venture to suggest that you will find my idea of sport more diverting than Ivan's?"

He nodded toward the corner to where the giant stood, scowling, his thick arms crossed on his hogshead of chest.

"You don't mean —" cried Rainsford.

"My dear fellow," said the general, "have I not told you I always mean what I say about hunting? This is really an inspiration. I drink to a foeman worthy of my steel — at last." The general raised his glass, but Rainsford sat staring at him.

"You'll find this game worth playing," the general said enthusiastically. "Your brain against mine. Your woodcraft against mine. Your strength and stamina against mine. Outdoor chess! And the stake is not without value, eh?"

"And if I win —" began Rainsford huskily.

"I'll cheerfully acknowledge myself defeated if I do not find you by midnight of the third day," said General Zaroff. "My sloop will place you on the mainland near a town." The general read what Rainsford was thinking.

"Oh, you can trust me," said the Cossack. "I will give you my word as a gentleman and a sportsman. Of course you, in turn, must agree to say nothing of your visit here."

"I'll agree to nothing of the kind," said Rainsford.

"Oh," said the general, "in that case — But why discuss that now? Three days hence we can discuss it over a bottle of *Veuve Cliquot,* unless —"

The general sipped his wine.

Then a businesslike air animated him. "Ivan," he said to Rainsford, "will supply you with hunting clothes, food, a knife. I suggest you wear moccasins; they leave a poorer trail. I suggest, too, that you avoid the big swamp in the southeast corner of the island. We call it Death Swamp. There's quicksand there. One foolish fellow tried it. The deplorable part of it was that Lazarus followed him. You can imagine my feelings, Mr. Rainsford. I loved Lazarus; he was the finest hound in my pack. Well, I must beg you to excuse me now. I always take a siesta after lunch. You'll hardly have time for a nap, I fear. You'll want to start, no doubt. I shall not follow till dusk. Hunting at night is so much more exciting than by day, don't you think? *Au revoir,* Mr. Rainsford, *au revoir.*" General Zaroff, with a deep, courtly bow, strolled from the room.

From another door came Ivan. Under one arm he carried khaki hunting clothes, a haversack of food, a leather sheath containing a long-bladed hunting knife; his right hand rested on a cocked revolver thrust in the crimson sash about his waist.

Rainsford had fought his way through the bush for two hours. "I must keep my nerve. I must keep my nerve," he said through tight teeth.

He had not been entirely clear-headed when the château gates snapped shut behind him. His whole idea at first was to put distance between himself and General Zaroff, and, to this end, he had plunged along, spurred on by the sharp rowels of something very like panic. Now he had got a grip on himself, had stopped, and was taking stock of himself and the situation. He saw that straight flight was futile; inevitably it would bring him face to face with the sea. He was in a picture with a frame of water, and his operations, clearly, must take place within that frame.

"I'll give him a trail to follow," muttered Rainsford, and he struck off from the rude path he had been following into the trackless wilderness. He executed a series of intricate loops; he doubled on his trail again and again, recalling all the lore of the fox hunt, and all the dodges of the fox. Night found him leg-weary, with hands and face lashed by the branches, on a thickly wooded ridge. He knew it would be insane to blunder on through the dark, even if he had the strength. His need for rest was imperative and he thought: "I have played the fox, now I must play the cat of the fable." A big tree with a thick trunk and outspread branches was near by, and, taking care to leave not the slightest mark, he climbed up into the crotch, and stretching out on one of the broad limbs, after a fashion, rested. Rest brought him new confidence and almost a feeling of security. Even so zealous a hunter as General Zaroff could not trace him there, he told himself; only the devil himself could follow that complicated trail through the jungle after dark. But, perhaps the general was a devil —

An apprehensive night crawled slowly by like a wounded snake, and sleep did not visit Rainsford, although the silence of a dead world was on the jungle. Toward morning when a dingy gray was varnishing the sky, the cry of some startled bird focused Rainsford's attention in that direction. Something was coming through the bush, coming slowly, carefully, coming by the same winding way Rainsford had come. He flattened himself down on the limb, and through a screen of leaves almost as thick as tapestry, he watched. . . . That which was approaching was a man.

It was General Zaroff. He made his way along with his eyes fixed in utmost concentration on the ground before him. He paused, almost beneath the tree, dropped to his knees and studied the ground. Rainsford's impulse was to hurl himself down like a panther, but he saw that the general's right hand held something metallic — a small automatic pistol.

The hunter shook his head several times, as if he were puzzled. Then he straightened up and took from his case one of his black cigarettes; its pungent incenselike smoke floated up to Rainsford's nostrils.

Rainsford held his breath. The general's eyes had left the ground and were traveling inch by inch up the tree. Rainsford froze there, every muscle tensed for a spring. But the sharp eyes of the hunter stopped before they reached the limb where Rainsford lay; a smile spread over his brown face. Very deliberately he blew a smoke ring into the air; then he turned his back on the tree and walked carelessly away, back along the trail he had come. The swish of the underbrush against his hunting boots grew fainter and fainter.

The pent-up air burst hotly from Rainsford's lungs. His first thought made him feel sick and numb. The general could follow a trail through the woods at night; he could follow an extremely difficult trail; he must have uncanny powers; only by the merest chance had the Cossack failed to see his quarry.

Rainsford's second thought was even more terrible. It sent a shudder of cold horror through his whole being. Why had the general smiled? Why had he turned back?

Rainsford did not want to believe what his reason told him was true, but the truth was as evident as the sun that had by now pushed through the morning mists. The general was playing with him! The general was saving him for another day's sport! The Cossack was the cat; he was the mouse. Then it was that Rainsford knew the full meaning of terror.

"I will not lose my nerve. I will not."

He slid down from the tree, and struck off again into the woods. His face was set and he forced the machinery of his mind to function. Three hundred yards from his hiding place he stopped where a huge dead tree leaned precariously on a smaller, living one. Throwing off his sack of food, Rainsford took his knife from its sheath and began to work with all his energy.

The job was finished at last, and he threw himself down behind a fallen log a hundred feet away. He did not have to wait long. The cat was coming again to play with the mouse.

Following the trail with the sureness of a bloodhound came General Zaroff. Nothing escaped those searching black eyes, no crushed blade of grass, no bent twig, no mark, no matter how faint, in the moss. So intent was the Cossack on his stalking that he was upon the thing Rainsford had made before he saw it. His foot touched the protruding bough that was the trigger. Even as he touched it, the general sensed his danger and leaped back with the agility of an ape. But he was not quite quick enough; the dead tree, delicately adjusted to rest on the cut living one, crashed down and struck the general a glancing blow on the shoulder as it fell; but for his alertness, he must have been smashed beneath it. He staggered, but he did not fall; nor did he drop his revolver. He stood there, rubbing his injured shoulder, and Rainsford, with fear again gripping his heart, heard the general's mocking laugh ring through the jungle.

"Rainsford," called the general, "if you are within sound of my voice, as I suppose you are, let me congratulate you. Not many men know how to make a Malay man-catcher. Luckily, for me, I too have hunted in Malacca. You are proving interesting, Mr. Rainsford. I am going now to have my wound dressed; it's only a slight one. But I shall be back. I shall be back."

When the general, nursing his bruised shoulder, had gone, Rainsford took up his flight again. It was flight now, a desperate, hopeless flight, that carried him on for some hours. Dusk came, then darkness, and still he pressed on. The ground grew softer under his moccasins; the vegetation grew ranker, denser; insects bit him savagely. Then, as he stepped forward, his foot sank into the ooze. He tried to wrench it back, but the muck sucked viciously at his foot as if it were a giant leech. With a violent effort, he tore his feet loose. He knew where he was now. Death Swamp and its quicksand.

His hands were tight closed as if his nerve were something tangible that someone in the darkness was trying to tear from his grip. The softness of the earth had given him an idea. He stepped back from the quicksand a dozen feet or so and, like some huge prehistoric beaver, he began to dig.

Rainsford had dug himself in in France when a second's delay meant death. That had been a placid pastime compared to his digging now. The pit grew deeper; when it was above his shoulders, he climbed out and from some hard saplings cut stakes and sharpened them to a fine point. These stakes he planted in the bottom of the pit with the points sticking up. With flying fingers he wove a rough carpet of weeds and branches and with it he covered the mouth of the pit. Then, wet with sweat and aching with tiredness, he crouched behind the stump of a lightning-charred tree.

He knew his pursuer was coming; he heard the padding sound of feet on the soft earth, and the night breeze brought him the perfume of the general's cigarette. It seemed to Rainsford that the general was coming with unusual swiftness; he was not feeling his way along, foot by foot. Rainsford, crouching there, could not see the general, nor could he see the pit. He lived a year in a minute. Then he felt an impulse to cry aloud with joy, for he heard the sharp crackle of the breaking branches as the cover of the pit gave way; he heard the sharp scream of pain as the pointed stakes found their mark. He leaped up from his place of concealment. Then he cowered back. Three feet from the pit a man was standing, with an electric torch in his hand.

"You've done well, Rainsford," the voice of the general called. "Your Burmese tiger pit has claimed one of my best dogs. Again you score. I think, Mr. Rainsford, I'll see what you can do against my whole pack. I'm going home for a rest now. Thank you for a most amusing evening."

At daybreak Rainsford, lying near the swamp, was awakened by a sound that made him know that he had new things to learn about fear. It was a distant sound, faint and wavering, but he knew it. It was the baying of a pack of hounds.

Rainsford knew he could do one of two things. He could stay where he was and wait. That was suicide. He could flee. That was postponing the inevitable. For a moment he stood there, thinking. An idea that held a wild chance came to him, and, tightening his belt, he headed away from the swamp.

The baying of the hounds drew nearer, then still nearer, nearer, ever nearer. On a ridge Rainsford climbed a tree. Down a watercourse, not a quarter of a mile away, he could see the bush moving. Straining his eyes, he saw the lean figure of General Zaroff; just ahead of him Rainsford made out another figure whose wide shoulders surged through the tall jungle weeds; it was the giant Ivan, and he seemed pulled forward by some unseen force; Rainsford knew that Ivan must be holding the pack in leash.

They would be on him any minute now. His mind worked frantically. He thought of a native trick he had learned in Uganda. He slid down the tree. He caught hold of a springy young sapling and to it he fastened his hunting knife, with the blade pointing down the trail; with a bit of wild grapevine he tied back the sapling. Then he ran for his life. The hounds raised their voices as they hit the fresh scent. Rainsford knew now how an animal at bay feels.

He had to stop to get his breath. The baying of the hounds stopped abruptly, and Rainsford's heart stopped too. They must have reached the knife.

He shinned excitedly up a tree and looked back. His pursuers had stopped. But the hope that was in Rainsford's brain when he climbed died, for he saw in the shallow valley that General Zaroff was still on his feet. But Ivan was not. The knife, driven by the recoil of the springing tree, had not wholly failed.

Rainsford had hardly tumbled to the ground when the pack took up the cry again.

"Nerve, nerve, nerve!" he panted, as he dashed along. A blue gap showed between the trees dead ahead. Ever nearer drew the hounds. Rainsford forced himself on toward that gap. He reached it. It was the shore of the sea. Across a cove he could see the gloomy gray stone of the château. Twenty feet below him the sea rumbled and hissed. Rainsford hesitated. He heard the hounds. Then he leaped far out into the sea. . . .

When the general and his pack reached the place by the sea, the Cossack stopped. For some minutes he stood regarding the blue-green expanse of water. He shrugged his shoulders. Then he sat down, took a drink of brandy from a silver flask, lit a cigarette, and hummed a bit from "Madame Butterfly."

General Zaroff had an exceedingly good dinner in his great paneled dining hall that evening. With it he had a bottle of *Pol Roger* and half a bottle of *Chambertin*. Two slight annoyances kept him from perfect enjoyment. One was the thought that it would be difficult to replace Ivan; the other was that his quarry had escaped him; of course the American hadn't played the game — so thought the general as he tasted his after-dinner liqueur. In his library he read, to soothe himself, from the works of Marcus Aurelius.[8] At ten he went up to his bedroom. He was deliciously tired, he said to himself, as he locked himself in. There was a little moonlight, so, before turning on his light, he went to the window and looked down at the courtyard. He could see the great hounds, and he called, "Better luck another time," to them. Then he switched on the light.

A man, who had been hiding in the curtains of the bed, was standing there.

"Rainsford!" screamed the general. "How in God's name did you get here?"

"Swam," said Rainsford. "I found it quicker than walking through the jungle."

The general sucked in his breath and smiled. "I congratulate you," he said. "You have won the game."

Rainsford did not smile. "I am still a beast at bay," he said, in a low, hoarse voice. "Get ready, General Zaroff."

The general made one of his deepest bows. "I see," he said. "Splendid! One of us is to furnish a repast for the hounds. The other will sleep in this very excellent bed. On guard, Rainsford."

He had never slept in a better bed, Rainsford decided.

* * *

EXAMINING THE STORY

1. The opening paragraph introduces the mystery of the island. As the mystery is explained — during Rainsford's dinner conversation with Zaroff — a second question is raised: must Rainsford himself play the game? The final section of the story is concerned with an even more urgent question. What is it? When is this question answered? The opening lines of the story promise suspense and strange adventure. How well is that promise fulfilled?
2. By what steps has General Zaroff come to play "the most dangerous game"? What qualities of character and mind made the idea appeal to him? led to his unique arrangements for pursuing the activity?

[8] **Marcus Aurelius:** Roman emperor and philosopher (A.D. 121–180).

Explain: "There is no greater bore than perfection" (page 27). How has Zaroff's upbringing contributed to his taste for this sport?

3. General Zaroff claims he likes to match wits with his quarry. Why does he hunt with a 22-caliber pistol? with dogs? How sporting a chance does he actually give his victims?

4. Rainsford's first four schemes of escape fail. How does each of these episodes demonstrate the physical and mental qualities of both Rainsford and Zaroff? On his fifth attempt, Rainsford succeeds. Why would such a swim have been futile, earlier? Does Rainsford win solely by his own strength and ingenuity, or is he aided by a weakness in Zaroff? (When Zaroff tracks Rainsford to the sea, what does he mean by "the American hadn't played the game"? Why does he assume this?)

5. **A Broader Perspective** • As "The Most Dangerous Game" shows, even a violent adventure story can raise important philosophical questions. Rainsford says, in the opening exchange with Whitney, ". . . the world is made up of two classes — the hunters and the huntees." Is that a statement of scientific fact, or is it one man's interpretation of life? Zaroff later tells Rainsford, "You'll find that my clothes will fit you. . . ." In how many ways are Rainsford and Zaroff alike? At what point do their ideas diverge? How do Rainsford's experiences on the island alter his earlier views about hunting?

   The story suggests that wanton hunting destroys important qualities in a man. What are they? Explain how this kind of sport can become a "dangerous game" for the hunter.

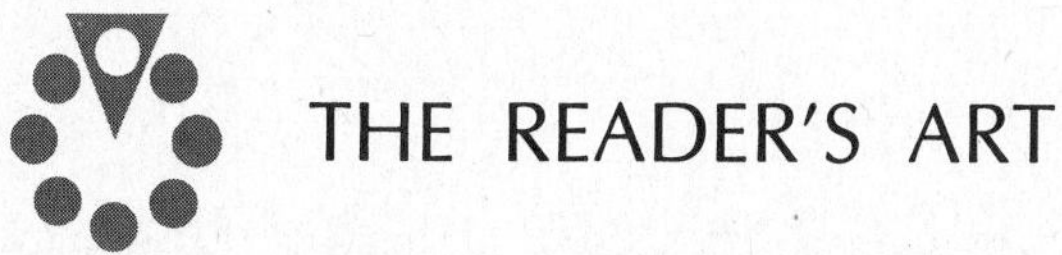

THE READER'S ART

Inferring the Meanings

The art of reading fiction is largely a matter of inferring meanings. To *infer* means to understand facts which are not directly stated — only suggested. Inference is one of the commonest ways of knowing things: a child holds his knee and cries; this action *implies* his feeling; an observer *infers* that the child is hurt. To infer accurately in everyday life requires alertness in observing; to infer skillfully in fiction requires alertness in reading; both require a disciplined imagination.

The short-story reader can expect to encounter certain basic elements in any story. For example, all stories involve a person or persons, in a particular setting, faced with a demand for a response. The response called for may be a physical action, such as defeating an adversary or escaping from a danger; or it may be a mental action, such as adjusting to others or within oneself. In either case, the short story is a revelation in two ways: first, it reveals the motives for a given human action; second, it makes a point about the general human situation. Such revelations, however, rather than being stated directly, usually are implied by the elements of the story.

These elements also imply information about each other. For example, *setting* implies *action:* the dustless horizon in "Early Marriage" implies that travelers ordinarily on the trail have been stopped by the Apaches, and the smoking cabin found by Rife and Nancy Belle implies what the Apaches have done. Again, *action* can imply *motive:* Rife buries the camp-fire before dark and from his action we infer its motive. Finally, *things* used in a story often imply *character:* when Nancy Belle examines her little trunk of possessions, the *things* in her trunk speak of her concern for her new household, of her skill in sewing, of her isolation from stores, of her family's past, and of her intention to make the best of circumstances.

The elements of a story also imply limits or definitions for each other. For example, the *setting* of General Zaroff's jungle island, with its maze of trails, hills, and swamps, limits the possibilities for *action* in the story; his château defines his self-indulgent *character.* The *setting* of the dangerous plain and storm define the *action* which Nancy Belle and Rife must take in order to achieve their purpose, and their *action* is further limited by the *things* they have.

When the reader of a story understands all the facts and their interrelationships, he is ready to infer the significance of the story as a whole — its comment on the human situation. This comment, or *theme,* is the seed from which the story grew. It is also the idea by which all the separate elements of the story are governed, while these in turn further shape and modify the theme. In addition to action, character, and setting, these elements include structure, mood, tone, and point of view. Each of these elements will be further explained in later sections of the book.

Fiction reading requires an awareness of all the ways in which a story communicates. It also requires attention to detail. What the author provides is a network of points which serve as clues to his meaning. He invites the reader to develop the meaning by inference, actually to create much of the story himself and so make it part of his own experience.

FOR WRITING

1. What personal qualities and skills are useful to Rainsford in his survival on Zaroff's island? to Nancy Belle and Rife in their journey to Gunstock? Which story pictures more complex danger? How are these dangers different from, or similar to, dangers people face today? What personal qualities and skills are needed to survive dangers in the community where you live?
2. Using characters from these stories as examples, explain some of the ways in which setting is related to personality. (Would a character like Zaroff be possible in Asa Putman's outpost? Why? Would Rife and Nancy Belle be different if they had been raised by Zaroff on his island? In what ways?)
3. Explain how later events of either story fulfill the expectations set up in the story's first paragraph.

2 Is it possible to seize happiness from life?

The Summer of the Beautiful White Horse

WILLIAM SAROYAN

One day back there in the good old days when I was nine and the world was full of every imaginable kind of magnificence, and life was still a delightful and mysterious dream, my cousin Mourad, who was considered crazy by everybody who knew him except me, came to my house at four in the morning and woke me up by tapping on the window of my room.

Aram, he said.

I jumped out of bed and looked out the window.

I couldn't believe what I saw.

It wasn't morning yet, but it was summer and with daybreak not many minutes around the corner of the world it was light enough for me to know I wasn't dreaming.

My cousin Mourad was sitting on a beautiful white horse.

I stuck my head out of the window and rubbed my eyes.

Yes, he said in Armenian. It's a horse. You're not dreaming. Make it quick if you want to ride.

I knew my cousin Mourad enjoyed being alive more than anybody else who had ever fallen into the world by mistake, but this was more than even I could believe.

In the first place, my earliest memories had been memories of horses and my first longings had been longings to ride.

This was the wonderful part.

In the second place, we were poor.

This was the part that wouldn't permit me to believe what I saw.

We were poor. We had no money. Our whole tribe was poverty-stricken. Every branch of the Garoghlanian family was living in the most amazing and comical poverty in the world. Nobody could understand where we ever got money enough to keep us with food in our bellies, not even the old men of the family. Most important of all, though, we were famous for our honesty. We had been famous for our honesty for something like eleven centuries, even when we had been the wealthiest family in what we liked to think was the world. We were proud first, honest next, and after that we believed in right and wrong. None of us would take advantage of anybody in the world, let alone steal.

Consequently, even though I could *see* the horse, so magnificent; even though I could *smell* it, so lovely; even though I could *hear* it breathing, so exciting; I couldn't *believe* the horse had anything to do with my cousin Mourad or with me or with any of the other members of our family, asleep or awake, because I *knew* my cousin Mourad couldn't have *bought* the horse, and if he couldn't have bought it he must have *stolen* it, and I refused to believe he had stolen it.

No member of the Garoghlanian family could be a thief.

I stared first at my cousin and then at the horse. There was a pious stillness and humor in each of them which on the one hand delighted me and on the other frightened me.

Mourad, I said, where did you steal this horse?

Leap out of the window, he said, if you want to ride.

It was true, then. He *had* stolen the horse. There was no question about it. He had come to invite me to ride or not, as I chose.

Well, it seemed to me stealing a horse for a ride was not the same thing as stealing something else, such as money. For all I knew, maybe it wasn't stealing at all. If you were crazy about horses the way my cousin Mourad and I were, it wasn't stealing. It wouldn't become stealing until we offered to sell the horse, which of course I knew we would never do.

Let me put on some clothes, I said.

All right, he said, but hurry.

I leaped into my clothes.

I jumped down to the yard from the window and leaped up onto the horse behind my cousin Mourad.

That year we lived at the edge of town, on Walnut Avenue. Behind our house was the country: vineyards, orchards, irrigation ditches, and country roads. In less than three minutes we were on Olive Avenue, and then the horse began to trot. The air was new and lovely to breathe. The feel of the horse running was wonderful. My cousin Mourad who was considered one of the craziest members of our family began to sing. I mean, he began to roar.

Every family has a crazy streak in it somewhere, and my cousin Mourad was considered the natural descendant of the crazy streak in our tribe. Before him was our uncle Khosrove, an enormous man with a powerful head of black hair and the largest mustache in the San Joaquin Valley, a man so furious in temper, so irritable, so impatient that he stopped anyone from talking by roaring, *It is no harm; pay no attention to it.*

That was all, no matter what anybody happened to be talking about. Once it was his own son Arak running eight blocks to the barber shop where his father was having his mustache trimmed to tell him their house was on fire. This man Khosrove sat up in the chair and roared, It is no harm; pay no attention to it. The barber said, But the boy says your house is on fire. So Khosrove roared, Enough, it is no harm, I say.

My cousin Mourad was considered the natural descendant of this man, although Mourad's father was Zorab, who was practical and nothing else. That's how it was in our tribe. A man could be the father of his son's flesh, but that did not mean that he was also the father of his spirit. The distribution of the various kinds of spirit of our tribe had been from the beginning capricious and vagrant.

We rode and my cousin Mourad sang. For all anybody knew we were still in the old country where, at least according to some of our neighbors, we belonged. We let the horse run as long as it felt like running.

At last my cousin Mourad said, Get down. I want to ride alone.

Will you let me ride alone? I said.

That is up to the horse, my cousin said. Get down.

The *horse* will let me ride, I said.

We shall see, he said. Don't forget that I have a way with a horse.

Well, I said, any way you have with a horse, I have also.

For the sake of your safety, he said, let us hope so. Get down.

All right, I said, but remember you've got to let me try to ride alone.

I got down and my cousin Mourad kicked his heels into the horse and shouted, *Vazire,* run. The horse stood on its hind legs, snorted, and burst into a fury of speed that was the loveliest thing I had ever seen. My cousin Mourad raced the horse across a field of dry grass to an irrigation ditch, crossed the ditch on the horse, and five minutes later returned, dripping wet.

The sun was coming up.

Now it's my turn to ride, I said.

My cousin Mourad got off the horse.

Ride, he said.

I leaped to the back of the horse and for a moment knew the awfulest fear imaginable. The horse did not move.

Kick into his muscles, my cousin Mourad said. What are you waiting for? We've got to take him back before everybody in the world is up and about.

I kicked into the muscles of the horse. Once again it reared and snorted. Then it began to run. I didn't know what to do. Instead of running across the field to the irrigation ditch the horse ran down the road to the vineyard of Dikran Halabian where it began to leap over vines. The horse leaped over seven vines before I fell. Then it continued running.

My cousin Mourad came running down the road.

I'm not worried about you, he shouted. We've got to get that horse. You go this way and I'll go this way. If you come upon him, be kindly. I'll be near.

I continued down the road and my cousin Mourad went across the field toward the irrigation ditch.

It took him half an hour to find the horse and bring him back.

All right, he said, jump on. The whole world is awake now.

What will we do? I said.

Well, he said, we'll either take him back or hide him until tomorrow morning.

He didn't sound worried and I knew he'd hide him and not take him back. Not for a while, at any rate.

Where will we hide him? I said.

I know a place, he said.

How long ago did you steal this horse? I said.

It suddenly dawned on me that he had been taking these early morning rides for some time and had come for me this morning only because he knew how much I longed to ride.

Who said anything about stealing a horse? he said.

Anyhow, I said, how long ago did you begin riding every morning?

Not until this morning, he said.

Are you telling the truth? I said.

Of course not, he said, but if we are found out, that's what you're to say. I don't want both of us to be liars. All you know is that we started riding this morning.

All right, I said.

He walked the horse quietly to the barn of a deserted vineyard which at one time had been the pride of a farmer named Fetvajian. There were some oats and dry alfalfa in the barn.

We began walking home.

It wasn't easy, he said, to get the horse to behave so nicely. At first it wanted to run wild, but, as I've told you, I have a way with a horse. I can get it to want to do anything *I* want it to do. Horses understand me.

How do you do it? I said.

I have an understanding with a horse, he said.

Yes, but what sort of an understanding? I said.

A simple and honest one, he said.

Well, I said, I wish I knew how to reach an understanding like that with a horse.

You're still a small boy, he said. When you get to be thirteen you'll know how to do it.

I went home and ate a hearty breakfast.

That afternoon my uncle Khosrove came to our house for coffee and cigarettes. He sat in the parlor, sipping and smoking and remembering the old country. Then another visitor arrived, a farmer named John Byro, an Assyrian who, out of loneliness, had learned to speak Armenian. My mother brought the lonely visitor coffee and tobacco and he rolled a cigarette and sipped and smoked, and then at last, sighing sadly, he said, My white horse which was stolen last month is still gone. I cannot understand it.

My uncle Khosrove became very irritated and shouted, It's no harm. What is the loss of a horse? Haven't we all lost the homeland? What is this crying over a horse?

That may be all right for you, a city dweller, to say, John Byro said, but what of my surrey? What good is a surrey without a horse?

Pay no attention to it, my uncle Khosrove roared.

I walked ten miles to get here, John Byro said.

You have legs, my uncle Khosrove shouted.

My left leg pains me, the farmer said.

Pay no attention to it, my uncle Khosrove roared.

That horse cost me sixty dollars, the farmer said.

I spit on money, my uncle Khosrove said.

He got up and stalked out of the house, slamming the screen door.

My mother explained.

He has a gentle heart, she said. It is simply that he is homesick and such a large man.

The farmer went away and I ran over to my cousin Mourad's house.

He was sitting under a peach tree, trying to repair the hurt wing of a young robin which could not fly. He was talking to the bird.

What is it? he said.

The farmer, John Byro, I said. He visited our house. He wants his horse. You've had it a month. I want you to promise not to take it back until I learn to ride.

It will take you *a year* to learn to ride, my cousin Mourad said.

We could keep the horse a year, I said.

My cousin Mourad leaped to his feet.

What? he roared. Are you inviting a member of the Garoghlanian family to steal? The horse must go back to its true owner.

When? I said.

In six months at the latest, he said.

He threw the bird into the air. The bird tried hard, almost fell twice, but at last flew away, high and straight.

Early every morning for two weeks my cousin Mourad and I took the horse out of the barn of the deserted vineyard where we were hiding it and rode it, and every morning the horse, when it was my turn to ride alone, leaped over grape vines and small trees and threw me and ran away. Nevertheless, I hoped in time to learn to ride the way my cousin Mourad rode.

One morning on the way to Fetvajian's deserted vineyard we ran into the farmer John Byro who was on his way to town.

Let me do the talking, my cousin Mourad said. I have a way with farmers.

Good morning, John Byro, my cousin Mourad said to the farmer.

The farmer studied the horse eagerly.

Good morning, sons of my friends, he said. What is the name of your horse?

My Heart, my cousin Mourad said in Armenian.

A lovely name, John Byro said, for a lovely horse. I could swear it is the horse that was stolen from me many weeks ago. May I look into its mouth?

Of course, Mourad said.

The farmer looked into the mouth of the horse.

Tooth for tooth, he said. I would swear it *is* my horse if I didn't know your parents. The fame of your family for honesty is well known to me. Yet the horse is the twin of my horse. A suspicious man would believe his eyes instead of his heart. Good day, my young friends.

Good day, John Byro, my cousin Mourad said.

Early the following morning we took the horse to John Byro's vineyard and put it in the barn. The dogs followed us around without making a sound.

The dogs, I whispered to my cousin Mourad. I thought they would bark.

They would at somebody else, he said. I have a way with dogs.

My cousin Mourad put his arms around the horse, pressed his nose into the horse's nose, patted it, and then we went away.

That afternoon John Byro came to our house in his surrey and showed my mother the horse that had been stolen and returned.

I do not know what to think, he said. The horse is stronger than ever. Better-tempered, too. I thank God.

My uncle Khosrove, who was in the parlor, became irritated and shouted, Quiet, man, quiet. Your horse has been returned. Pay no attention to it.

* * *

EXAMINING THE STORY

1. The Garoghlanians, Aram tells us, are famous for their honesty. Yet Mourad allows himself the pleasure of riding a stolen horse. How does he justify his behavior to Aram? to himself? Do you consider Mourad and Aram honest? dishonest? Why?
2. When the farmer John Byro meets the boys on the road, he does not claim his horse on the spot. Why not? Explain how his action leads to the return of his horse. (What do his Armenian neighbors like about John Byro's actions?) At the end of the story, John Byro brings the horse to the Garoghlanians' house. Why? How does this gesture further reveal the kind of man he is?
3. Mourad "enjoyed being alive more than anybody else." Does this fact help to explain Mourad's "understanding" with horses, birds, and farmers? (The robin with the hurt wing recovers; the farmer is not angry at Mourad's theft; the horse enjoys better health and temper than ever before.) Is the secret of Mourad's power revealed in the name he gives the horse? Explain.
4. "It is simply that he is homesick and such a large man." By this remark, Aram's mother tries to explain two of Uncle Khosrove's ways of behaving. What are they? Does Uncle Khosrove put a high value on material possessions? Defend your answer. In what ways is Uncle Khosrove similar to Mourad?
5. **A Broader Perspective •** In this story, Armenian farmers with very few material things are shown to possess something else of immense value. What is it? How is it shown in the way they treat animals? In their regard for the feelings of other people? In what way are these people unfailingly honest? In what sense are their lives rich? What qualities of character are most honored by this story?

Antaeus

BORDEN DEAL

This was during the wartime, when lots of people were coming North for jobs in factories and war industries, when people moved around a lot more than they do now and sometimes kids were thrown into new groups and new lives that were completely different from anything they had ever known before. I remember this one kid, T.J. his name was, from somewhere down South, whose family moved into our building during that time. They'd come North with everything they owned piled into the back seat of an old-model sedan that you wouldn't expect could make the trip, with T.J. and his three younger sisters riding shakily on top of the load of junk.

Our building was just like all the others there, with families crowded into a few rooms, and I guess there were twenty-five or thirty kids about my age in that one building. Of course, there were a few of us who formed a gang and ran together all the time after school, and I was the one who brought T.J. in and started the whole thing.

The building right next door to us was a factory where they made walking dolls. It was a low building with a flat, tarred roof that had a parapet[1] all around it about head-high, and we'd found out a long time before that no one, not even the watchman, paid any attention to the roof, because it was higher than any of the other buildings around. So my gang used the roof as a headquarters. We could get up there by crossing over to the fire escape from our own roof on a plank and then going on up. It was a secret place for us, where nobody else could go without our permission.

Antaeus: pronounced an · tē'əs.
[1] **parapet:** low protective wall around a roof.

I remember the day I first took T.J. up there to meet the gang. He was a stocky, robust kid with a shock of white hair, nothing sissy about him except his voice; he talked in this slow, gentle voice like you never heard before. He talked different from any of us, and you noticed it right away. But I liked him anyway, so I told him to come on up.

We climbed up over the parapet and dropped down on the roof. The rest of the gang were already there.

"Hi," I said. I jerked my thumb at T.J. "He just moved into the building yesterday."

He just stood there, not scared or anything, just looking, like the first time you see somebody you're not sure you're going to like.

"Hi," Blackie said. "Where are you from?"

"Marion County," T.J. said.

We laughed. "Marion County?" I said. "Where's that?"

He looked at me for a moment like I was a stranger too. "It's in Alabama," he said, like I ought to know where it was.

"What's your name?" Charley said.

"T.J.," he said, looking back at him. He had pale blue eyes that looked washed-out, but he looked directly at Charley, waiting for his reaction. He'll be all right, I thought. No sissy in him, except that voice. Who ever talked like that?

"T.J.," Blackie said. "That's just initials. What's your real name? Nobody in the world has just initials."

"I do," he said. "And they're T.J. That's all the name I got." His voice was resolute with the knowledge of his rightness, and for a moment no one had anything to say. T.J. looked around at the rooftop and down at the black tar under his feet. "Down yonder where I come from," he said, "we played out in the woods. Don't you-all have no woods around here?"

"Naw" Blackie said. "There's the park a few blocks over, but it's full of kids and cops and old women. You can't do a thing."

T.J. kept looking at the tar under his feet. "You mean you ain't got no fields to raise nothing in, no watermelons or nothing?"

"Naw," I said scornfully. "What do you want to grow something for? The folks can buy everything they need at the store."

He looked at me again with that strange, unknowing look. "In Marion County," he said, "I had my own acre of cotton and my own acre of corn. It was mine to plant and make ever' year."

He sounded like it was something to be proud of, and in some obscure way it made the rest of us angry. Blackie said, "Who'd want to have their own acre of cotton and corn? That's just work. What can you do with an acre of cotton and corn?"

T.J. looked at him. "Well you get part of the bale offen your acre," he said seriously. "And I fed my acre of corn to my calf."

We didn't really know what he was talking about, so we were more puzzled than angry; otherwise, I guess, we'd have chased him off the roof and wouldn't let him be part of our gang. But he was strange and different, and we were all attracted by his stolid sense of rightness and belonging, maybe by the strange softness of his voice contrasting our own tones of speech into harshness.

He moved his foot against the black tar. "We could make our own field right here," he said softly, thoughtfully. "Come spring we could raise us what we want to — watermelons and garden truck and no telling what all."

"You'd have to be a good farmer to make these tar roofs grow any watermelons," I said. We all laughed.

But T.J. looked serious. "We could haul us some dirt up here," he said. "And spread it out even and water it, and before you know it, we'd have us a crop in here." He looked at us intently. "Wouldn't that be fun?"

"They wouldn't let us," Blackie said quickly.

"I thought you said this was you-all's roof," T.J. said to me. "That you-all could do anything you wanted to up here."

"They've never bothered us," I said. I felt the idea beginning to catch fire in me. It was a big idea, and it took a while for it to sink in; but the more I thought about it, the better I liked it. "Say," I said to the gang. "He might have something there. Just make us a regular roof garden, with flowers and grass and trees and everything. And all ours, too," I said. "We wouldn't let anybody up here except the ones we wanted to."

"It'd take a while to grow trees," T.J. said quickly, but we weren't paying any attention to him. They were all talking about it suddenly, all excited with the idea after I'd put it in a way they could catch hold of it. Only rich people had roof gardens, we knew, and the idea of our own private domain excited them.

"We could bring it up in sacks and boxes," Blackie said. "We'd have to do it while the folks weren't paying any attention to us, for we'd have to come up to the roof of our building and then cross over with it."

"Where could we get the dirt?" somebody said worriedly.

"Out of those vacant lots over close to school," Blackie said. "Nobody'd notice if we scraped it up."

I slapped T.J. on the shoulder. "Man, you had a wonderful idea," I said, and everybody grinned at him, remembering that he had started it. "Our own private roof garden."

He grinned back. "It'll be ourn," he said. "All ourn." Then he looked thoughtful again. "Maybe I can lay my hands on some cotton seed, too. You think we could raise us some cotton?"

We'd started big projects before at one time or another, like any gang of kids, but they'd always petered out for lack of organization and direction. But this one didn't; somehow or other T.J. kept it going all through the winter months. He kept talking about the watermelons and the cotton we'd raise, come spring, and when even that wouldn't work, he'd switch around to my idea of flowers and grass and trees, though he was always honest enough to add that it'd take a while to get any trees started. He always had it on his mind and he'd mention it in school, getting them lined up to carry dirt that afternoon, saying in a casual way that he reckoned a few more weeks ought to see the job through.

Our little area of private earth grew slowly. T.J. was smart enough to start in one corner of the building, heaping up the carried earth two or three feet thick so that we had an immediate result to look at, to contemplate with awe. Some of the evenings T.J. alone was carrying earth up to the building, the rest of the gang distracted by other enterprises or interests, but T.J. kept plugging along on his own, and eventually we'd all come back to him again and then our own little acre would grow more rapidly.

He was careful about the kind of dirt he'd let us carry up there, and more than once he dumped a sandy load over the parapet into the areaway below because it wasn't good enough. He found out the kinds of earth in all the vacant lots for blocks around. He'd pick it up and feel it and smell it, frozen though it was sometimes, and then he'd say it was good growing soil or it wasn't worth anything, and we'd have to go on somewhere else.

Thinking about it now, I don't see how he kept us at it. It was hard work, lugging paper sacks and boxes of dirt all the way up the stairs of our own building, keeping out of the way of the grownups so they wouldn't catch on to what we were doing. They probably wouldn't have cared, for they didn't pay much attention to us, but we wanted to keep it secret anyway. Then we had to go through the trapdoor to our roof, teeter over a plank to the fire escape, then climb two or three stories to the parapet and drop down onto the roof. All that for a small pile of earth that sometimes didn't seem worth the effort. But T.J. kept the vision bright within us, his words shrewd and calculated toward the fulfillment of his dream; and he worked harder than any of us. He seemed driven toward a goal that we couldn't see, a particular point in time that would be definitely marked by signs and wonders that only he could see.

The laborious earth just lay there during the cold months, inert and lifeless, the clods lumpy and cold under our feet when we walked over it. But one day it rained, and afterward there was a softness in the air, and the earth was live and giving again with moisture and warmth.

That evening T.J. smelled the air, his nostrils dilating with the odor of the earth under his feet. "It's spring," he said, and there was a gladness rising in his voice that filled us all with the same feeling. "It's mighty late for it, but it's spring. I'd just about decided it wasn't never gonna get here at all."

We were all sniffing at the air, too, trying to smell it the way that T.J. did, and I can still remember the sweet odor of the earth under our feet. It was the first time in my life that spring and spring earth had meant anything to me. I looked at T.J. then, knowing in a faint way the hunger within him through the toilsome winter months, knowing the dream that lay behind his plan. He was a new Antaeus, preparing his own bed of strength.

"Planting time," he said. "We'll have to find us some seed."

"What do we do?" Blackie said. "How do we do it?"

"First we'll have to break up the clods," T.J. said. "That won't be hard to do. Then we plant the seed, and after a while they come up. Then you got you a crop." He frowned. "But you ain't got it raised yet. You got to tend it and hoe it and take care of it, and all the time it's growing and growing, while you're awake and while you're asleep. Then you lay it by when it's growed and let it ripen, and then you got you a crop."

"There's those wholesale seed houses over on Sixth," I said. "We could probably swipe some grass seed over there."

T.J. looked at the earth. "You-all seem mighty set on raising some grass," he said. "I ain't never put no effort into that. I spent all my life trying not to raise grass."

"But it's pretty," Blackie said. "We could play on it and take sunbaths on it. Like having our own lawn. Lots of people got lawns."

"Well," T.J. said. He looked at the rest of us, hesitant for the first time. He kept on looking at us for a moment. "I did have it in mind to raise some corn and vegetables. But we'll plant grass."

He was smart. He knew where to give in. And I don't suppose it made any difference to him, really. He just wanted to grow something, even if it was grass.

"Of course," he said, "I do think we ought to plant a row of watermelons. They'd be mighty nice to eat while we was a-laying on that grass."

We all laughed. "All right," I said. "We'll plant us a row of watermelons."

Things went very quickly then. Perhaps half the roof was covered with the earth, the half that wasn't broken by ventilators, and we swiped pocketfuls of grass seed from the open bins in the wholesale seed house, mingling among the buyers on Saturdays and during the school lunch hour. T.J. showed us how to prepare the earth, breaking up the clods and smoothing it and sowing the grass seed. It looked rich and black now with moisture, receiving of the seed, and it seemed that the grass sprang up overnight, pale green in the early spring.

We couldn't keep from looking at it, unable to believe that we had created this delicate growth. We looked at T.J. with understanding now, knowing the fulfillment of the plan he had carried along within his mind. We had worked without full understanding of the task, but he had known all the time.

We found that we couldn't walk or play on the delicate blades, as we had expected to, but we didn't mind. It was enough just to look at it, to realize that it was the work of our own hands, and each evening the whole gang was there, trying to measure the growth that had been achieved that day.

One time a foot was placed on the plot of ground, one time only, Blackie stepping onto it with sudden bravado. Then he looked at the crushed blades and there was shame in his face. He did not do it again. This was his grass, too, and not to be desecrated. No one said anything, for it was not necessary.

T.J. had reserved a small section for watermelons, and he was still trying to find some seed for it. The wholesale house didn't have any watermelon seed, and we didn't know where we could lay our hands on them. T.J. shaped the earth into mounds, ready to receive them, three mounds lying in a straight line along the edge of the grass plot.

We had just about decided that we'd have to buy the seed if we were to get them. It was a violation of our principles, but we were anxious to get the watermelons started. Somewhere or other, T.J. got his hands on a seed catalog and brought it one evening to our roof garden.

"We can order them now," he said, showing us the catalog. "Look!"

We all crowded around, looking at the fat, green watermelons pictured in full color on the pages. Some of them were split open, showing the red, tempting meat, making our mouths water.

"Now we got to scrape up some seed money," T.J. said, looking at us. "I got a quarter. How much you-all got?"

We made up a couple of dollars between us and T.J. nodded his head. "That'll be more than enough. Now we got to decide what kind to get. I think them Kleckley Sweets. What do you-all think?"

He was going into esoteric matters beyond our reach. We hadn't even known there were different kinds of melons. So we just nodded our heads and agreed that yes, we thought the Kleckley Sweets too.

"I'll order them tonight," T.J. said. "We ought to have them in a few days."

"What are you boys doing up here?" an adult voice said behind us.

It startled us, for no one had ever come up here before in all the time we had been using the roof of the factory. We jerked around and saw three men standing near the trapdoor at the other end of the roof. They weren't policemen or night watchmen, but three men in plump business suits, looking at us. They walked toward us.

"What are you boys doing up here?" the one in the middle said again.

We stood still, guilt heavy among us, levied by the tone of voice, and looked at the three strangers.

The men stared at the grass flourishing behind us. "What's this?" the man said. "How did this get up here?"

"Sure is growing good, ain't it?" T.J. said conversationally. "We planted it."

The men kept looking at the grass as if they didn't believe it. It was a thick carpet over the earth now, a patch of deep greenness startling in the sterile industrial surroundings.

"Yes, sir," T.J. said proudly. "We toted that earth up here and planted that grass." He fluttered the seed catalog. "And we're just fixing to plant us some watermelon."

The man looked at him then, his eyes strange and faraway. "What do you mean, putting this on the roof of my building?" he said. "Do you want to go to jail?"

T.J. looked shaken. The rest of us were silent, frightened by the authority of his voice. We had grown up aware of adult authority, of policemen and night watchmen and teachers, and this man sounded like all the others. But it was a new thing to T.J.

"Well, you wan't using the roof," T.J. said. He paused a moment and added shrewdly, "So we just thought to pretty it up a little bit."

"And sag it so I'd have to rebuild it," the man said sharply. He started turning away, saying to another man beside him, "See that all that junk is shoveled off by tomorrow."

"Yes, sir," the man said.

T.J. started forward. "You can't do that," he said. "We toted it up here, and it's our earth. We planted it and raised it and toted it up here."

The man stared at him coldly. "But it's my building," he said. "It's to be shoveled off tomorrow."

"It's our earth," T.J. said desperately. "You ain't got no right!"

The men walked on without listening and descended clumsily through the trapdoor. T.J. stood looking after them, his body tense with anger, until they had disappeared. They wouldn't even argue with him, wouldn't let him defend his earthrights.

He turned to us. "We won't let 'em do it," he said fiercely. "We'll stay up here all day tomorrow and the day after that, and we won't let 'em do it."

We just looked at him. We knew that there was no stopping it.

He saw it in our faces, and his face wavered for a moment before he gripped it into determination. "They ain't got no right," he said. "It's our earth. It's our land. Can't nobody touch a man's own land."

We kept on looking at him, listening to the words but knowing that it was no use. The adult world had descended on us even in our richest dream, and we knew there was no calculating the adult world, no fighting it, no winning against it.

We started moving slowly toward the parapet and the fire escape, avoiding a last look at the green beauty of the earth that T.J. had planted for us, had planted deeply in our minds as well as in our experience. We filed slowly over the edge and down the steps to the plank, T.J. coming last, and all of us could feel the weight of his grief behind us.

"Wait a minute," he said suddenly, his voice harsh with the effort of calling.

We stopped and turned, held by the tone of his voice, and looked up at him standing above us on the fire escape.

"We can't stop them?" he said, looking down at us, his face strange in the dusky light. "There ain't no way to stop 'em?"

"No," Blackie said with finality. "They own the building."

We stood still for a moment, looking up at T.J., caught into inaction by the decision working in his face. He stared back at us, and his face was pale and mean in the poor light, with a bald nakedness in his skin like cripples have sometimes.

"They ain't gonna touch my earth," he said fiercely. "They ain't gonna lay a hand on it! Come on."

He turned around and started up the fire escape again, almost running against the effort of climbing. We followed more slowly, not knowing what he intended. By the time we reached him, he had seized a board and thrust it into the soil, scooping it up and flinging it over the parapet into the areaway below. He straightened and looked at us.

"They can't touch it," he said. "I won't let 'em lay a dirty hand on it!"

We saw it then. He stooped to his labor again and we followed, the gusts of his anger moving in frenzied labor among us as we scattered along the edge of earth, scooping it and throwing it over the parapet, destroying with anger the growth we had nurtured with such tender care. The soil carried so laboriously upward to the light and the sun cascaded swiftly into the dark areaway, the green blades of grass crumpled and twisted in the falling.

It took less time than you would think; the task of destruction is infinitely easier than that of creation. We stopped at the end, leaving only a scattering of loose soil, and when it was finally over, a stillness stood among the group and over the factory building. We looked down at the bare sterility of black tar, felt the harsh texture of it under the soles of our shoes, and the anger had gone out of us, leaving only a sore aching in our minds like overstretched muscles.

T.J. stood for a moment, his breathing slowing from anger and effort, caught into the same contemplation of destruction as all of us. He stooped slowly, finally, and picked up a lonely blade of grass left trampled under our feet and put it between his teeth, tasting it, sucking the greenness out of it into his mouth. Then he started walking toward the fire escape, moving before any of us were ready to move, and disappeared over the edge.

We followed him, but he was already halfway down to the ground, going on past the board where we crossed over, climbing down into the areaway. We saw the last section swing down with his weight, and then he stood on the concrete below us, looking at the small pile of anonymous earth scattered by our throwing. Then he walked across the place where we could see him and disappeared toward the street without glancing back, without looking up to see us watching him.

They did not find him for two weeks. Then the Nashville police caught him just outside the Nashville freight yards. He was walking along the railroad track, still heading south, still heading home.

As for us, who had no remembered home to call us, none of us ever again climbed the escapeway to the roof.

* * *

EXAMINING THE STORY

1. T.J. is driven by a vision the other boys do not share. What is it? Why does his idea take fire with the other boys only after it is labeled a "roof garden"? (What advantages do the boys associate with a roof garden?)

2. During the winter months, T.J. manages to keep alive interest in the roof garden. In what ways does he show faith? drive? flexibility? an understanding of people? Does he *know* more than the other boys about the project they have undertaken? Is he lacking in any important quality of leadership?

3. The boys get grass seed by stealing, because to purchase anything is "a violation of [their] principles." Are their principles different from those of the adult world they live in? Why? When the men confront the boys on the roof, how do principles conflict? Does the landlord have the right to do what he does?

4. Why does T.J. throw the soil of his beloved garden off the roof? In Greek mythology, Antaeus was invincible while he could touch the earth (and was killed while being held off the ground). Does the title of the story help to explain T.J.'s behavior? Does it help to emphasize the story's theme?

5. **A Broader Perspective •** "Antaeus" takes place in the modern industrial world where greenbelts are rare and adults are often too busy earning a living to give care to their children's development. In such a setting, why has contact with the earth a special importance? (Notice that T.J., who has always felt a bond with the earth, has "a sense of rightness and belonging" which is recognized by the other boys, and that they all feel delight and awe as the grass actually takes root and grows.) The story suggests that the ancient myth of Antaeus has an urgent message for modern society. Explain what that message is.

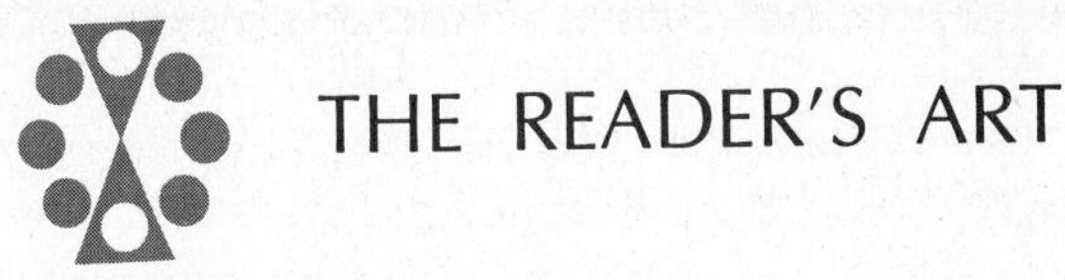

THE READER'S ART

Understanding Character

Action excites the reader while he reads — but only because he cares what is happening to the people in the story. Their purposes for behaving as they do give meaning to their actions. Long after we have forgotten specific incidents of a story, certain figures go on living vividly in memory — Scrooge, Huckleberry Finn, and Saul of the Old Testament, for example.

The character who is vital — who goes on living in the reader's mind — is always believable in two ways. First, his inner life of feeling and motive is real to us. The character may be placed in strange circumstances — like Scrooge in his long night's encounter with otherworld phantoms — but his response must be what the reader can accept as true to human experience: Scrooge feels terror and remorse when he is shown the person he really is. The second way in which a character must be believable is in his self-consistency: his actions, as the story goes on, must be plausible in the light of what we already know about him. He may change, of course, but the change must result understandably from his experiences. (When Huckleberry Finn decides to break the law of his day to shield the runaway slave, Jim, he does so because a long series of first-hand experiences has shown him that Jim is noble and important.)

With these comments in mind, consider the characters T.J. and Mourad. What is the "strangeness" the boys first notice in T.J.? What is the cause of it? How does T.J. show inner consistency in his work on the garden? Is his destruction of the garden true to his character? How and why does T.J. change during the story?

Mourad also is considered strange by others. What observation does Aram make that points out Mourad's difference from other people? (Although Aram, who tells the story, does not fully understand his cousin, does this prevent *you* from understanding Mourad? Why?) Mourad steals a horse. Is this conduct nevertheless guided by a clear and consistent set of values? What does Mourad value?

Which boy, T.J. or Mourad, is more like someone you know? Can you explain how?

FOR WRITING

1. Compare Mourad's use of the white horse with T.J.'s use of the roof. Is the principle the same? The adults in these stories have differing attitudes toward the boys' actions — why? Under what circumstances is it possible for individuals to seize happiness from life?
2. Choose any character from either of these stories. Do the feelings he shows in a given episode of the story seem to you natural? Are his actions in this episode characteristic — that is, consistent with other information given about him?

3 How does war distort human relationships?

The Sniper

LIAM O'FLAHERTY

The long June twilight faded into night. Dublin lay enveloped in darkness but for the dim light of the moon that shone through fleecy clouds, casting a pale light as of approaching dawn over the streets and the dark waters of the Liffey. Around the beleaguered Four Courts the heavy guns roared. Here and there through the city machine guns and rifles broke the silence of the night spasmodically, like dogs barking on lone farms. Republicans and Free Staters[1] were waging civil war.

On a rooftop near O'Connell Bridge a Republican sniper lay watching. Beside him lay his rifle, and over his shoulders were slung a pair of field glasses. His face was the face of a student — thin and ascetic — but his eyes had the cold gleam of the fanatic. They were deep and thoughtful, the eyes of a man who is used to look at death.

He was eating a sandwich hungrily. He had eaten nothing since morning. He had been too excited to eat. He finished the sandwich and paused for a moment, considering whether he should risk a smoke. It was dangerous. The flash might be seen in the darkness and there were enemies watching. He decided

Liam O'Flaherty: The author's first name is pronounced lē'əm.

[1] **Republicans and Free Staters:** The Republicans favored the unification of northern and southern Ireland in a republic, independent of Great Britain. Their opponents supported the Irish Free State (southern Ireland), which had been granted home rule by Britain but remained a part of the British Empire.

to take the risk. Placing a cigarette between his lips, he struck a match, inhaled the smoke hurriedly, and put out the light. Almost immediately, a bullet flattened itself against the parapet[2] of the roof. The sniper took another whiff and put out the cigarette. Then he swore softly and crawled away to the left.

Cautiously he raised himself and peered over the parapet. There was a flash, and a bullet whizzed over his head. He dropped immediately. He had seen the flash. It came from the opposite side of the street.

He rolled over the roof to a chimney stack in the rear, and slowly drew himself up behind it until his eyes were level with the top of the parapet. There was nothing to be seen — just the dim outline of the opposite housetop against the blue sky. His enemy was under cover.

Just then an armored car came across the bridge and advanced slowly up the street. It stopped on the opposite side of the street fifty yards ahead. The sniper could hear the dull panting of the motor. His heart beat faster. It was an enemy car. He wanted to fire, but he knew it was useless. His bullets would never pierce the steel that covered the gray monster.

Then round the corner of a side street came an old woman, her head covered by a tattered shawl. She began to talk to the man in the turret of the car. She was pointing to the roof where the sniper lay. An informer.

The turret opened. A man's head and shoulders appeared, looking towards the sniper. The sniper raised his rifle and fired. The head fell heavily on the turret wall. The woman darted toward the side street. The sniper fired again. The woman whirled round and fell with a shriek into the gutter.

Suddenly from the opposite roof a shot rang out, and the sniper dropped his rifle with a curse. The rifle clattered to the roof. The sniper thought the noise would wake the dead. He stopped to pick the rifle up. He couldn't lift it. His forearm was dead. He muttered, "I'm hit."

Dropping flat onto the roof, he crawled back to the parapet. With his left hand he felt the injured right forearm. The blood was oozing through the sleeve of his coat. There was no pain — just a deadened sensation, as if the arm had been cut off.

Quickly he drew his knife from his pocket, opened it on the breastwork of the parapet, and ripped open the sleeve. There

[2] **parapet:** low protective wall around a roof.

was a small hole where the bullet had entered. On the other side there was no hole. The bullet had lodged in the bone. It must have fractured it. He bent the arm below the wound. The arm bent back easily. He ground his teeth to overcome the pain.

Then, taking out his field dressing, he ripped open the packet with his knife. He broke the neck of the iodine bottle and let the bitter fluid drip into the wound. A paroxysm of pain swept through him. He placed the cotton wadding over the wound and wrapped the dressing over it. He tied the end with his teeth. Then he lay still against the parapet, and closing his eyes, he made an effort of will to overcome the pain.

In the street beneath all was still. The armored car had retired speedily over the bridge, with the machine gunner's head hanging lifeless over the turret. The woman's corpse lay still in the gutter.

The sniper lay for a long time nursing his wounded arm and planning escape. Morning must not find him wounded on the roof. The enemy on the opposite roof covered his escape. He must kill that enemy and he could not use his rifle. He had only a revolver to do it. Then he thought of a plan.

Taking off his cap, he placed it over the muzzle of his rifle. Then he pushed the rifle slowly upwards over the parapet until the cap was visible from the opposite side of the street. Almost immediately there was a report, and a bullet pierced the center of the cap. The sniper slanted the rifle forward. The cap slipped down into the street. Then, catching the rifle in the middle, the sniper dropped his left hand over the roof and let it hang, lifelessly. After a few moments he let the rifle drop to the street. Then he sank to the roof, dragging his hand with him.

Crawling quickly to the left, he peered up at the corner of the roof. His ruse had succeeded. The other sniper, seeing the cap and rifle fall, thought that he had killed his man. He was now standing before a row of chimney pots, looking across, with his head clearly silhouetted against the western sky.

The Republican sniper smiled and lifted his revolver above the edge of the parapet. The distance was about fifty yards — a hard shot in the dim light — and his right arm was paining him like a thousand devils. He took a steady aim. His hand trembled with eagerness. Pressing his lips together, he took a deep breath through his nostrils and fired. He was almost deafened with the report, and his arm shook with the recoil.

Then, when the smoke cleared, he peered across and uttered a cry of joy. His enemy had been hit. He was reeling over the parapet in his death agony. He struggled to keep his feet, but he was slowly falling forward, as if in a dream. The rifle fell from his grasp, hit the parapet, fell over, bounded off the pole of a barber's shop beneath, and then clattered onto the pavement.

Then the dying man on the roof crumpled up and fell forward. The body turned over and over in space and hit the ground with a dull thud. Then it lay still.

The sniper looked at his enemy falling and he shuddered. The lust of battle died in him. He became bitten by remorse. The sweat stood out in beads on his forehead. Weakened by his wound and the long summer day of fasting and watching on the roof, he revolted from the sight of the shattered mass of his dead enemy. His teeth chattered. He began to gibber to himself, cursing the war, cursing himself, cursing everybody.

He looked at the smoking revolver in his hand and with an oath he hurled it to the roof at his feet. The revolver went off with the concussion, and the bullet whizzed past the sniper's head. He was frightened back to his senses by the shock. His nerves steadied. The cloud of fear scattered from his mind and he laughed.

He decided to leave the roof and look for his company commander to report. Everywhere around was quiet. There was not much danger in going through the streets. He picked up his revolver and put it in his pocket. Then he crawled down through the skylight to the house underneath.

When the sniper reached the laneway on the street level, he felt a sudden curiosity as to the identity of the enemy sniper whom he had killed. He decided that he was a good shot whoever he was. He wondered if he knew him. Perhaps he had been in his own company before the split in the army. He decided to risk going over to have a look at him. He peered around the corner into O'Connell Street. In the upper part of the street there was heavy firing, but around here all was quiet.

The sniper darted across the street. A machine gun tore up the ground around him with a hail of bullets, but he escaped. He threw himself face downwards beside the corpse. The machine gun stopped.

Then the sniper turned over the dead body and looked into his brother's face.

EXAMINING THE STORY

1. The Republican sniper is described as "a student" but also "a fanatic." How many of his actions are expressions of one of these two characteristics? (Consider, for example, the fact that he does not shoot the armored car, does shoot the old woman, tries to bend his arm bone to make sure it is broken, and is curious to know whom he has killed.) Is he also brave? resourceful? understandable? Why or why not?
2. What does the Republican sniper respect about his adversary? Why does he notice more details about this death than about others he has caused that day? Does the change in his condition — by then he is wounded, tired, and hungry — account for his sudden remorse when the Free State sniper dies? Explain.
3. In what ways are the two snipers alike? In what sense, even before he sees the dead man's face, does the Republican sniper realize that he has killed a brother?
4. **A Broader Perspective** • The Republican sniper is never given a name. Why? Why aren't the political differences between the Republicans and Free Staters explained? (Are they important to the author's purpose?) Is the setting essential to this story, or is the Irish episode mainly a way to raise a more general question about the meaning of war?

The Enemy

PEARL BUCK

Dr. Sadao Hoki's house was built on a spot of the Japanese coast where as a little boy he had often played. The low square stone house was set upon rocks well above a narrow beach that was outlined with bent pines. As a boy Sadao had climbed the pines, supporting himself on his bare feet as he had seen men do in the South Seas when they climbed for coconuts. His father had taken him often to the islands of those seas, and never had he failed to say to the little grave boy at his side, "Those islands yonder, they are the steppingstones to the future for Japan."

"Where shall we step from them?" Sadao had asked seriously.

"Who knows?" his father had answered. "Who can limit our future? It depends on what we make it."

Sadao had taken this into his mind as he did everything his father said, his father who never joked or played with him but who spent infinite pains upon him who was his only son. Sadao knew that his education was his father's chief concern. For this reason he had been sent at twenty-two to America to learn all that could be learned of surgery and medicine. He had come back at thirty, and before his father died he had seen Sadao become famous not only as a surgeon but as a scientist. Because he was now perfecting a discovery which would render wounds entirely clean, he had not been sent abroad with the troops. Also, he knew, there was some slight danger that the old General might need an operation for a condition for which he was now being treated medically, and for this possibility Sadao was being kept in Japan.

Clouds were rising from the ocean now. The unexpected warmth of the last few days had at night drawn heavy fog from the cold waves. He watched mists hide outlines of a little island near the shore and then come creeping up the beach below the house, wreathing around the pines. In a few minutes it would be wrapped about the house, too. Then he would go into the room where Hana, his wife, would be waiting for him with the two children.

But at this moment the door opened and she looked out, a dark blue woolen *haori* over her kimono. She came to him affectionately and put her arm through his as he stood, smiled and said nothing. He had met Hana in America, but he had waited to fall in love with her until he was sure she was Japanese. His father would never have received her unless she had been pure in her race. He wondered often whom he would have married if he had not met Hana, and by what luck he had found her in the most casual way, by chance, literally, at an American professor's house. The professor and his wife had been kind people, anxious to do something for their few foreign students, and the students, though bored, had accepted this kindness. Sadao had often told Hana how nearly he had not gone to Professor Harley's house that night — the rooms were so small, the food so bad, the professor's wife so voluble. But he had gone, and there he had found Hana, a new student, and had felt he would love her, if it were at all possible.

Now he felt her hand on his arm and was aware of the pleasure it gave him, even though they had been married years enough to have the two children. For they had not married heedlessly in America. They had finished their work at school and had come home to Japan, and when his father had seen her, the marriage had been arranged in the old Japanese way, although Sadao and Hana had talked everything over beforehand. They were perfectly happy. She laid her cheek against his arm.

It was at this moment that both of them saw something black come out of the mists. It was a man. He was flung up out of the ocean — flung, it seemed, to his feet by a breaker. He staggered a few steps, his body outlined against the mist, his arms above his head. Then the curled mists hid him again.

"Who is that?" Hana cried. She dropped Sadao's arm and they both leaned over the railing of the veranda. Now they saw him again. The man was on his hands and knees, crawling. Then they saw him fall on his face and lie there.

"A fisherman, perhaps," Sadao said, "washed from his boat." He ran quickly down the steps and behind him Hana came, her wide sleeves flying. A mile or two away on either side there were fishing villages, but here was only the bare and lonely coast, dangerous with rocks. The surf beyond the beach was spiked with rocks. Somehow the man had managed to come through them — he must be badly torn.

They saw when they came toward him that indeed it was so. The sand on one side of him had already a stain of red soaking through.

"He is wounded!" Sadao exclaimed. He made haste to the man, who lay motionless, his face in the sand. An old cap stuck to his head, soaked with sea water. He was in wet rags of garments. Sadao stooped, Hana at his side, and turned the man's head. They saw the face.

"A white man!" Hana whispered.

Yes, it was a white man. The wet cap fell away and there was his wet yellow hair, long, as though for many weeks it had not been cut, and upon his young and tortured face was a ragged yellow beard. He was unconscious and knew nothing that they did to him.

Now Sadao remembered the wound, and with his expert fingers he began to search for it. Blood flowed freshly at his touch. On the right side of his lower back Sadao saw that a ragged gun wound had been reopened. The flesh was blackened with powder. Sometime, not many days ago, the man had been shot and had not been tended. It was bad chance that the rock had struck the wound.

"Oh, how he is bleeding!" Hana whispered again in a solemn voice. The mists screened them now completely, and at this time of day no one came by here. The fishermen had gone home and even the chance beachcombers would have considered the day at an end.

"What shall we do with this man?" Sadao muttered. But his trained hands seemed of their own will to be doing what they could to staunch the fearful bleeding. He packed the wound with the sea moss that strewed the beach. The man moaned with pain in his stupor, but he did not awaken.

"The best thing that we could do would be to put him back in the sea," Sadao said, answering himself.

Now that the bleeding was stopped for the moment he stood up and dusted the sand from his hands.

"Yes, undoubtedly that would be best," Hana said steadily. But she continued to stare down at the motionless man.

"If we sheltered a white man in our house, we would be arrested, and if we turned him over as a prisoner, he would certainly die," Sadao said.

"The kindest thing would be to put him back into the sea," Hana said. But neither of them moved. They were staring with a curious repulsion upon the inert figure.

"What is he?" Hana whispered.

"There is something about him that looks American," Sadao said. He took up the battered cap. Yes, there, almost gone, was the faint lettering. "A sailor," he said, "from an American battleship." He spelled it out, "U.S. Navy." The man was a prisoner of war!

"He has escaped," Hana cried softly, "and that is why he is wounded."

"In the back," Sadao agreed.

They hesitated, looking at each other. Then Hana said with resolution, "Come, are we able to put him back into the sea?"

"If I am able, are you?" Sadao asked.

"No," Hana said. "But if you can do it alone . . ."

Sadao hesitated again. "The strange thing is," he said, "that if the man were whole I could turn him over to the police without difficulty. I care nothing for him. He is my enemy. All Americans are my enemy. And he is only a common fellow. You see how foolish his face is. But since he is wounded . . ."

"You also cannot throw him back to the sea," Hana said. "Then there is only one thing to do. We must carry him into the house."

"But the servants?" Sadao inquired.

"We must simply tell them that we intend to give him to the police — as indeed we must, Sadao. We must think of the children and your position. It would endanger all of us if we did not give this man over as a prisoner of war."

"Certainly," Sadao agreed. "I would not think of doing anything else."

Thus agreed, together they lifted the man. He was very light, like a fowl that has been half-starved for a long time until it is only feathers and skeleton. So, his hand and arms hanging, they carried him up the steps and into the side door of the house. This door opened into a passage and down the passage they carried the man toward an empty bedroom. It had been the bedroom of Sadao's father, and since his death it had not been used. They laid the man on the deeply matted floor. Everything here had been Japanese to please the old man, who would never, in his own home, sit on a chair or sleep in a foreign bed. Hana went to the wall cupboards and slid back a door and took out a soft quilt. She hesitated. The quilt was covered with flowered silk, and the lining was pure white silk.

"He is so dirty," she murmured in distress.

"Yes, he had better be washed," Sadao agreed. "If you will fetch hot water, I will wash him."

"I cannot bear for you to touch him," she said. "We shall have to tell the servants he is here. I will tell Yumi. She can leave the children for a few minutes."

Sadao considered a moment. "Let it be so," he agreed. "You tell Yumi and I will tell the others."

But the utter pallor of the man's unconscious face moved him first to stoop and feel his pulse. It was faint but it was there. He put his hand against the man's cold breast. The heart, too, was yet alive.

"He will die unless he is operated on," Sadao said, considering. "The question is whether he will die if he is operated on, too."

Hana cried out in fear. "Don't try to save him! What if he should live?"

"What if he should die?" Sadao replied. He stood gazing down on the motionless man. This man must have extraordinary vitality or he would have been dead by now. But then he was very young — perhaps not yet twenty-five.

"You mean from the operation?" Hana asked.

"Yes," Sadao said.

Hana considered this doubtfully, and when she did not answer Sadao turned away. "At any rate something must be done with him," he said, "and first he must be washed." He went quickly out of the room and Hana came behind him. She did not wish to be left alone with the white man. He was the first she had seen since she left America and now he seemed to have nothing to do with those whom she had known there. Here he was her enemy, a menace, living or dead.

She turned to the nursery and called, "Yumi!"

But the children heard her voice and she had to go in for a moment and smile at them and play with the baby boy, now nearly three months old.

Over the baby's soft black hair she motioned with her mouth, "Yumi — come with me!"

"I will put him to bed," Yumi replied. "He is ready."

She went with Yumi into the bedroom next to the nursery and stood with the boy in her arms while Yumi spread the sleeping quilts on the floor and laid the baby between them.

Then Hana led the way quickly and softly to the kitchen. There two servants were frightened at what their master had just told them. The old gardener who was also a house servant pulled the few hairs on his upper lip.

"The master ought not to heal the wound of this white man," he said bluntly to Hana. "The white man ought to die. First he was shot. Then the sea caught him and wounded him with her rocks. If the master heals what the gun did and what the sea did, they will take revenge on us."

"I will tell him what you say," Hana replied courteously. But she herself was also frightened, although she was not superstitious as the old man was. Could it ever be well to help an enemy? Nevertheless she told Yumi to fetch the hot water and bring it to the room where the white man was.

She went ahead and slid back the partitions. Sadao was not yet there. Yumi put down her wooden bucket. Then she went over to the white man. When she saw him her thick lips folded themselves into stubbornness. "I have never washed a white man," she said, "and I will not wash so dirty a one now."

Hana cried at her severely, "You will do what your master commands you!"

"My master ought not to command me to wash the enemy," Yumi said stubbornly.

There was so fierce a look of resistance upon Yumi's round dull face that Hana felt unreasonably afraid. After all, if the servants should report something that was not as it happened?

"Very well," she said with dignity. "You understand we only want to bring him to his senses so that we can turn him over as a prisoner?"

"I will have nothing to do with it," Yumi said. "I am a poor person and it is not my business."

"Then please," Hana said gently, "return to your own work."

At once Yumi left the room. But this left Hana with the white man alone. She might have been too afraid to stay, had not her anger at Yumi's stubbornness now sustained her.

"Stupid Yumi," she muttered fiercely. "Is this anything but a man? And a wounded, helpless man!"

In the conviction of her own superiority she bent impulsively and untied the knotted rags that kept the white man covered. When she had his breast bare, she dipped the small clean towel that Yumi had brought into the steaming hot water and washed his face carefully. The man's skin, though rough with exposure, was of a fine texture and must have been very blond when he was a child.

While she was thinking these thoughts, though not really liking the man better now that he was no longer a child, she kept on washing him until his upper body was quite clean. But she dared not turn him over. Where was Sadao? Now her anger was ebbing and she was anxious again and she rose, wiping her hands on the wrung towel. Then lest the man be chilled she put the quilt over him.

"Sadao!" she called softly.

He had been about to come in when she called. His hand had been on the door so that now it opened. She saw that he had brought his surgeon's emergency bag and that he wore his surgeon's coat.

"You have decided to operate!" she cried.

"Yes," he said shortly. He turned his back to her and unfolded a sterilized towel upon the floor of the *takonoma* alcove, and put his instruments out upon it.

"Fetch towels," he said.

She went obediently, but how anxious now, to the linen shelves and took out the towels. There ought, also, to be old pieces of matting so that the blood would not ruin the deep floor covering. She went out to the back veranda where the gardener kept strips of matting with which to protect delicate shrubs on cold nights and took an armful of them.

But when she went back into the room, she saw this was useless. The blood had already soaked through the packing in the man's wound and had ruined the mat under him.

"Oh, the mat!" she cried.

"Yes, it is ruined." Sadao replied, as though he did not care. "Help me to turn him," he commanded her.

She obeyed him without a word, and he began to wash the man's back carefully.

"Yumi would not wash him," she said.

"Did you wash him, then?" Sadao asked, not stopping for a moment his swift concise movements.

"Yes," she said.

He did not seem to hear her. But she was used to his absorption when he was at work. She wondered for a moment if it mattered to him what was the body upon which he worked so long as it was the thing he did so excellently.

"You will have to give the anesthetic if he needs it," he said.

"I?" she repeated blankly. "But never have I."

"It is easy enough," he said impatiently.

He was taking out the packing now and the blood began to flow more quickly. He peered into the wound with his bright surgeon's light fastened on his forehead. "The bullet is still there," he said with cool interest. "Now I wonder how deep this rock wound is. If it is not too deep, it may be that I can get the bullet. But the bleeding is not superficial. He has lost much blood."

At this moment Hana choked. He looked up and saw her face the color of sulphur.

"Don't faint," he said sharply. He did not put down his exploring instrument. "If I stop now, the man will surely die." She clapped her hands to her mouth and leaped up and ran out of the room. Outside in the garden he heard her retching. But he went on with his work.

"It will be better for her to empty her stomach," he thought. He had forgotten that of course she had never seen an operation. But her distress and his inability to go to her at once made him impatient and irritable with this man who lay as though dead under his knife.

"This man," he thought, "there is no reason under heaven why he should live."

Unconsciously this thought made him ruthless and he proceeded swiftly. In his dream the man moaned, but Sadao paid no heed except to mutter at him.

"Groan," he muttered, "groan if you like. I am not doing this for my own pleasure. In fact, I do not know why I am doing it."

The door opened and there was Hana again. She had not stopped even to smooth back her hair.

"Where is the anesthetic?" she asked in a clear voice.

Sadao motioned with his chin. "It is as well that you came back," he said. "This fellow is beginning to stir."

She had the bottle and some cotton in her hand.

"But how shall I do it?" she asked.

"Simply saturate the cotton and hold it near his nostrils," Sadao replied without delaying for one moment the intricate detail of his work. "When he breathes badly, move it away a little."

She crouched close to the sleeping face of the young American. It was a piteously thin face, she thought, and the lips were twisted. The man was suffering whether he knew it or not. Watching him, she wondered if the stories they heard sometimes of the sufferings of prisoners were true. They came like flickers of rumor, told by word of mouth and always contradicted. In the newspapers the reports were always that wherever the Japanese armies went the people received them gladly, with cries of joy at their liberation. But sometimes she remembered such men as General Takima, who beat his wife cruelly at home, though no one mentioned it now that he had fought so victorious a battle in Manchuria. If a man like that could be so cruel to a woman in his power, would he not be cruel to one like this, for instance?

She hoped anxiously that this young man had not been tortured. It was at this moment that she observed deep red scars on his neck, just under the ear. "Those scars," she murmured, lifting her eyes to Sadao.

But he did not answer.

At this moment he felt the tip of his instrument strike against something hard, dangerously near the kidney. All thought left him. He felt only the purest pleasure. He probed with his fingers, delicately, familiar with every atom of this human body. His old American professor of anatomy had seen to that knowledge. "Ignorance of the human body is the surgeon's cardinal sin, sirs!" he had thundered at his classes year after year. "To operate without a complete knowledge of the body as if you had made it — anything less is murder."

"It is not quite at the kidney, my friend," Sadao murmured. It was his habit to murmur to the patient when he forgot himself in an operation. "My friend," he always called his patients, and so now he did, forgetting that this was his enemy.

Then, quickly, with the cleanest and most precise of incisions, the bullet was out. The man quivered but he was still unconscious. Nevertheless, he muttered a few English words.

"Guts," he muttered, choking. "They got . . . my guts . . ."

"Sadao!" Hana cried sharply.

"Hush," Sadao said.

The man sank again into silence so profound that Sadao took up his wrist, hating the touch of it. Yes, there was still a pulse so faint, so feeble, but enough, if he wanted the man to live, to give hope.

"But certainly I do not want this man to live," he thought.

"No more anesthetic," he told Hana.

He turned as swiftly as though he had never paused, and from his medicines he chose a small vial and from it filled a hypodermic and thrust it into the patient's left arm. Then putting down the needle he took the man's wrist again. The pulse under his fingers fluttered once or twice and then grew stronger.

"This man will live in spite of all," he said to Hana and sighed.

The young man woke, so weak, his blue eyes so piteous when he perceived where he was, that Hana felt compelled to apology. She served him herself, for none of the servants would enter the room.

When she came in the first time she saw him summon his small strength to be prepared for some fearful thing.

"Don't be afraid," she begged him softly.

"How come . . . you speak English . . ." he gasped.

"I was a long time in America," she replied.

She saw that he wanted to reply to that but he could not and so she knelt and fed him gently from the porcelain spoon. He ate unwillingly, but still he ate.

"Now you will soon be strong," she said, not liking him and yet moved to comfort him.

He did not answer.

When Sadao came in the third day after the operation he found the young man sitting up in bed, his face bloodless with the effort.

"Lie down!" Sadao cried. "Do you want to die?"

He forced the man down gently and strongly, and examined the wound. "You may kill yourself if you do this sort of thing," he scolded.

"What are you going to do with me?" the boy muttered. He looked just now barely seventeen. "Are you going to hand me over?"

For a moment Sadao did not answer. He finished his examination and then pulled the silk quilt over the man.

"I do not know myself what I shall do with you," he said. "I ought of course to give you to the police. You are a prisoner of war . . . no, do not tell me anything." He put up his hand as he saw the young man about to speak. "Do not even tell me your name unless I ask it."

They looked at each other for a moment, and then the young man closed his eyes and turned his face to the wall.

"Okay," he whispered, his mouth a bitter line.

Outside the door Hana was waiting for Sadao. He saw at once that she was in trouble.

"Sadao, Yumi tells me the servants feel that they cannot stay if we hide this man here any more," she said. "She says they are thinking that you and I were so long in America that we have forgotten to think of our own country first. They think we like Americans."

"It is not true," Sadao said harshly. "Americans are our enemies. But I have been trained not to let a man die if I can help it."

"The servants cannot understand that," she said anxiously.

"No," he agreed.

Neither seemed able to say more, and somehow the household dragged on. The servants grew daily more watchful. Their courtesy was as careful as ever, but their eyes were cold upon the pair to whom they were hired.

"It is clear what our master ought to do," the old gardener said one morning. He had worked with flowers all his life, and had been a specialist, too, in moss. For Sadao's father he had made one of the finest moss gardens in Japan, sweeping the bright green carpet constantly so that not a leaf or a pine needle marred the velvet of its surface. "My old master's son knows very well what he ought to do," he now said, pinching a bud from a bush as he spoke. "When the man was so near death, why did he not let him bleed?"

"That young master is so proud of his skill to save life that he saves any life," the cook said contemptuously. She split a fowl's neck skillfully and held the fluttering bird and let its blood flow into the roots of a wistaria vine. Blood is the best of fertilizers and the old gardener would not let her waste a drop of it.

"It is the children of whom we must think," Yumi said sadly. "What will be their fate if their father is condemned as a traitor?"

They did not try to hide what they said from the ears of Hana as she stood arranging the day's flowers in the veranda near by, and she knew that they spoke on purpose that she might hear. That they were right she knew in most of her being. But there was another part of her which she herself could not understand. It was not sentimental liking of the prisoner. She had come to think of him as a prisoner. She had not liked him even yesterday when he had said in his impulsive way, "Anyway, let me tell you that my name is Tom." She had only bowed her little distant bow. She saw hurt in his eyes, but she did not wish to assuage it. Indeed he was a great trouble in this house.

As for Sadao, every day he examined the wound carefully. The last stitches had been pulled out today, and the young man would in a fortnight be nearly as well as ever. Sadao went back to his office and carefully typed a letter to the chief of police reporting the whole matter. "On the twenty-first day of February an escaped prisoner was washed upon the shore in front of my house." So far he typed, and then he opened a secret drawer of his desk and put the unfinished report into it.

On the seventh day after that, two things happened. In the morning the servants left together, their belongings tied in large square cotton kerchiefs. When Hana got up in the morning nothing was done, the house not cleaned and the food not prepared, and she knew what it meant. She was dismayed and even terrified, but her pride as a mistress would not allow her to show it. Instead, she inclined her head gracefully when they appeared before her in the kitchen, and she paid them off and thanked them for all that they had done for her. They were crying, but she did not cry. The cook and the gardener had served Sadao since he was a little boy in his father's house, and Yumi cried because of the children. She was so grieving that after she had gone she ran back to Hana.

"If the baby misses me too much tonight, send for me. I am going to my own house and you know where it is."

"Thank you," Hana said smiling. But she told herself she would not send for Yumi however the baby cried.

She made the breakfast and Sadao helped with the children. Neither of them spoke of the servants beyond the fact that they were gone. But after Hana had taken morning food to the prisoner she came back to Sadao.

"Why is it we cannot see clearly what we ought to do?" she asked him. "Even the servants see more clearly than we do. Why are we different from other Japanese?"

Sadao did not answer. But a little later he went into the room where the prisoner was and said brusquely, "Today you may get up on your feet. I want you to stay up only five minutes at a time. Tomorrow you may try it twice as long. It would be well that you get back your strength as quickly as possible."

He saw the flicker of terror on the young face that was still very pale.

"Okay," the boy murmured. Evidently he was determined to

say more. "I feel I ought to thank you, doctor, for having saved my life."

"Don't thank me too early," Sadao said coldly. He saw the flicker of terror again in the boy's eyes — terror as unmistakable as an animal's. The scars on his neck were scarlet for a moment. Those scars! What were they? Sadao did not ask.

In the afternoon the second thing happened. Hana, working hard at unaccustomed labor, saw a messenger come to the door in official uniform. Her hands went weak and she could not draw her breath. The servants must have told already. She ran to Sadao, gasping, unable to utter a word. But by then the messenger had simply followed her through the garden and there he stood. She pointed at him futilely.

Sadao looked up from his book. He was in his office, the outer partition of which was thrown open to the garden for the southern sunshine.

"What is it?" he asked the messenger and then he rose, seeing the man's uniform.

"You are to come to the palace," the man said. "The old General is in pain again."

"Oh," Hana breathed, "is that all?"

"All?" the messenger exclaimed. "Is it not enough?"

"Indeed, it is," she replied. "I am very sorry."

When Sadao came to tell her good-by she was in the kitchen, but doing nothing. The children were asleep and she sat merely resting for a moment, more exhausted from her fright than from work.

"I thought they had come to arrest you," she said.

He gazed down into her anxious eyes. "I must get rid of this man for your sake," he said in distress. "Somehow I must get rid of him."

"Of course," the General said weakly, "I understand fully. But that is because I once took a degree in Princeton. So few Japanese have."

"I care nothing for the man, Excellency," Sadao said, "but having operated on him with such success . . ."

"Yes, yes," the General said. "It only makes me feel you more indispensable to me. You say you think I can stand one more such attack as I have had today?"

"Not more than one," Sadao said.

"Then certainly I can allow nothing to happen to you," the General said with anxiety. His long pale Japanese face became expressionless, which meant that he was in deep thought. "You cannot be arrested," the General said, closing his eyes. "Suppose you were condemned to death and the next day I had to have my operation?"

"There are other surgeons, Excellency," Sadao suggested.

"None that I trust," the General replied. "The best ones have been trained by Germans and would consider the operation successful even if I died. I do not care for their point of view." He sighed. "It seems a pity that we cannot better combine the German ruthlessness with the American sentimentality. Then you could turn your prisoner over to execution, and yet I could be sure you would not murder me while I was unconscious." The General laughed. He had an unusual sense of humor. "As a Japanese, could you not combine these two foreign elements?" he asked.

Sadao smiled. "I am not quite sure," he said, "but for your sake I would be willing to try, Excellency."

The General shook his head. "I had rather not be the test case," he said. He felt suddenly weak and overwhelmed with the cares of his life as an official in times such as these when repeated victory brought great responsibilities all over the south Pacific. "It is very unfortunate that this man should have been washed up on your doorstep," he said irritably.

"I feel it so myself," Sadao said gently.

"It would be best if he could be quietly killed," the General said. "Not by you, but by someone who does not know him. I have my own private assassins. Suppose I send two of them to your house tonight — or better, any night. You need know nothing about it. It is now warm — what would be more natural than that you should leave the outer partition of the white man's room open to the garden while he sleeps?"

"Certainly it would be very natural," Sadao agreed. "In fact, it is so left open every night."

"Good," the General said, yawning. "They are very capable assassins — they make no noise and they know the trick of inward bleeding. If you like, I can even have them remove the body."

Sadao considered. "That perhaps would be best, Excellency," he agreed, thinking of Hana.

He left the General's presence then, and went home, thinking over the plan. In this way, the whole thing would be taken out of his hands. He would tell Hana nothing, since she would be timid at the idea of assassins in the house, and yet certainly such persons were essential in an absolute state such as Japan was. How else could rulers deal with those who opposed them?

He refused to allow anything but reason to be the atmosphere of his mind as he went into the room where the American was in bed. But as he opened the door he found the young man out of bed to his surprise, and preparing to go out into the garden.

"What is this?" he exclaimed. "Who gave you permission to leave your room?"

"I'm not used to waiting for permission," Tom said gaily. "Gosh, I feel pretty good again! But will the muscles on this side always feel stiff?"

"Is it so?" Sadao inquired, surprised. He forgot all else. "Now I thought I had provided against that," he murmured. He lifted the edge of the man's shirt and gazed at the healing scar. "Massage may do it," he said, "if exercise does not."

"It won't bother me much," the young man said. His young face was gaunt under the stubbly blond beard. "Say, doctor, I've got something I want to say to you. If I hadn't met a Jap like you, well, I wouldn't be alive today. I know that."

Sadao bowed, but he could not speak.

"Sure, I know that," Tom went on warmly. His big thin hands gripping a chair were white at the knuckles. "I guess if all the Japs were like you there wouldn't have been a war."

"Perhaps," Sadao said with difficulty. "And now I think you had better go back to bed."

He helped the boy back into bed and then bowed. "Good night," he said.

He slept badly that night. Time and time again he woke, thinking he heard the rustling of footsteps, the sound of a twig broken or a stone displaced in the garden, such sounds as men might make who carried a burden.

The next morning he made the excuse to go first into the guest room. If the American were gone, he then could simply tell Hana, and so the General had directed. But when he opened the door he saw at once that it was not done last night. There, on the pillow, was the shaggy blond head. He could hear the peaceful breathing of sleep, and he closed the door again quietly.

"He is asleep," he told Hana. "He is almost well to sleep like that."

"What shall we do with him?" Hana whispered her old refrain.

Sadao shook his head. "I must decide in a day or two," he promised.

But certainly, he thought, the second night must be the night. There rose a wind that night, and he listened to the sounds of bending boughs and whistling partitions.

Hana woke too. "Ought we not to go and close the sick man's partition?" she asked.

"No," Sadao said. "He is able now to do it for himself."

But the next morning the American was still there.

Then the third night, of course, must be the night. The wind changed to quiet rain and the garden was full of the sound of dripping eaves and running springs. Sadao slept a little better, but he woke at the sound of a crash and leaped to his feet.

"What was that?" Hana cried. The baby woke at her voice and began to wail. "I must go and see." But he held her and would not let her move. "Sadao," she cried, "what is the matter with you?"

"Don't go," he muttered. "Don't go!"

His terror infected her and she stood breathless, waiting. There was only silence. Together they crept back into the bed, the baby between them.

Yet, when he opened the door of the guest room in the morning, there was the young man. He was very gay and had already washed and was on his feet. He had asked for a razor yesterday and had shaved himself, and today there was a faint color in his cheeks.

"I am well," he said joyously.

Sadao drew his kimono around his weary body. He could not, he decided suddenly, go through another night. It was not that he cared for this young man's life. No, simply it was not worth the strain.

"You are well," Sadao agreed. He lowered his voice. "You are so well that I think if I put my boat on the shore tonight, with food and extra clothing in it, you might be able to row to that little island not far from the coast. It is so near the coast that it has not been worth fortifying. Nobody lives on it because in storm it is submerged. But this is not the season of storm. You could live there until you saw a fishing boat pass by. They pass quite near the island because the water is many fathoms deep there."

The young man stared at him, slowly comprehending. "Do I have to?" he asked.

"I think so," Sadao said gently. "You understand . . . it is not hidden that you are here . . ."

The young man nodded in perfect comprehension. "Okay," he said simply.

Sadao did not see him again until evening. As soon as it was dark he had dragged the stout boat down to the shore and in it he put food and bottled water that he had bought secretly during the day, as well as two quilts he had bought at a pawnshop. The boat he tied to a post in the water, for the tide was high. There was no moon and he worked without a flashlight.

When he came to the house he entered as though he were just back from his work, and Hana knew nothing. "Yumi was here today," she said as she served his supper. Though she was so modern, still she did not eat with him. "Yumi cried over the baby," she went on with a sigh. "She misses him so."

"The servants will come back as soon as the foreigner is gone," Sadao said.

He went into the guest room that night before he went to bed, and himself checked carefully the American's temperature, the state of the wound, and his heart and pulse. The pulse was irregular but that was perhaps because of excitement. The young man's pale lips were pressed together and his eyes burned. Only the scars on his neck were red.

"I realize that you are saving my life again," he told Sadao.

"Not at all," Sadao said. "It is only inconvenient to have you here any longer."

He had hesitated a good deal about giving the man a flashlight. But he had decided to give it to him after all. It was a small one, his own, which he used at night when he was called.

"If your food runs out before you catch a boat," he said, "signal me two flashes at the same instant the sun drops over the horizon.

Do not signal in darkness for it will be seen. If you are all right but still there, signal me once. You will find fish easy to catch but you must eat them raw. A fire would be seen."

"Okay," the young man breathed.

He was dressed now in the Japanese clothes which Sadao had given him, and at the last moment Sadao wrapped a black cloth about his blond head.

"Now," Sadao said.

The young American without a word shook Sadao's hand warmly, and then walked quite well across the floor and down the step into the darkness of the garden. Once . . . twice . . . Sadao saw his light flash to find his way. But that would not be suspected. He waited until from the shore there was one more flash. Then he closed the partition. That night he slept.

"You say the man escaped?" the General asked faintly. He had been operated upon a week ago, an emergency operation to which Sadao had been called in the night. For twelve hours Sadao had not been sure the General would live. The gall bladder was much involved. Then the old man began to breathe deeply again and to ask for food. Sadao had not been able to ask about the assassins. So far as he knew, they had never come. The servants returned, and Yumi had cleaned the guest room thoroughly and had burned sulphur in it to get the white man's smell out of it. Nobody said anything. Only the gardener was cross because he had got behind with his chrysanthemum cuttings.

After a week Sadao had felt the General was well enough to be spoken to about the prisoner.

"Yes, Excellency, he escaped," Sadao said. He coughed, signifying that he had not said all that he might have said, but was unwilling to disturb the General further. But the old man opened his eyes suddenly.

"That prisoner," he said with some energy, "did I not promise you I would kill him for you?"

"You did, Excellency," Sadao said.

"Well, well!" the old man said in a tone of amazement. "So I did! But you see, I was suffering a good deal. The truth is, I thought of nothing but myself. In short, I forgot my promise to you."

"I wondered, Your Excellency," Sadao murmured.

"It was certainly very careless of me," the General said. "But you understand it was not lack of patriotism or dereliction of duty." He looked anxiously at his doctor. "If the matter should come out, you would understand that, wouldn't you?"

"Certainly, Your Excellency," Sadao said. He suddenly comprehended that the General was in the palm of his hand and that as a consequence he himself was perfectly safe. "I can swear to your loyalty, Excellency," he said to the old General, "and to your zeal against the enemy."

"You are a good man," the General murmured, and closed his eyes. "You will be rewarded."

But Sadao, searching the spot of black in the twilighted sea that night, had his reward. There was no prick of light in the dusk. No one was on the island. His prisoner was gone — safe, doubtless, for he had warned him to wait only for a Korean fishing boat.

He stood for a moment on the veranda, gazing out to the sea from whence the young man had come that other night. And into his mind, although without reason, there came other white faces he had known — the professor at whose house he had met Hana, a dull man, and his wife, who had been a silly, talkative woman, in spite of her wish to be kind. He remembered his old teacher of anatomy, who had been so insistent on mercy with his knife, and then he remembered the face of his fat and slatternly landlady. He had had great difficulty in finding a place to live because he was a Japanese. The Americans were full of prejudice and it had been bitter to live in it, knowing himself their superior. How he had despised the ignorant and dirty old woman who had at last consented to house him in her miserable home! He had once tried to be grateful to her because she had, in his last year, nursed him through influenza, but it was difficult, for she was no less repulsive to him in her kindness. But then white people were repulsive, of course. It was a relief to be openly at war with them at last. Now he remembered the youthful, haggard face of his prisoner — white and repulsive.

"Strange," he thought. "I wonder why I could not kill him."

* * *

EXAMINING THE STORY

1. At the end of the story, Dr. Hoki still cannot understand why he could not kill the American sailor. Would the fact that Dr. Hoki had been "trained not to let a man die if I can help it" account for all his actions? Would it explain the feeling of "purest pleasure" he experienced while operating on the sailor? What fact does Dr. Hoki forget at the moment of operating?
2. How does the mere fact of constantly seeing and tending the American increase the difficulty for Sadao and Hana? Why do they both refuse to let the man tell his name? Is Hana's cooperation in this matter anything more than the usual obedience of a Japanese wife? Explain.
3. Sadao decides to report the American's presence to the General rather than to the chief of police. Why? How does the General propose to help Sadao out of his dilemma? What is the General's motive in doing this? Why don't the assassins ever arrive? (Is it because, as the General says, his illness caused him to think of nothing but himself — or do you think he may have intended the prisoner to escape?) Why is Sadao sure, after speaking with the General, that he himself is safe?
4. At the end of the story, why does Dr. Hoki remind himself of his hatred for Americans? Describe the private war taking place within the Japanese doctor. Is Dr. Hoki a believable, consistent character? (See page 61.) Why or why not?
5. **A Broader Perspective** • When nations are at war, the people of each nation are expected to regard all members of the other as "the enemy." But this contradicts a deeper and more permanent feeling men have for each other. Why is this feeling stronger in Dr. Hoki than in most men? For such men, who — or what — is the real "enemy"?

Old Man at the Bridge

ERNEST HEMINGWAY

An old man with steel rimmed spectacles and very dusty clothes sat by the side of the road. There was a pontoon bridge across the river and carts, trucks, and men, women and children were crossing it. The mule-drawn carts staggered up the steep bank from the bridge with soldiers helping push against the spokes of the wheels. The trucks ground up and away heading out of it all and the peasants plodded along in the ankle deep dust. But the old man sat there without moving. He was too tired to go any farther.

It was my business to cross the bridge, explore the bridgehead beyond and find out to what point the enemy had advanced. I did this and returned over the bridge. There were not so many carts now and very few people on foot, but the old man was still there.

"Where do you come from?" I asked him.

"From San Carlos," he said, and smiled.

That was his native town and so it gave him pleasure to mention it and he smiled.

"I was taking care of animals," he explained.

"Oh," I said, not quite understanding.

"Yes," he said, "I stayed, you see, taking care of animals. I was the last one to leave the town of San Carlos."

He did not look like a shepherd nor a herdsman and I looked at his dusty clothes and his gray dusty face and his steel rimmed spectacles and said, "What animals were they?"

"Various animals," he said, and shook his head. "I had to leave them."

I was watching the bridge and the African looking country of the Ebro Delta[1] and wondering how long now it would be before

[1] **Ebro Delta:** mouth of the Ebro River, on the northeastern coast of Spain.

we would see the enemy, and listening all the while for the first noises that would signal that ever mysterious event called contact, and the old man still sat there.

"What animals were they?" I asked.

"There were three animals altogether," he explained. "There were two goats and a cat and then there were four pairs of pigeons."

"And you had to leave them?" I asked.

"Yes. Because of the artillery. The captain told me to go because of the artillery."

"And you have no family?" I asked, watching the far end of the bridge where a few last carts were hurrying down the slope of the bank.

"No," he said "only the animals I stated. The cat, of course, will be all right. A cat can look out for itself, but I cannot think what will become of the others."

"What politics have you?" I asked.

"I am without politics," he said. "I am seventy-six years old. I have come twelve kilometers now and I think now I can go no further."

"This is not a good place to stop," I said. "If you can make it, there are trucks up the road where it forks for Tortosa."

"I will wait a while," he said, "and then I will go. Where do the trucks go?"

"Towards Barcelona," I told him.

"I know no one in that direction," he said, "but thank you very much. Thank you again very much."

He looked at me very blankly and tiredly, then said, having to share his worry with some one, "The cat will be all right, I am sure. There is no need to be unquiet about the cat. But the others. Now what do you think about the others?"

"Why they'll probably come through it all right."

"You think so?"

"Why not," I said, watching the far bank where now there were no carts.

"But what will they do under the artillery when I was told to leave because of the artillery?"

"Did you leave the dove cage unlocked?" I asked.

"Yes."

"Then they'll fly."

"Yes, certainly they'll fly. But the others. It's better not to think about the others," he said.

"If you are rested I would go," I urged. "Get up and try to walk now."

"Thank you," he said and got to his feet, swayed from side to side and then sat down backwards in the dust.

"I was taking care of animals," he said dully, but no longer to me. "I was only taking care of animals."

There was nothing to do about him. It was Easter Sunday and the Fascists were advancing toward the Ebro.[2] It was a gray overcast day with a low ceiling so their planes were not up. That and the fact that cats know how to look after themselves was all the good luck that old man would ever have.

* * *

EXAMINING THE STORY

1. The old man has been dislocated from the village where he has always lived and from the only work he knows how to do. In what other ways does he appear lonely and aimless? Does he understand what the fighting is about? In what ways does he resemble the animals he leaves behind?
2. Does the old man seem to pity himself? Does the author ever appeal directly to the reader to pity this character? Would self-pity or direct appeal have increased your feeling for the old man? Why or why not?
3. Can the soldier-narrator do anything to help the old man? What does he imply will happen when the weather clears? In the last sentence, the soldier refers to the old man's "good luck." What is the tone (see Glossary) of the soldier's remark? Is this tone strengthened by the reference to Easter Sunday?
4. **A Broader Perspective** • This story is hardly more than a sketch, yet it suggests broad meanings. The reader is told almost nothing about the old man, neither his name, history, dress, nor facial features. What the reader *is* shown is the old man's helpless, and hopeless, situation. In what ways is his situation like that of millions of displaced persons in this century? Is the soldier, in his relationship to the old man and in the action he must take, also representative of millions?

[2] **"It was Easter . . . Ebro":** In April, 1938, General Francisco Franco's troops, having reached the sea below the Ebro, were moving north toward the Loyalist capital at Barcelona. They were to win the war in less than a year.

4 Can man defy the laws of nature?

To Build a Fire

JACK LONDON

Day had broken cold and gray, exceedingly cold and gray, when the man turned aside from the main Yukon trail[1] and climbed the high earth-bank, where a dim and little-traveled trail led eastward through the fat spruce timberland. It was a steep bank, and he paused for breath at the top, excusing the act to himself by looking at his watch. It was nine o'clock. There was no sun nor hint of sun, though there was not a cloud in the sky. It was a clear day, and yet there seemed an intangible pall over the face of things, a subtle gloom that made the day dark, and that was due to the absence of sun. This fact did not worry the man. He was used to the lack of sun. It had been days since he had seen the sun, and he knew that a few more days must pass before that cheerful orb, due south, would just peep above the sky-line and dip immediately from view.

The man flung a look back along the way he had come. The Yukon lay a mile wide and hidden under three feet of ice. On top of this ice were as many feet of snow. It was all pure white, rolling in gentle undulations where the ice-jams of the freeze-up had formed. North and south, as far as his eye could see, it was unbroken white, save for a dark hairline that curved and twisted

[1] **Yukon trail:** The Yukon trail follows the course of the Yukon River east from Norton Sound on the west coast of Alaska to Dawson, in the Klondike area of Canada. A southern branch of the trail led North to Dawson from Chilcoot Pass, near Juneau, in the Alaska panhandle. The Yukon trail was made famous by the Gold Rush of 1898.

"To Build a Fire" by Jack London. Reprinted by permission of Irving Shepard.

from around the spruce-covered island to the south, and that curved and twisted away into the north, where it disappeared behind another spruce-covered island. This dark hair-line was the trail — the main trail — that led south five hundred miles to the Chilcoot Pass, Dyea, and salt water; and that led north seventy miles to Dawson, and still on to the north a thousand miles to Nulato, and finally to St. Michael on Bering Sea, a thousand miles and half a thousand more.

But all this — the mysterious, far-reaching hair-line trail, the absence of sun from the sky, the tremendous cold, and the strangeness and weirdness of it all — made no impression on the man. It was not because he was long used to it. He was a newcomer in the land, a chechago,[2] and this was his first winter. The trouble with him was that he was without imagination. He was quick and alert in the things of life, but only in the things, and not in the significances. Fifty degrees below zero meant eighty-odd degrees of frost. Such fact impressed him as being cold and uncomfortable, and that was all. It did not lead him to meditate upon his frailty as a creature of temperature, and upon man's frailty in general, able only to live within certain narrow limits of heat and cold; and from there on it did not lead him to the conjectural field of immortality and man's place in the universe. Fifty degrees below zero stood for a bite of frost that hurt and that must be guarded against by the use of mittens, ear flaps, warm moccasins, and thick socks. Fifty degrees below zero was to him just precisely fifty degrees below zero. That there should be anything more to it than that was a thought that never entered his head.

As he turned to go on, he spat speculatively. There was a sharp, explosive crackle that startled him. He spat again. And again, in the air, before it could fall to the snow, the spittle crackled. He knew that at fifty below spittle crackled on the snow, but this spittle had crackled in the air. Undoubtedly it was colder than fifty below — how much colder he did not know. But the temperature did not matter. He was bound for the old claim on the left fork of Henderson Creek, where the boys were already. They had come over across the divide from the Indian Creek country, while he had come the roundabout way to take a look at the possibilities of getting out logs in the spring from

[2] **chechago:** a Chinook Indian word meaning *tenderfoot.*

the islands in the Yukon. He would be in to camp by six o'clock; a bit after dark, it was true, but the boys would be there, a fire would be going, and a hot supper would be ready. As for lunch, he pressed his hand against the protruding bundle under his jacket. It was also under his shirt, wrapped up in a handkerchief and lying against the naked skin. It was the only way to keep the biscuits from freezing. He smiled agreeably to himself as he thought of those biscuits, each cut open and sopped in bacon grease, and each inclosing a generous slice of fried bacon.

He plunged in among the big spruce trees. The trail was faint. A foot of snow had fallen since the last sled had passed over, and he was glad he was without a sled, traveling light. In fact he carried nothing but the lunch wrapped in the handkerchief. He was surprised, however, at the cold. It certainly was cold, he concluded, as he rubbed his numb nose and cheek-bones with his mittened hand. He was a warm-whiskered man, but the hair on his face did not protect the high cheek-bones and the eager nose that thrust itself aggressively into the frosty air.

At the man's heels trotted a dog, a big native husky, the proper wolf-dog, gray-coated and without any visible or temperamental difference from its brother, the wild wolf. The animal was depressed by the tremendous cold. It knew that it was no time for traveling. Its instinct told it a truer tale than was told to the man by the man's judgment. In reality, it was not merely colder than fifty below zero; it was colder than sixty below, than seventy below. It was seventy-five below zero. Since the freezing point is thirty-two above zero, it meant that one hundred and seven degrees of frost obtained. The dog did not know anything about thermometers. Possibly in its brain there was no sharp consciousness of a condition of very cold such as was in the man's brain. But the brute had its instinct. It experienced a vague but menacing apprehension that subdued it and made it slink along at the man's heels, and that made it question eagerly every unwonted movement of the man as if expecting him to go into camp or to seek shelter somewhere and build a fire. The dog had learned fire, and it wanted fire, or else to burrow under the snow and cuddle its warmth away from the air.

The frozen moisture of its breathing had settled on its fur in a fine powder of frost, and especially were its jowls, muzzle, and eyelashes whitened by its crystalled breath. The man's red beard and mustache were likewise frosted, but more solidly, the deposit taking the form of ice and increasing with every warm, moist breath he exhaled. Also, the man was chewing tobacco, and the muzzle of ice held his lips so rigidly that he was unable to clear his chin when he expelled the juice. The result was that a crystal beard of the color and solidity of amber was increasing its length on his chin. If he fell down it would shatter itself, like glass, into brittle fragments. But he did not mind the appendage. It was the penalty all tobacco chewers paid in that country, and he had been out before in two cold snaps. They had not been so cold as this, he knew, but by the spirit thermometer at Sixty Mile he knew they had been registered at fifty below and at fifty-five.

He held on through the level stretch of woods for several miles, crossed a wide flat of niggerheads,[3] and dropped down a bank to the frozen bed of a small stream. This was Henderson Creek, and he knew he was ten miles from the forks. He looked at his watch. It was ten o'clock. He was making four miles an hour, and he calculated that he would arrive at the forks at half-past twelve. He decided to celebrate that event by eating his lunch there.

The dog dropped in again at his heels, with a tail drooping discouragement, as the man swung along the creek-bed. The furrow of the old sled-trail was plainly visible, but a dozen inches of snow covered the marks of the last runners. In a month no man had come up or down that silent creek. The man held steadily on. He as not much given to thinking, and just then particularly he had nothing to think about save that he would eat lunch at the forks and that at six o'clock he would be in camp with the boys. There was nobody to talk to; and, had there been, speech would have been impossible because of the ice muzzle on his mouth. So he continued monotonously to chew tobacco and to increase the length of his amber beard.

Once in a while the thought reiterated itself that it was very cold and that he had never experienced such cold. As he walked along he rubbed his cheek-bones and nose with the back of his mittened hand. He did this automatically, now and again changing hands. But rub as he would, the instant he stopped his cheek-bones went numb, and the following instant the end of his nose went numb. He was sure to frost his cheeks; he knew that, and

[3] **niggerheads:** clumps of swamp grass such as are found in the far north.

experienced a pang of regret that he had not devised a nose strap of the sort Bud wore in cold snaps. Such a strap passed across the cheeks as well, and saved them. But it didn't matter much, after all. What were frosted cheeks? A bit painful, that was all; they were never serious.

Empty as the man's mind was of thoughts, he was keenly observant, and he noticed the changes in the creek, the curves and bends and timber-jams, and always he sharply noted where he placed his feet. Once, coming around a bend, he shied abruptly, like a startled horse, curved away from the place where he had been walking, and retreated several paces back along the trail. The creek, he knew, was frozen clear to the bottom, — no creek could contain water in that artic winter, — but he knew also that there were springs that bubbled out from the hillsides and ran along under the snow and on top of the ice of the creek. He knew that the coldest snaps never froze these springs, and he knew likewise their danger. They were traps. They hid pools of water under the snow that might be three inches deep, or three feet. Sometimes a skin of ice half an inch thick covered them, and in turn was covered by the snow. Sometimes there were alternate layers of water and ice-skin, so that when one broke through he kept on breaking through for a while, sometimes wetting himself to the waist.

That was why he had shied in such panic. He had felt the give under his feet and heard the crackle of a snow-hidden ice-skin. And to get his feet wet in such a temperature meant trouble and danger. At the very least it meant delay, for he would be forced to stop and build a fire, and under its protection to bare his feet while he dried his socks and moccasins. He stood and studied the creek-bed and its banks, and decided that the flow of water came from the right. He reflected a while, rubbing his nose and cheeks, then skirted to the left, stepping gingerly and testing the footing for each step. Once clear of the danger, he took a fresh chew of tobacco and swung along at his four-mile gait.

In the course of the next two hours he came upon several similar traps. Usually the snow above the hidden pools had a sunken, candied appearance that advertised the danger. Once again, however, he had a close call; and once, suspecting danger, he compelled the dog to go on in front. The dog did not want to go. It hung back until the man shoved it forward, and then it went quickly across the white, unbroken surface. Suddenly it broke through, floundered to one side, and got away to firmer footing. It had wet its forefeet and legs, and almost immediately the water that clung to it turned to ice. It made quick efforts to lick the ice off its legs, then dropped down in the snow and began to bite out the ice that had formed between the toes. This was a matter of instinct. To permit the ice to remain would mean sore feet. It did not know this. It merely obeyed the mysterious prompting that arose from the deep crypts of its being. But the man knew, having achieved a judgment on the subject, and he removed the mitten from his right hand and helped tear out the ice-particles. He did not expose his fingers more than a minute, and was astonished at the swift numbness that smote them. It certainly was cold. He pulled on the mitten hastily, and beat the hand savagely across his chest.

At twelve o'clock the day was at its brightest. Yet the sun was too far south on its winter journey to clear the horizon. The bulge of the earth intervened between it and Henderson Creek, where the man walked under a clear sky at noon and cast no shadow. At half-past twelve, to the minute, he arrived at the forks of the creek. He was pleased at the speed he had made. If he kept it up, he would certainly be with the boys by six. He unbuttoned his jacket and shirt and drew forth his lunch. The action consumed no more than a quarter of a minute, yet in that brief moment the numbness laid hold of the exposed fingers. He did not put the mitten on, but, instead, struck the fingers a dozen sharp smashes against his leg. Then he sat down on a snow-covered log to eat. The sting that followed upon the striking of his fingers against his leg ceased so quickly that he was startled. He had had no chance to take a bite of biscuit. He struck the fingers repeatedly and returned them to the mitten, baring the other hand for the purpose of eating. He tried to take a mouthful, but the ice-muzzle prevented. He had forgotten to build a fire and thaw out. He chuckled at his foolishness, and as he chuckled he noted the numbness creeping into the exposed fingers. Also he noted that the stinging which had first come to his toes when he sat down was already passing away. He wondered whether the toes were warm or numb. He moved them inside the moccasins and decided that they were numb.

He pulled the mitten on hurriedly and stood up. He was a bit frightened. He stamped up and down until the stinging returned into the feet. It certainly was cold, was his thought. That man from Sulphur Creek had spoken the truth when telling how cold it sometimes got in the country. And he had laughed at him at the time! That showed one must not be too sure of things. There was no mistake about it, it *was* cold. He strode up and down, stamping his feet and threshing his arms, until reassured by the returning warmth. Then he got out matches and proceeded to make a fire. From the undergrowth, where high water of the previous spring had lodged a supply of seasoned twigs, he got his firewood. Working carefully from a small beginning, he soon had a roaring fire, over which he thawed the ice from his face and in the protection of which he ate his biscuits. For the moment the cold of space was outwitted. The dog took satisfaction in the fire, stretching out close enough for warmth and far enough away to escape being singed.

When the man had finished, he filled his pipe and took his comfortable time over a smoke. Then he pulled on his mittens, settled the ear-flaps of his cap firmly about his ears, and took the creek trail up the left fork. The dog was disappointed and yearned back toward the fire. This man did not know cold. Possibly all the generations of his ancestry had been ignorant of cold, of real cold, of cold one hundred and seven degrees below freezing point. But the dog knew; all its ancestry knew, and it had inherited the knowledge. And it knew that it was not good to walk abroad in such fearful cold. It was the time to lie snug in a hole in the snow and wait for a curtain of cloud to be drawn across the face of outer space whence this cold came. On the other hand, there was no keen intimacy between the dog and the man. The one was the toil-slave of the other, and the only caresses it had ever received were the caresses of the whip-lash and of harsh and menacing throat-sounds that threatened the whip-lash. So the dog made no effort to communicate its apprehension to the man. It was not concerned in the welfare of the man; it was for its own sake that it yearned back toward the fire. But the man whistled, and spoke to it with the sound of whip-lashes, and the dog swung in at the man's heels and followed after.

The man took a chew of tobacco and proceeded to start a new amber beard. Also, his moist breath quickly powdered with white his mustache, eyebrows, and lashes. There did not seem to be so many springs on the left fork of the Henderson, and for half an hour the man saw no signs of any. And then it happened. At a place where there were no signs, where the soft, unbroken snow seemed to advertise solidity beneath, the man broke through. It was not deep. He wet himself halfway to the knees before he floundered out to the firm crust.

He was angry, and cursed his luck aloud. He had hoped to get into camp with the boys at six o'clock, and this would delay him an hour, for he would have to build a fire and dry out his foot-gear. This was imperative at that low temperature — he knew that much; and he turned aside to the bank, which he climbed. On top, tangled in the underbrush about the trunks of several small spruce trees, was a high-water deposit of dry firewood — sticks and twigs, principally, but also larger portions of seasoned branches and fine, dry, last year's grasses. He threw down several large pieces on top of the snow. This served for a foundation and prevented the young flame from drowning itself in the snow it otherwise would melt. The flame he got by touching a match to a small shred of birch-bark that he took from his pocket. This burned even more readily than paper. Placing it on the foundation, he fed the young flame with wisps of dry grass and with the tiniest dry twigs.

He worked slowly and carefully, keenly aware of his danger. Gradually, as the flame grew stronger, he increased the size of the twigs with which he fed it. He squatted in the snow, pulling the twigs out from their entanglement in the brush and feeding directly to the flame. He knew there must be no failure. When it is seventy-five below zero, a man must not fail in his first attempt to build a fire — that is, if his feet are wet. If his feet are dry, and he fails, he can run along the trail for half a mile and restore his circulation. But the circulation of wet and freezing feet cannot be restored by running when it is seventy-five below. No matter how fast he runs, the wet feet will freeze the harder.

All this the man knew. The old-timer on Sulphur Creek had told him about it the previous fall, and now he was appreciating the advice. Already all sensation had gone out of his feet. To build the fire he had been forced to remove his mittens, and the fingers had quickly gone numb. His pace of four miles an hour had kept his heart pumping blood to the surface of his body and to all the extremities. But the instant he stopped, the action of the pump eased down. The cold of space smote the unprotected tip of the planet, and he, being on that unprotected tip, received the full force of the blow. The blood of his body recoiled before it. The blood was alive, like the dog, and like the dog it wanted to hide away and cover itself up from the fearful cold. So long as he walked four miles an hour, he pumped that blood, willy-nilly, to the surface; but now it ebbed away and sank down into the recesses of his body. The extremities were the first to feel its absence. His wet feet froze the faster, and his exposed fingers numbed the faster, though they had not yet begun to freeze. Nose and cheeks were already freezing, while the skin of all his body chilled as it lost its blood.

But he was safe. Toes and nose and cheeks would be only touched by the frost, for the fire was beginning to burn with strength. He was feeding it with twigs the size of his finger. In another minute he would be able to feed it with branches the size of his wrist, and then he could remove his wet foot-gear, and, while it dried, he could keep his naked feet warm by the fire, rubbing them at first, of course, with snow. The fire was a success. He was safe. He remembered the advice of the old-timer on Sulphur Creek, and smiled. The old-timer had been very serious in laying down the law that no man must travel alone in the Klondike after fifty below. Well, here he was; he had had the accident; he was alone; and he had saved himself. Those old-timers were rather womanish, some of them, he thought. All a man had to do was to keep his head, and he was all right. Any man who was a man could travel alone. But it was surprising the rapidity with which his cheeks and nose were freezing. And he had not thought his fingers could go lifeless in so short a time. Lifeless they were, for he could scarcely make them move together to grip a twig, and they seemed remote from his body and from him. When he touched a twig, he had to look and see whether or not he had hold of it. The wires were pretty well down between him and his finger-ends.

All of which counted for little. There was the fire, snapping and crackling and promising life with every dancing flame. He started to untie his moccasins. They were coated with ice; the thick German socks were like sheaths of iron halfway to the knees; and the moccasin strings were like rods of steel all twisted and knotted as by some conflagration. For a moment he tugged with his numb fingers, then, realizing the folly of it, he drew his sheath knife.

But before he could cut the strings it happened. It was his own fault, or rather, his mistake. He should not have built the fire under the spruce tree. He should have built it in the open. But it had been easier to pull the twigs from the brush and drop them directly on the fire. Now the tree under which he had done this carried a weight of snow on its boughs. No wind had blown for weeks, and each bough was fully freighted. Each time he had pulled a twig he had communicated a slight agitation to the tree — an imperceptible agitation, so far as he was concerned, but an agitation sufficient to bring about the disaster. High up in the tree one bough capsized its load of snow. This fell on the boughs beneath, capsizing them. This process continued, spreading out and involving the whole tree. It grew like an avalanche, and it descended without warning upon the man and the fire, and the fire was blotted out! Where it had burned was a mantle of fresh and disordered snow.

The man was shocked. It was as though he had just heard his own sentence of death. For a moment he sat and stared at the spot where the fire had been. Then he grew very calm. Perhaps the old-timer on Sulphur Creek was right. If he had only had a trail-mate he would have been in no danger now. The trail-mate could have built the fire. Well, it was up to him to build the fire over again, and this second time there must be no failure. Even if he succeeded, he would most likely lose some toes. His feet must be badly frozen by now, and there would be some time before the second fire was ready.

Such were his thoughts, but he did not sit and think them. He was busy all the time they were passing through his mind. He made a new foundation for a fire, this time in the open, where no treacherous tree could blot it out. Next he gathered dry grasses and tiny twigs from the high-water flotsam. He could not bring his fingers together to pull them out, but he was able to gather them by the handful. In this way he got many rotten twigs and bits of green moss that were undesirable, but it was the best he could do. He worked methodically, even collecting an armful of the larger branches to be used later when the fire gathered strength. And all the while the dog sat and watched him, a certain yearning wistfulness in its eyes, for it looked upon him as the fire-provider, and the fire was slow in coming.

When all was ready, the man reached in his pocket for a second piece of birch-bark. He knew the bark was there, and, though he could not feel it with his fingers, he could hear its crisp rustling as he fumbled for it. Try as he would, he could not clutch hold of it. And all the time, in his consciousness, was the knowledge that each instant his feet were freezing. This thought tended to put him in a panic, but he fought against it and kept calm. He pulled on his mittens with his teeth, and threshed his arms back and forth, beating his hands with all his might against his sides. He did this sitting down, and he stood up to do it; and all the while the dog sat in the snow, its wolf-brush of a tail curled around warmly over its forefeet, its sharp wolf-ears pricked forward intently as it watched the man. And the man, as he beat and threshed with his arms and hands, felt a great surge of envy as he regarded the creature that was warm and secure in its natural covering.

After a time he was aware of the first faraway signals of sensation in his beaten fingers. The faint tingling grew stronger till it evolved into a stinging ache that was excruciating, but which the man hailed with satisfaction. He stripped the mitten from his right hand and fetched forth the birch-bark. The exposed fingers were quickly going numb again. Next he brought out his bunch of sulphur matches. But the tremendous cold had already driven the life out of his fingers. In his effort to separate one match from the others, the whole bunch fell in the snow. He tried to pick it out of the snow, but failed. The dead fingers could neither touch nor clutch. He was very careful. He drove the thought of his freezing feet, and nose, and cheeks, out of his mind, devoting his whole soul to the matches. He watched, using the sense of vision in place of that of touch, and when he saw his fingers on each side the bunch, he closed them — that is, he willed to close them, for the wires were down, and the fingers did not obey. He pulled the mitten on the right hand, and beat it fiercely against his knee. Then, with both mittened hands, he scooped the bunch of matches, along with much snow, into his lap. Yet he was no better off.

After some manipulation he managed to get the bunch between the heels of his mittened hands. In this fashion he carried it to his mouth. The ice crackled and snapped when by a violent effort he opened his mouth. He drew the lower jaw in, curled the upper lip out of the way, and scraped the bunch with his upper teeth in order to separate a match. He succeeded in getting one, which he dropped on his lap. He was no better off. He could not pick it up. Then he devised a way. He picked it up in his teeth and scratched it on his leg. Twenty times he scratched before he succeeded in lighting it. As it flamed he held it with his teeth to the birch-bark. But the burning brimstone[4] went up his nostrils and into his lungs, causing him to cough spasmodically. The match fell into the snow and went out.

The old-timer on Sulphur Creek was right, he thought in the moment of controlled despair that ensued: after fifty below, a man should travel with a partner. He beat his hands, but failed in exciting any sensation. Suddenly he bared both hands, removing the mittens with his teeth. He caught the whole bunch between the heels of his hands. His arm muscles, not being frozen, enabled him to press the hand-heels tightly against the matches. Then he scratched the bunch along his leg. It flared into flame, seventy sulphur matches at once! There was no wind to blow them out. He kept his head to one side to escape the strangling fumes, and held the blazing bunch to the birch-bark. As he so held it, he became aware of sensation in his hand. His flesh was burning. He could smell it. Deep down below the surface he could feel it. The sensation developed into pain that grew acute. And still he endured it, holding the flame of the matches clumsily to the bark that would not light readily because his own burning hands were in the way, absorbing most of the flame.

At last, when he could endure no more, he jerked his hands apart. The blazing matches fell sizzling into the snow, but the birch-bark was alight. He began laying dry grasses and the tiniest twigs on the flame. He could not pick and choose, for he had to lift the fuel between the heels of his hands. Small pieces of rotten wood and green moss clung to the twigs, and he bit them off as well as he could with his teeth. He cherished the flame carefully and awkwardly. It meant life, and it must not perish. The withdrawal of blood from the surface of his body now made him begin to shiver, and he grew more awkward. A large piece of green moss fell squarely on the little fire. He

[4] **brimstone:** sulphur.

tried to poke it out with his fingers, but his shivering frame made him poke too far, and he disrupted the nucleus of the little fire, the burning grasses and tiny twigs separating and scattering. He tried to poke them together again, but in spite of the tenseness of the effort, his shivering got away with him, and the twigs were hopelessly scattered. Each twig gushed a puff of smoke and went out. The fire-provider had failed. As he looked apathetically about him, his eyes chanced on the dog, sitting across the ruins of the fire from him, in the snow, making restless, hunching movements, slightly lifting one fore foot and then the other, shifting its weight back and forth on them with wistful eagerness.

The sight of the dog put a wild idea into his head. He remembered the tale of the man, caught in a blizzard, who killed a steer and crawled inside the carcass, and so was saved. He would kill the dog and bury his hands in the warm body until the numbness went out of them. Then he could build another fire. He spoke to the dog, calling it to him; but in his voice was a strange note of fear that frightened the animal, who had never known the man to speak in such way before. Something was the matter, and its suspicious nature sensed danger — it knew not what danger, but somewhere, somehow, in its brain arose an apprehension of the man. It flattened its ears down at the sound of the man's voice, and its restless, hunching movements and the liftings and shiftings of its fore feet became more pronounced; but it would not come to the man. He got on his hands and knees and crawled toward the dog. This unusual posture again excited suspicion, and the animal sidled mincingly away.

The man sat up in the snow for a moment and struggled for calmness. Then he pulled on his mittens, by means of his teeth, and got upon his feet. He glanced down at first in order to assure himself that he was really standing up, for the absence of sensation in his feet left him unrelated to the earth. His erect position in itself started to drive the webs of suspicion from the dog's mind; and when he spoke peremptorily with the sound of whiplashes in his voice, the dog rendered its customary allegiance and came to him. As it came within reaching distance, the man lost his control. His arms flashed out to the dog, and he experienced genuine surprise when he discovered that his hands could not clutch, that there was neither bend nor feeling in the fingers. He had forgotten for the moment that they were frozen and that they were freezing more and more. All this happened quickly, and before the animal could get away, he encircled its body with his arms. He sat down in the snow, and in this fashion held the dog, while it snarled and whined and struggled.

But it was all he could do, hold its body encircled in his arms and sit there. He realized that he could not kill the dog. There was no way to do it. With his helpless hands he could neither draw nor hold his sheath-knife nor throttle the animal. He released it, and it plunged wildly away, with tail between its legs, and still snarling. It halted forty feet away and surveyed him curiously, with ears sharply pricked forward. The man looked down at his hands in order to locate them, and found them hanging on the ends of his arms. It struck him as curious that one should have to use his eyes in order to find out where his hands were. He began threshing his arms back and forth, beating the mittened hands against his sides. He did this for five minutes, violently, and his heart pumped enough blood up to the surface to put a stop to his shivering. But no sensation was aroused in the hands. He had an impression that they hung like weights on the ends of his arms, but when he tried to run the impression down, he could not find it.

A certain fear of death, dull and oppressive, came to him. This fear quickly became poignant as he realized that it was no longer a mere matter of freezing his fingers and toes, or of losing his hands and feet, but that it was a matter of life and death, with the chances against him. This threw him into a panic, and he turned and ran up the creek-bed along the old dim trail. The dog joined in behind and kept up with him. He ran blindly, without intention, in fear such as he had never known in his life. Slowly, as he plowed and floundered through the snow, he began to see things again, — the banks of the creek, the old timber-jams, the leafless aspens, and the sky. The running made him feel better. He did not shiver. Maybe, if he ran on, his feet would thaw out; and, anyway, if he ran far enough, he would reach the camp and the boys. Without doubt he would lose some fingers and toes and some of his face; but the boys would take care of him, and save the rest of him when he got there. And at the same time there was another thought in his mind that said he would never get to the camp and the boys; that it was too many miles away, that the freezing had too great a start on him, and that he would soon be stiff and dead. This thought he kept in the background and refused to consider. Sometimes it pushed itself forward and demanded to be heard, but he thrust it back and strove to think of other things.

It struck him as curious that he could run at all on feet so frozen that he could not feel them when they struck the earth and took the weight of his body. He seemed to himself to skim along above the surface, and to have no connection with the earth. Somewhere he had once seen a winged Mercury, and he wondered if Mercury felt as he felt when skimming over the earth.

His theory of running until he reached camp and the boys had one flaw in it: he lacked the endurance. Several times he stumbled, and finally he tottered, crumpled up, and fell. When he tried to rise, he failed. He must sit and rest, he decided, and next time he would merely walk and keep on going. As he sat and regained his breath, he noted that he was feeling quite warm and comfortable. He was not shivering, and it even seemed that a warm glow had come to his chest and trunk. And yet, when he touched his nose or cheeks, there was no sensation. Running would not thaw them out. Nor would it thaw out his hands and feet. Then the thought came to him that the frozen portions of his body must be extending. He tried to keep this thought down, to forget it, to think of something else; he was aware of the panicky feeling that it caused, and he was afraid of the panic. But the thought asserted itself, and persisted, until it produced a vision of his body totally frozen. This was too much, and he made another wild run along the trail. Once he slowed down to a walk, but the thought of the freezing extending itself made him run again.

And all the time the dog ran with him, at his heels. When he fell down a second time, it curled its tail over its fore feet and sat in front of him, facing him, curiously eager and intent. The warmth and security of the animal angered him, and he cursed it till it flattened down its ears appeasingly. This time the shivering came more quickly upon the man. He was losing in his battle with the frost. It was creeping into his body from all sides. The thought of it drove him on, but he ran no more than a hundred feet, when he staggered and pitched headlong. It was his last panic. When he had recovered his breath and control, he sat up and entertained in his mind the conception of meeting death with dignity. However, the conception did not come to him in such terms. His idea of it was that he had been making a fool of himself, running around like a chicken with its head cut off—such was the simile that occurred to him. Well, he was bound to freeze anyway, and he might as well take it decently. With this new-found peace of mind came the first glimmerings of drowsiness. A good idea, he thought, to sleep off to death. It was like taking an anesthetic. Freezing was not so bad as people thought. There were lots worse ways to die.

He pictured the boys finding his body next day. Suddenly he found himself with them, coming along the trail and looking for himself. And, still with them, he came around a turn in the trail and found himself lying in the snow. He did not belong with himself any more, for even then he was out of himself, standing with the boys and looking at himself in the snow. It certainly was cold, was his thought. When he got back to the States, he could tell the folks what real cold was. He drifted on from this to a vision of the old-timer on Sulphur Creek. He could see him quite clearly, warm and comfortable, and smoking a pipe.

"You were right, old hoss; you were right," the man mumbled to the old-timer of Sulphur Creek.

Then the man drowsed off into what seemed to him the most comfortable and satisfying sleep he had ever known. The dog sat facing him and waiting. The brief day drew to a close in a long, slow twilight. There were no signs of a fire to be made, and, besides, never in the dog's experience had it known a man to sit like that in the snow and make no fire. As the twilight drew on, its eager yearning for the fire mastered it, and with a great lifting and shifting of fore feet, it whined softly, then flattened its ears down in anticipation of being chidden by the man. But the man remained silent. Later, the dog whined loudly. And still later it crept close to the man and caught the scent of death. This made the animal bristle and back away. A little longer it delayed, howling under the stars that leaped and danced and shone brightly in the cold sky. Then it turned and trotted up the trail in the direction of the camp it knew, where were the other food-providers and fire-providers.

* * *

EXAMINING THE STORY

1. Several times, the man is astonished by the cold. Which of his observations surprise him? Need he have been surprised at these evidences of the cold? What warnings from the old-timer at Sulphur Creek did the man ignore?
2. We are told that the man lacks imagination. What are some ways in which imagination might have suggested to him better preparations for his trip? What might imagination have suggested about planning to arrive "a bit after dark"?
3. The man does not foresee his reaction to the cold. In what other way does he underestimate his endurance? Consider his plan of running until he reaches the camp. What earlier incident (paragraph 1) should have warned the man of his limited endurance?
4. We are told that man is "able to live only within certain narrow limits." When does this man recognize these limits?
5. **A Broader Perspective** • The man struggles to build a fire necessary for his survival; why does he fail? In what ways is the dog better equipped to survive in this environment than the man? Does the dog show any feeling for the man? Does the man show any feeling for the dog? for the men who will find him? How does he think they will react to his death? What laws govern the action of this story? Do they provide one answer to "the conjectural field of immortality and man's place in the universe"? (Page 94)

The Interlopers

SAKI

In a forest of mixed growth somewhere on the eastern spurs of the Carpathians[1] a man stood one winter night watching and listening, as though he waited for some beast of the woods to

Saki: pronounced sä'kē.

[1] **spurs . . . Carpathians:** ridges of the mountain range between Czechoslovakia and Poland.

come within the range of his vision and, later, of his rifle. But the game for whose presence he kept so keen an outlook was none that figured in the sportsman's calendar as lawful and proper for the chase; Ulrich von Gradwitz patrolled the dark forest in quest of a human enemy.

The forest lands of Gradwitz were of wide extent and well stocked with game; the narrow strip of precipitous woodland that lay on its outskirt was not remarkable for the game it harbored or the shooting it afforded, but it was the most jealously guarded of all its owner's territorial possessions. A famous lawsuit in the days of his grandfather had wrested it from the illegal possession of a neighboring family of petty landowners; the dispossessed party had never acquiesced in the judgment of the courts, and a long series of poaching affrays[2] and similar scandals had embittered the relationships between the families for three generations. The neighbor feud had grown into a personal once since Ulrich had come to be head of his family; if there was a man in the world whom he detested and wished ill to, it was Georg Znaeym, the inheritor of the quarrel and the tireless game-snatcher and raider of the disputed border-forest.

The feud might, perhaps, have died down or been compromised if the personal ill will of the two men had not stood in the way: as boys they had thirsted for one another's blood, as men each prayed that misfortune might fall on the other; and this wind-scourged winter night Ulrich had banded together his foresters to watch the dark forest, not in quest of four-footed quarry, but to keep a lookout for the prowling thieves whom he suspected of being afoot from across the land boundary. The roebuck, which usually kept in the sheltered hollows during a storm wind, were running like driven things tonight, and there was movement and unrest among the creatures that were wont to sleep through the dark hours. Assuredly there was a disturbing element in the forest, and Ulrich could guess the quarter from whence it came.

He strayed away by himself from the watchers whom he had placed in ambush on the crest of the hill, and wandered far down the steep slopes amid the wild tangle of undergrowth, peering through the tree trunks and listening through the whistling and

[2] **poaching affrays:** fights that broke out when the neighbors trespassed in order to steal game.

skirling of the wind and the restless beating of the branches for sight or sound of the marauders. If only on this wild night, in this dark, lone spot, he might come across Georg Znaeym man to man, with none to witness—that was the wish that was uppermost in his thoughts.

And as he stepped round the trunk of a huge beech, he came face to face with the man he sought.

The two enemies stood glaring at one another for a long, silent moment. Each had a rifle in his hand; each had hate in his heart and murder uppermost in his mind. The chance had come to give full play to the passions of a lifetime. But a man who has been brought up under the code of a restraining civilization cannot easily nerve himself to shoot down his neighbor in cold blood and without word spoken, except for an offense against his hearth and honor. And before the moment of hesitation had given way to action, a deed of Nature's own violence overwhelmed them both.

A fierce shriek of the storm had been answered by a splitting crash over their heads, and ere they could leap aside, a mass of falling beech tree had thundered down on them. Ulrich von Gradwitz found himself stretched on the ground, one arm numb beneath him and the other held almost as helplessly in a tight tangle of forked branches, while both legs were pinned beneath the fallen mass. His heavy shooting boots had saved his feet from being crushed to pieces, but if his fractures were not as serious as they might have been, at least it was evident that he could not move from his present position till someone came to release him. The descending twigs had slashed the skin of his face, and he had to wink away some drops of blood from his eyelashes before he could take in a general view of the disaster. At his side, so near that under ordinary circumstances he could almost have touched him, lay Georg Znaeym, alive and struggling but obviously as helplessly pinioned down as himself. All round them lay a thick-strewn wreckage of splintered branches and broken twigs.

Relief at being alive and exasperation at his captive plight brought a strange medley of pious thank-offerings and sharp curses to Ulrich's lips.

Georg, who was nearly blinded with the blood which trickled across his eyes, stopped his struggling for a moment to listen, and then gave a short, snarling laugh. "So you're not killed, as you ought to be, but you're caught anyway," he cried, "caught fast! Ho, what a jest — Ulrich von Gradwitz snarled in his stolen forest. There's real justice for you!" And he laughed again, mockingly and savagely.

"I'm caught in my own forest land," retorted Ulrich. "When my men come to release us, you will wish, perhaps, that you were in a better plight than caught poaching on a neighbor's land — shame on you!"

Georg was silent for a moment; then he answered quietly: "Are you sure that your men will find much to release? I have men, too, in the forest tonight, close behind me, and *they* will be here first and do the releasing. When they drag me out from under these branches, it won't need much clumsiness on their part to roll this mass of trunk right over on the top of you. Your men will find you dead under a fallen beech tree. For form's sake I shall send my condolences to your family."

"It is a useful hint," said Ulrich fiercely. "My men had orders to follow in ten minutes' time — seven of which must have gone by already — and when they get me out, I will remember the hint. Only, as you will have met your death poaching on my lands, I don't think I can decently send any message of condolence to your family."

"Good," snarled Georg, "good. We fight this quarrel out to the death, you and I and our foresters, with no cursed interlopers to come between us. Death and damnation to you, Ulrich von Gradwitz."

"The same to you, Georg Znaeym, forest-thief, game-snatcher."

Both men spoke with the bitterness of possible defeat before them, for each knew that it might be long before his men would seek him out or find him; it was a bare matter of chance which party would arrive first on the scene.

Both had now given up the useless struggle to free themselves from the mass of wood that held them down; Ulrich limited his endeavors to an effort to bring his one partially free arm near enough to his outer coat pocket to draw out his wine flask. Even when he had accomplished that operation, it was long before he could manage the unscrewing of the stopper or get any of the liquid down his throat. But what a heaven-sent draft it seemed! It was an open winter, and little snow had fallen as yet; hence the captives suffered less from the cold than might have been the case at that season of the year; nevertheless, the wine was warming and reviving to the wounded man, and he looked across with something like a throb of pity to where his enemy lay, just keeping the groans of pain and weariness from crossing his lips.

"Could you reach this flask if I threw it over to you?" asked Ulrich suddenly. "There is good wine in it, and one may as well be as comfortable as one can. Let us drink, even if tonight one of us dies."

"No, I can scarcely see anything, there is so much blood caked round my eyes," said Georg, "and in any case I don't drink wine with an enemy."

Ulrich was silent for a few minutes, and lay listening to the weary screeching of the wind. An idea was slowly forming and growing in his brain, an idea that gained strength every time that he looked across at the man who was fighting so grimly against pain and exhaustion. In the pain and languor that Ulrich himself was feeling, the old fierce hatred seemed to be dying down.

"Neighbor," he said presently, "do as you please if your men come first. It was a fair compact. But as for me, I've changed my mind. If my men are the first to come, you shall be the first to be helped, as though you were my guest. We have quarreled like devils all our lives over this stupid strip of forest, where the trees can't even stand upright in a breath of wind. Lying here tonight, thinking, I've come to think we've been rather fools; there are better things in life than getting the better of a boundary dispute. Neighbor, if you will help me to bury the old quarrel, I — I will ask you to be my friend."

Georg Znaeym was silent for so long that Ulrich thought perhaps he had fainted with the pain of his injuries. Then he spoke slowly and in jerks. "How the whole region would stare and gabble if we rode into the market square together. No one living can remember seeing a Znaeym and a von Gradwitz talking to one another in friendship. And what peace there would be among the forester folk if we ended our feud tonight. And if we chose to make peace among our people, there is none other to interfere, no interlopers from outside. You would come and keep the Sylvester night[3] beneath my roof, and I would come and feast on some high day at your castle. I would never fire a shot on your land save when you invited me as a guest, and you should come and shoot with me down in the marshes where the wildfowl are. In all the countryside there are none that could hinder if we willed to make peace. I never thought to have wanted to do other than hate you all my life, but I think I have changed my mind about things too this last half hour. And you offered me your wine flask. Ulrich von Gradwitz, I will be your friend."

For a space both men were silent, turning over in their minds the wonderful changes that this dramatic reconciliation would bring about. In the cold, gloomy forest, with the wind tearing in fitful gusts through the naked branches and whistling round the tree trunks, they lay and waited for the help that would now bring release and succor to both parties. And each prayed a private prayer that his men might be the first to arrive, so that he might be the first to show honorable attention to the enemy that had become a friend.

Presently, as the wind dropped for a moment, Ulrich broke silence. "Let's shout for help," he said. "In this lull our voices may carry a little way."

"They won't carry far through the trees and undergrowth," said Georg, "but we can try. Together, then."

The two raised their voices in a prolonged hunting call.

"Together again," said Ulrich a few minutes later, after listening in vain for an answering hallo. "I heard something that time, I think," said Ulrich.

"I heard nothing but the pestilential wind," said Georg hoarsely.

There was silence again for some minutes, and then Ulrich gave a joyful cry. "I can see figures coming through the wood. They are following in the way I came down the hillside."

Both men raised their voices in as loud a shout as they could muster.

"They hear us! They've stopped. Now they see us. They're running down the hill towards us," cried Ulrich.

"How many of them are there?" asked Georg.

[3] **the Sylvester night:** a festival on December 31 honoring St. Sylvester, who was bishop of Rome from 314 to 335.

"I can't see distinctly," said Ulrich. "Nine or ten."

"Then they are yours," said Georg. "I had only seven out with me."

"They are making all the speed they can, brave lads," said Ulrich gladly.

"Are they your men?" asked Georg. "Are they your men?" he repeated impatiently, as Ulrich did not answer.

"No," said Ulrich with a laugh, the idiotic chattering laugh of a man unstrung with hideous fear.

"Who are they?" asked Georg quickly, straining his eyes to see what the other would gladly not have seen.

"Wolves."

* * *

EXAMINING THE STORY

1. Both Ulrich and Georg seek each other out in the forest, alone. Why? In the larger view, how important is the feud that absorbs all their energies and attention?
2. What finally prompts the men to forget their quarrel? (Is this typical of human behavior?) How is their reconciliation made ironic by the events that follow? (See *irony* in the Glossary.)
3. ". . . there was a disturbing element in the forest" (page 110). What larger meaning does this phrase take on as the story progresses?
4. **A Broader Perspective** • An *interloper* is one who intrudes where he has no right to be. The natural forces of the forest operate without regard to the men: lightning strikes, the tree falls, the wolves come . . . and the forest remains. When you consider the story as a whole, who are the interlopers? How do they forfeit their right to enjoy the forest?

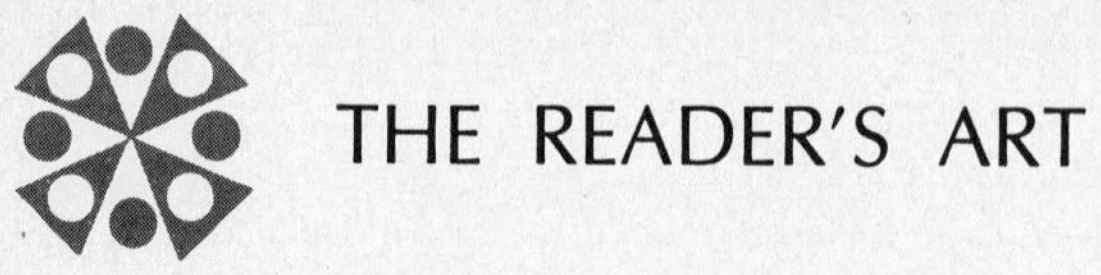

THE READER'S ART

Understanding Symbols

All characters and events in fiction are to some degree symbols — that is, they suggest human tendencies and situations which exist in the world *outside* the story. Similarly, all the objects used by people in a story, and all the settings in which action occurs, are to some degree symbols — just as things in the world itself can be symbolic. One might say, for example, that a church is a symbol — of man's engineering accomplishments, of fellowship among the church's members, of man's spiritual aspiration. Any object, in or out of stories, may be considered symbolic of several ideas.

In some stories, however, the people and circumstances function as symbols *primarily*. The fact that they are not individualized calls attention to their general qualities. A character so drawn may stand for a large group of people, perhaps for mankind itself; similarly, a setting or object may symbolize an abstract force or an idea.

The man in "To Build a Fire" is such a character. Although he is individualized to a small degree by his lack of imagination and unrealistic judgment, the story stresses the physical limitations the man shares with all human beings: a limited endurance and an ability to survive only within a narrow range of temperature. Because of these limitations and the man's refusal to give thought to "immortality and man's place in the universe," the man becomes a symbol of the answer — or of one answer — to that fundamental question. The story shows the man destroyed by the universe. What does it suggest about immortality?

Sometimes characters, things, and settings in a story can do more than represent a whole class of people, experiences, or places; they can symbolize moral ideas. Consider "The Interlopers." While the two men in this story lose their lives (like the man in the Yukon) for want of taking a few elementary precautions against the dangers in nature, their blindness is the result not of ignorance but of hatred born of greed. These men live in a *moral* forest — tangled, dark, restless, and menacing, shut off from the light of love and reason. When they do see their folly, it is too late to escape its consequences. The pack of ravenous wolves is like the destructive greed these men once permitted to rage unchecked within themselves. The wolf pack represents a trait in human nature itself.

There are two major pitfalls in interpreting symbols. Inexperienced readers often assume either that a symbol has a single, fixed meaning or that, since the author is "just telling a story," the search for symbolic meanings is futile. But "telling a story" is nothing else than arranging symbols, and without symbols there would be no story at all. A truer view is that symbols tend to have a life of their own, with meanings that tend to be fluid and variable. Thus the wolves, in "The Interlopers," might also be seen to represent vengeance or retribution for the evil the men have done.

One helpful question to ask in dealing with symbols is: In how many ways is this story true to life? and a second is: Which of the possible meanings helps to reinforce other implications in the story? Answering these questions will help you acquire a sense of how symbols work in fiction.

FOR WRITING

1. A single character can be seen as a symbol of humanity. Justify this statement by reference to one of the following stories: "Antaeus," "The Sniper," "To Build a Fire," "The Interlopers."
2. Compare and/or contrast the themes in one of the following pairs of stories: "The Sniper" and "The Interlopers"; "The Interlopers" and "To Build a Fire"; "Old Man at the Bridge" and "The Enemy."

5 Can a man be master of his own conduct?

Quality

JOHN GALSWORTHY

I knew him from the days of my extreme youth, because he made my father's boots, inhabiting with his elder brother two little shops let into one, in a small bystreet — now no more, but then most fashionably placed in the West End.

That tenement had a certain quiet distinction; there was no sign upon its face that he made for any of the Royal Family — merely his own German name of Gessler Brothers, and in the window a few pairs of boots. I remember that it always troubled me to account for those unvarying boots in the window, for he made only what was ordered, reaching nothing down,[1] and it seemed so inconceivable that what he made could ever have failed to fit. Had he bought them to put there? That, too, seemed inconceivable. He would never have tolerated in his house leather on which he had not worked himself. Besides, they were too beautiful — the pair of pumps, so inexpressibly slim; the patent leathers with cloth tops, making water come into one's mouth; the tall brown riding boots with marvelous sooty glow, as if, though new, they had been worn a hundred years. Those pairs could only have been made by one who saw before him the Soul of Boot — so truly were they prototypes incarnating[2] the

[1] **reaching nothing down:** taking nothing from the shelves; that is, selling no ready-made boots.

[2] **prototypes incarnating:** original models embodying.

very spirit of all footgear. These thoughts, of course, came to me later, though even when I was promoted to him, at the age of perhaps fourteen, some inkling haunted me of the dignity of himself and brother. For, to make boots — such boots as he made — seemed to me then, and still seems to me, mysterious and wonderful.

I remember well my shy remark one day while stretching out to him my youthful foot: "Isn't it awfully hard to do, Mr. Gessler?"

And his answer, given with a sudden smile from out of the sardonic redness of his beard: "Id is an ardt!"

Himself, he was a little as if made from leather, with his yellow crinkly face, and crinkly reddish hair and beard, and neat folds slanting down his cheeks to the corners of his mouth, and his guttural and one-toned voice — for leather is a sardonic substance, and stiff and slow of purpose. And that was the character of his face save that his eyes, which were gray-blue, had in them the simple gravity of one secretly possessed by the Ideal. His elder brother was so very like him — though watery, paler in every way, with a great industry — that sometimes in early days I was not quite sure of him until the interview was over. Then I knew that it was he if the words "I will ask my brudder" had not been spoken, and that if they had, it was his elder brother.

When one grew old and wild and ran up bills, one somehow never ran them up with Gessler Brothers. It would not have seemed becoming to go in there and stretch out one's foot to that blue iron-spectacled glance, owing him for more than — say — two pairs, just the comfortable reassurance that one was still his client.

For it was not possible to go to him very often — his boots lasted terribly,[3] having something beyond the temporary — some, as it were, essence of boot stitched into them.

One went in, not as into most shops, in the mood of "Please serve me, and let me go!" but restfully, as one enters a church, and, sitting on the single wooden chair, waited — for there was never anybody there. Soon, over the top edge of that sort of well — rather dark, and smelling soothingly of leather — which formed the shop, there would be seen his face, or that of his elder brother, peering down. A guttural sound and the tip-tap

[3] **terribly:** that is, terribly well.

of bast[4] slippers beating the narrow wooden stairs, and he would stand before one without coat, a little bent, in leather apron, with sleeves turned back, blinking — as if awakened from some dream of boots, or like an owl surprised in daylight and annoyed at this interruption.

And I would say, "How do you do, Mr. Gessler? Could you make me a pair of Russia leather boots?"

Without a word he would leave me, retiring whence he came or into the other portion of the shop, and I would continue to rest in the wooden chair, inhaling the incense of his trade. Soon he would come back, holding in his thin, veined hand a piece of gold-brown leather. With eyes fixed on it, he would remark, "What a beaudiful biece!" When I, too, had admitted it, he would speak again: "When do you wand dem?"

And I would answer, "Oh, as soon as you conveniently can."

And he would say, "Tomorrow fordnighd?" Or if he were his elder brother: "I will ask my brudder!"

Then I would murmur, "Thank you! Good morning, Mr. Gessler."

"Goot-morning!" he would reply, still looking at the leather in his hand.

And as I moved to the door, I would hear the tip-tap of his bast slippers restoring him, up the stairs, to his dream of boots. But if it were some new kind of footgear that he had not yet made me, then indeed he would observe ceremony — divesting me of my boot and holding it long in his hand, looking at it with eyes at once critical and loving, as if recalling the glow with which he had created it, and rebuking the way in which one had disorganized this masterpiece. Then, placing my foot on a piece of paper, he would two or three times tickle the outer edges with a pencil and pass his nervous fingers over my toes, feeling himself into the heart of my requirements.

I cannot forget that day on which I had occasion to say to him, "Mr. Gessler, that last pair of town walking-boots creaked, you know."

He looked at me for a time without replying, as if expecting me to withdraw or qualify the statement, then said, "Id shouldn'd 'ave greaked."

"It did, I'm afraid."

"You goddem wed before dey found demselves?"

[4] **bast:** rope.

"I don't think so."

At that he lowered his eyes, as if hunting for memory of those boots, and I felt sorry I had mentioned this grave thing. "Zend dem back!" he said. "I will look at dem."

A feeling of compassion for my creaking boots surged up in me, so well could I imagine the sorrowful, long curiosity of regard which he would bend on them.

"Zome boods," he said slowly, "are bad from birdt. If I can do noding wid dem, I dake dem off your bill."

Once (once only) I went absent-mindedly into his shop in a pair of boots bought in an emergency at some large firm. He took my order without showing me any leather, and I could feel his eyes penetrating the inferior integument[5] of my foot. At last he said, "Dose are nod my boods."

The tone was not one of anger nor of sorrow, not even of contempt, but there was in it something quiet that froze the blood. He put his hand down and pressed a finger on the place where the left boot, endeavoring to be fashionable, was not quite comfortable.

"Id 'urds you dere," he said. "Dose big virms 'ave no self-respect. Drash!" And then, as if something had given way within him, he spoke long and bitterly. It was the only time I ever heard him discuss the conditions and hardships of his trade.

"Dey get id all," he said. "Dey get id by adverdisement, nod by work. Dey dake it away from us, who lofe our boods. Id gomes to this — bresently I haf no work. Every year id gets less — you will see."

And looking at his lined face I saw things I had never noticed before, bitter things and bitter struggle — and what a lot of gray hairs there seemed suddenly in his red beard!

As best I could, I explained the circumstances of the purchase of those ill-omened boots. But his face and voice made so deep an impression that during the next few minutes I ordered many pairs. Nemesis[6] fell! They lasted more terribly than ever. And I was not able conscientiously to go to him for nearly two years.

When at last I went, I was surprised to find that outside one of the two little windows of his shop another name was painted, also that of a bootmaker — making, of course, for the Royal

[5] **integument:** covering.

[6] **Nemesis** (nem'ə · sis): unavoidable penalty.

Family. The old familiar boots, no longer in dignified isolation, were huddled in the single window. Inside, the now-contracted well of the one little shop was more scented and darker than ever. And it was longer than usual, too, before a face peered down and the tip-tap of the bast slippers began.

At last he stood before me and, gazing through those rusty iron spectacles, said, "Mr. ——, isn'd it?"

"Ah! Mr. Gessler," I stammered, "but your boots are really *too* good, you know! See, these are quite decent still!" And I stretched out to him my foot.

He looked at it. "Yes," he said, "beople do nod wand good boods, id seems."

To get away from his reproachful eyes and voice, I hastily remarked, "What have you done to your shop?"

He answered quietly, "Id was too exbensif. Do you wand some boods?"

I ordered three pairs, though I had only wanted two, and quickly left. I had I do not know quite what feeling of being part, in his mind, of a conspiracy against him, or not perhaps so much against him as against his idea of boot. One does not, I suppose, care to feel like that, for it was again many months before my next visit to his shop, paid, I remember, with the feeling "Oh! well, I can't leave the old boy — so here goes! Perhaps it'll be his elder brother!" For his elder brother, I knew, had not character enough to reproach me, even dumbly.

And, to my relief, in the shop there did appear to be his elder brother, handling a piece of leather.

"Well, Mr. Gessler," I said, "how are you?"

He came close, and peered at me. "I am breddy well," he said slowly, "but my elder brudder is dead."

And I saw that it was indeed himself — but how aged and wan! And never before had I heard him mention his brother. Much shocked, I murmured, "Oh! I am sorry!"

"Yes," he answered, "he was a good man; he made a good bood; but he is dead." And he touched the top of his head, where the hair had suddenly gone as thin as it had been on that of his poor brother, to indicate, I suppose, the cause of death. "He could nod ged over losing de oder shop. Do you wand any boods?" And he held up the leather in his hand: "Id's a beautiful biece."

I ordered several pairs. It was very long before they came — but they were better than ever. One simply could not wear them out. And soon after that I went abroad.

It was over a year before I was again in London. And the first shop I went to was my old friend's. I had left a man of sixty; I came back to one of seventy-five, pinched and worn and tremulous, who genuinely, this time, did not at first know me.

"Oh! Mr. Gessler," I said, sick at heart, "how splendid your boots are! See, I've been wearing this pair nearly all the time I've been abroad, and they're not half worn out, are they?"

He looked long at my boots — a pair of Russia leather — and his face seemed to regain steadiness. Putting his hand on my instep, he said, "Do dey vid you here? I'ad drouble wid dat bair, I remember."

I assured him that they had fitted beautifully.

"Do you wand any boods?" he said. "I can make dem quickly; id is a slack dime."

I answered, "Please, please! I want boots all round — every kind!"

"I will make a vresh model. Your food must be bigger." And with utter slowness, he traced round my foot and felt my toes, only once looking up to say, "Did I dell you my brudder was dead?"

To watch him was painful, so feeble had he grown; I was glad to get away.

I had given those boots up, when one evening they came. Opening the parcel, I set the four pairs out in a row. Then one by one I tried them on. There was no doubt about it. In shape and fit, in finish and quality of leather, they were the best he had ever made me. And in the mouth of one of the town walking-boots I found his bill. The amount was the same as usual, but it gave me quite a shock. He had never before sent it in till quarter day. I flew downstairs and wrote a check and posted it at once with my own hand.

A week later, passing the little street, I thought I would go in and tell him how splendidly the new boots fitted. But when I came to where his shop had been, his name was gone. Still there in the window were the slim pumps, the patent leathers with cloth tops, the sooty riding boots.

I went in, very much disturbed. In the two little shops —

again made into one — was a young man with an English face.

"Mr. Gessler in?" I said.

He gave me a strange, ingratiating look. "No, sir," he said, "no. But we can attend to anything with pleasure. We've taken the shop over. You've seen our name, no doubt, next door. We make for some very good people."

"Yes, yes," I said, "but Mr. Gessler?"

"Oh!" he answered, "dead."

"Dead! But I only received these boots from him last Wednesday week."

"Ah!" he said, "a shockin' go. Poor old man starved 'imself."

"Good God!"

"Slow starvation, the doctor called it! You see, he went to work in such a way! Would keep the shop on, wouldn't have a soul touch his boots except himself. When he got an order, it took him such a time. People won't wait. He lost everybody. And there he'd sit, goin' on and on — I will say that for him — not a man in London made a better boot! But look at the competition! He never advertised! Would 'ave the best leather, too, and do it all 'imself. Well, there it is. What could you expect with his ideas?"

"But starvation —"

"That may be a bit flowery, as the sayin' is — but I know myself he was sittin' over his boots day and night, to the very last. You see, I used to watch him. Never gave 'imself time to eat, never had a penny in the house. All went in rent and leather. How he lived so long I don't know. He regular let his fire go out. He was a character. But he made good boots."

"Yes," I said, "he made good boots."

And I turned and went out quickly, for I did not want that youth to know that I could hardly see.

* * *

EXAMINING THE STORY

1. What are Mr. Gessler's ideas about the right way to make boots? to run a business? Rather than try to compete with the advertising of the big firms, he keeps the same boots in the window. Why? What enables Mr. Gessler to survive his older brother? What finally causes his death — pride? lack of food? of appreciation? of hope?

2. "People do not want good boots," Mr. Gessler says. Is that the whole truth? What are the real causes of the decline in his business? Why are none of these causes explained in the story? Does Mr. Gessler understand them? Does the narrator?
3. Describe the patron's attitude toward Mr. Gessler. Why doesn't he offer either condolences or outright financial assistance to the bootmaker? Does he do anything to indicate concern? Do you consider his detached ways a sign of good breeding or of coldness? (To what social class does he belong?)
4. **A Broader Perspective** • It is possible to view the Gessler brothers as victims of inevitable change (like some species of animals who could not adapt to changes in their natural environments). They show what can happen to men who choose to disregard trends in the world around them. Were the Gesslers right to set their uncompromising standards of handcraftsmanship against machine production? "Quality" poses that question, without attempting to answer it. How might a historian's view of the situation differ from that of a fiction writer?

The Heyday of the Blood

DOROTHY CANFIELD FISHER

The older professor looked up at the assistant, fumbling fretfully with a pile of papers. "Farrar, what's the *matter* with you lately?" he said sharply.

The younger man started, "Why . . . why . . ." the brusqueness of the other's manner shocked him suddenly into confession. "I've lost my nerve, Professor Mallory, that's what's the matter with me. I'm frightened to death," he said melodramatically.

"What *of?*" asked Mallory, with a little challenge in his tone.

The flood-gates were open. The younger man burst out in exclamations, waving his thin, nervous, knotted fingers, his face twitching as he spoke. "Of myself . . . no, not myself, but my body! I'm not well . . . I'm getting worse all the time. The doctors don't make out what is the matter . . . I don't sleep . . . I worry . . . I forget things, I take no interest in life . . . the doctors intimate a nervous breakdown ahead of me . . . and yet I rest . . . I rest . . . more than I can afford to! I never go out. Every evening I'm in bed by nine o'clock. I take no part in college life beyond my work, for fear of the nervous strain. I've refused to take charge of that summer-school in New York, you know, that would be such an opportunity for me . . . if I could only sleep! But though I never do anything exciting in the evening . . . heavens! what nights I have. Black hours of seeing myself in a sanitarium, dependent on my brother! I never . . . why, I'm in hell . . . that's what's the matter with me, a perfect hell of ignoble terror!"

He sat silent, his drawn face turned to the window. The older man looked at him speculatively. When he spoke it was with a cheerful, casual quality in his voice which made the other look up at him surprised.

"You don't suppose those great friends of yours, the nerve specialists, would object to my telling you a story, do you? It's very quiet and unexciting. You're not too busy?"

"Busy! I've forgotten the meaning of the word! I don't dare to be!"

"Very well, then; I mean to carry you back to the stony little farm in the Green Mountains, where I had the extreme good luck to be born and raised. You've heard me speak of Hillsboro; and the story is all about my great-grandfather, who came to live with us when I was a little boy."

"Your great-grandfather?" said the other incredulously. "People don't remember their great-grandfathers!"

"Oh, yes, they do, in Vermont. There was my father on one farm, and my grandfather on another, without a thought that he was no longer young, and there was 'gran'ther' as we called him, eighty-eight years old and just persuaded to settle back, let his descendants take care of him, and consent to be an old man. He had been in the War of 1812 — think of that, you mushroom! — and had lost an arm and a good deal of his health there. He had lately begun to get a pension of twelve dollars a month, so that for an old man he was quite independent financially, as poor Vermont farmers look at things; and he was a most extraordinary character, so that his arrival in our family was quite an event.

"He took precedence at once of the oldest man in the township, who was only eighty-four and not very bright. I can remember bragging at school about Gran'ther Pendleton, who'd be eighty-nine come next Woodchuck day, and could see to read without glasses. He had been ailing all his life, ever since the fever he took in the war. He used to remark triumphantly that he had now outlived six doctors who had each given him but a year to live; 'and the seventh is going downhill fast, so I hear!' This last was his never-failing answer to the attempts of my conscientious mother and anxious, dutiful father to check the old man's reckless indifference to any of the rules of hygiene.

"They were good disciplinarians with their children, and this naughty old man, who would give his weak stomach frightful attacks of indigestion by stealing out to the pantry and devouring a whole mince pie because he had been refused two pieces at the table — this rebellious, unreasonable, whimsical old madcap was an electric element in our quiet, orderly life. He insisted on going to every picnic and church sociable, where he ate recklessly of all the indigestible dainties he could lay his hands on, stood in drafts, tired himself to the verge of fainting away by playing games with the children, and returned home, exhausted, animated, and quite ready to pay the price of a day in bed, groaning and screaming out with pain as heartily and unaffectedly as he had laughed with the pretty girls the evening before.

"The climax came, however, in the middle of August, when he announced his desire to go to the county fair, held some fourteen miles down the valley from our farm. Father never dared let gran'ther go anywhere without himself accompanying the old man, but he was perfectly sincere in saying that it was not because he could not spare a day from the haying that he refused pointblank to consider it. The doctor who had been taking care of gran'ther since he came to live with us said that it would be crazy to think of such a thing. He added that the wonder was that gran'ther lived at all, for his heart was all wrong, his asthma was enough to kill a young man, and he had no digestion; in short, if father wished to kill his old grandfather, there was no surer way than to drive fourteen miles in the heat of August to the noisy excitement of a county fair.

"So father for once said 'No,' in the tone that we children had come to recognize as final. Gran'ther grimly tied a knot in his empty sleeve — a curious, enigmatic mode of his to express strong emotion — put his one hand on his cane, and his chin on his hand, and withdrew himself into that incalculable distance from the life about him where very old people spend so many hours.

"He did not emerge from this until one morning toward the middle of fair-week, when all the rest of the family were away — father and the bigger boys on the far-off upland meadows haying, and mother and the girls off blackberrying. I was too little to be of any help, so I had been left to wait on gran'ther, and to set out our lunch of bread and milk and huckleberries. We had not been alone half an hour when gran'ther sent me to extract, from under the mattress of his bed, the wallet in which he kept his pension money. There was six dollars and forty-three cents — he counted it over carefully, sticking out his tongue like a schoolboy doing a sum, and when he had finished he began to laugh and snap his fingers and sing out in his high, crackled old voice: "'We're goin' to go a-skylarkin'! Little Jo Mallory is going to the county fair with his Granther Pendleton, an' he's goin' to have more fun than ever was in the world, and he ——'

"'But, gran'ther, father said we mustn't!' I protested, horrified.

"'But I say we *shall!* I was your gre't-gran'ther long before he was your feyther, and anyway I'm here and he's not — so, *march!* Out to the barn!'

"He took me by the collar, and, executing a shuffling fandango[1] of triumph, he pushed me ahead of him to the stable, where old white Peggy, the only horse left at home, looked at us amazed.

"'But it'll be twenty-eight miles, and Peg's never driven over eight!' I cried, my old-established world of rules and orders reeling before my eyes.

"'Eight — and — twenty-eight!
But I — am — *eighty*-eight!'

[1] **fandango:** a lively Spanish dance.

"Gran'ther improvised a sort of whooping chant of scorn as he pulled the harness from the peg. 'It'll do her good to drink some pink lemonade — old Peggy! An' if she gits tired comin' home, I'll git out and carry her part way myself!'

"His adventurous spirit was irresistible. I made no further objection, and we hitched up together, I standing on a chair to fix the check-rein, and gran'ther doing wonders with his one hand. Then, just as we were — gran'ther in a hickory shirt, and with an old hat flapping over his wizened face, I bare-legged, in ragged old clothes — so we drove out of the grassy yard, down the steep, stony hill that led to the main valley road, and along the hot, white turnpike, deep with the dust which had been stirred up by the teams on their way to the fair. Gran'ther sniffed the air jubilantly, and exchanged hilarious greetings with the people who constantly overtook old Peg's jogging trot. Between times he regaled me with spicy stories of the hundreds of thousands — they seemed no less numerous to me then — of county fairs he had attended in his youth. He was horrified to find that I had never been even to one.

"'Why, Joey, how old be ye? 'Most eight, ain't it? When I was your age I had run away and been to two fairs an' a hangin'.'

"'But didn't they lick you when you got home?' I asked shudderingly.

"'You *bet* they did!' cried gran'ther with gusto.

"I felt the world changing into an infinitely larger place with every word he said.

"'Now, this is somethin' *like!*' he exclaimed, as we drew near to Granville and fell into a procession of wagons all filled with country people in their best clothes, who looked with friendly curiosity at the little, shriveled cripple, his face shining with perspiring animation, and at the little boy beside him, his bare feet dangling high above the floor of the battered buckboard, overcome with the responsibility of driving a horse for the first time in his life, and filled with such a flood of new emotions and ideas that he must have been quite pale."

Professor Mallory leaned back and laughed aloud at the vision he had been evoking — laughed with so joyous a relish in his reminiscences that the drawn, impatient face of his listener relaxed a little. He drew a long breath, he even smiled a little absently.

"Oh, that was a day!" went on the professor, still laughing

and wiping his eyes. "Never will I have such another! At the entrance to the grounds gran'ther stopped me while he solemnly untied the knot in his empty sleeve. I don't know what kind of hairbrained vow he had tied up in it, but with the little ceremony disappeared every trace of restraint, and we plunged head over ears into the saturnalia[2] of delights that was an old-time county fair.

"People had little cash in those days, and gran'ther's six dollars and forty-three cents lasted like the widow's cruse of oil.[3] We went to see the fat lady, who, if she was really as big as she looked to me then, must have weighed at least a ton. My admiration for gran'ther's daredevil qualities rose to infinity when he entered into free-and-easy talk with her, about how much she ate, and could she raise her arms enough to do up her own hair, and how many yards of velvet it took to make her gorgeous, gold-trimmed robe. She laughed a great deal at us, but she was evidently touched by his human interest, for she confided to him that it was not velvet at all, but furniture covering; and when we went away she pressed on us a bag of peanuts. She said she had more peanuts than she could eat — a state of unbridled opulence which fitted in for me with all the other superlatives of that day.

"We saw the dog-faced boy, whom we did not like at all; gran'ther expressing, with a candidly outspoken cynicism, his belief that 'them whiskers was glued to him.' We wandered about the stock exhibit, gazing at the monstrous oxen, and hanging over the railings where the prize pigs liked to scratch their backs. In order to miss nothing, we even conscientiously passed through the Woman's Building, where we were very much bored by the serried ranks of preserve jars.

"'Sufferin' Hezekiah!' cried gran'ther irritably. 'Who cares how gooseberry jel *looks*. If they'd give a felly a taste, now ——'

"This reminded him that we were hungry, and we went to a restaurant under a tent, where, after taking stock of the wealth that yet remained of gran'ther's hoard, he ordered the most expensive things on the bill of fare."

[2] **saturnalia:** festival, from the ancient Roman celebration in honor of Saturn, the god of agriculture.

[3] **like the widow's cruse of oil:** that is, a long time. This is a reference to the biblical story in which a widow's single potful of oil is miraculously turned into an inexhaustible supply (II Kings 4:1–7).

Professor Mallory suddenly laughed out again. "Perhaps in heaven, but certainly not until then, shall I ever taste anything so ambrosial as that fried chicken and coffee ice-cream! I have not lived in vain that I have such a memory back of me!"

This time the younger man laughed with the narrator, settling back in his chair as the professor went on:

"After lunch we rode on the merry-go-round, both of us, gran'ther clinging desperately with his one hand to his red camel's wooden hump, and crying out shrilly to me to be sure and not lose his cane. The merry-go-round had just come in at that time, and gran'ther had never experienced it before. After the first giddy flight we retired to a lemonade-stand to exchange impressions, and finding that we both alike had fallen completely under the spell of the new sensation, gran'ther said that we 'sh'd keep on a-ridin' till we'd had enough! King Solomon couldn't tell when we'd ever git a chance again!' So we returned to the charge, and rode and rode and rode, through blinding clouds of happy excitement, so it seems to me now, such as I was never to know again. The sweat was pouring off from us, and we had tried all the different animals on the machine before we could tear ourselves away to follow the crowd to the race-track.

"We took reserved seats, which cost a quarter apiece, instead of the unshaded ten-cent benches, and gran'ther began at once to pour out to me a flood of horse-talk and knowing race-track aphorisms, which finally made a young fellow sitting next to us laugh superciliously. Gran'ther turned on him heatedly.

" 'I bet-che fifty cents I pick the winner in the next race!' he said sportily.

" 'Done!' said the other, still laughing.

"Gran'ther picked a big black mare, who came in almost last, but he did not flinch. As he paid over the half-dollar he said: 'Everybody's likely to make mistakes about *some* things; King Solomon was a fool in the head about women-folks! I bet-che a dollar I pick the winner in *this* race!' and 'Done!' said the disagreeable young man, still laughing. I gasped, for I knew we had only eighty-seven cents left, but gran'ther shot me a command to silence out of the corner of his eyes, and announced that he bet on the sorrel gelding.

"If I live to be a hundred and break the bank at Monte Carlo three times a week," said Mallory, shaking his head reminiscently, "I could not know a tenth part of the frantic excitement of that race or of the mad triumph when our horse won. Gran'ther cast his hat upon the ground, screaming like a steam-calliope with exultation as the sorrel swept past the judges' stand ahead of all the others, and I jumped up and down in an agony of delight which was almost more than my little body could hold.

"After that we went away, feeling that the world could hold nothing more glorious. It was five o'clock, and we decided to start back. We paid for Peggy's dinner out of the dollar we had won on the race — I say 'we,' for by that time we were welded into one organism — and we still had a dollar and a quarter left. 'While ye're about it, always go the whole hog!' said gran'ther, and we spent twenty minutes in laying out that money in trinkets for all the folks at home. Then, dusty, penniless, laden with bundles, we bestowed our exhausted bodies and our uplifted hearts in the old buckboard, and turned Peg's head toward the mountains. We did not talk much during that drive, and though I thought at the time only of the carnival of joy we had left, I can now recall every detail of the trip — how the sun sank behind Indian Mountain, a peak I had known before only through distant views; then, as we journeyed on, how the stars came out above Hemlock Mountain — our own home mountain behind our house, and later, how the fireflies filled the darkening meadows along the river below us, so that we seemed to be floating between the steady stars of heaven and their dancing, twinkling reflection in the valley.

"Gran'ther's dauntless spirit still surrounded me. I put out of mind doubts of our reception at home, and lost myself in delightful ruminatings on the splendors of the day. At first, every once in a while, gran'ther made a brief remark, such as, ''Twas the hind-quarters of the sorrel I bet on. He was the only one in the hull kit and bilin' of 'em that his quarters didn't fall away'; or, 'You needn't tell *me* that them Siamese twins ain't unpinned every night as separate as you and me!' But later on, as the damp evening air began to bring on his asthma, he subsided into silence, only broken by great gasping coughs.

"These were heard by the anxious, heart-sick watchers at home, and, as old Peg stumbled wearily up the hill, father came running down to meet us. 'Where you be'n?' he demanded, his face pale and stern in the light of his lantern. 'We be'n to the county fair!' croaked gran'ther with a last flare of triumph, and fell over sideways against me. Old Peg stopped short, hanging her head as if she, too, were at the limit of her strength. I was frightfully tired myself, and frozen with terror of what father would say. Gran'ther's collapse was the last straw. I began to cry loudly, but father ignored my distress with an indifference which cut me to the heart. He lifted gran'ther out of the buckboard, carrying the unconscious little old body into the house without a glance backward at me. But when I crawled down to the ground, sobbing and digging my fists into my eyes, I felt mother's arms close around me.

"'Oh, poor, naughty little Joey!' she said. 'Mother's bad, dear little boy!'"

Professor Mallory stopped short.

"Perhaps that's something else I'll know again in heaven," he said soberly, and waited a moment before he went on: "Well, that was the end of our day. I was so worn out that I fell asleep over my supper, in spite of the excitement in the house about sending for a doctor for gran'ther, who was, so one of my awestruck sisters told me, having some kind of 'fits.' Mother must have put me to bed, for the next thing I remember, she was shaking me by the shoulder and saying, 'Wake up, Joey. Your great-grandfather wants to speak to you. He's been suffering terribly all night, and the doctor think's he's dying.'

"I followed her into gran'ther's room, where the family was assembled about the bed. Gran'ther lay drawn up in a ball, groaning so dreadfully that I felt a chill like cold water at the roots of my hair; but a moment or two after I came in, all at once he gave a great sigh and relaxed, stretching out his legs and laying his arms down on the coverlid. He looked at me and attempted a smile.

"'Well, it was wuth it, warn't it, Joey?' he said gallantly, and closed his eyes peacefully to sleep."

"Did he die?" asked the younger professor, leaning forward eagerly.

"Die? Gran'ther Pendleton? Not much! He came tottering down to breakfast the next morning, as white as an old ghost, with no voice left, his legs trembling under him, but he kept the whole family an hour and a half at the table, telling them in a loud whisper all about the fair, until father said really he would have to take us to the one next year. Afterward he sat out on the porch watching old Peg graze around the yard. I thought he was in one of his absent-minded fits, but when I came out, he called me to him, and, setting his lips to my ear, he whispered:

"'An' the seventh is a-goin' down-hill fast, so I hear!' He chuckled to himself over this for some time, wagging his head feebly, and then he said: 'I tell ye, Joey, I've lived a long time, and I've larned a lot about the way folks is made. The trouble with most of 'em is, they're 'fraid-cats! As Jeroboam Warner used to say — he was in the same rigiment with me in 1812 — the only way to manage this business of livin' is to give a whoop and let her rip! If ye just about half-live, ye just the same as half-die; and if ye spend yer time half-dyin', some day ye turn in and die all over, without rightly meanin' to at all — just a kind o' bad habit ye've got yerself inter.' Gran'ther fell into a meditative silence for a moment. 'Jeroboam, he said that the evenin' before the battle of Lundy's Lane, and he got killed the next day. Some live, and some die; but folks that live all over die happy, anyhow! Now I tell you what's my motto, an' what I've lived to be eighty-eight on ——"

Professor Mallory stood up and, towering over the younger man, struck one hand into the other as he cried: "This was the motto he told me: 'Live while you live, and then die and be done with it!'"

* * *

EXAMINING THE STORY

1. What are the symptoms of Farrar's illness? Of what does he say he is afraid? What has he rejected because of his poor health? Why does Mallory tell him the story of Grandfather Pendleton?
2. "Exhausted bodies and uplifted hearts" — how does Grandfather Pendleton demonstrate these ideas of what makes the good life? Which of them is cause and which is effect? (What pattern repeats in Grandfather Pendleton's illnesses and activities?) What does he tell Joey is the trouble with most folks? Is that the trouble with Farrar?
3. How did Grandfather Pendleton's escapade change the attitude of Mallory's father? What effect did it have on his grandson? How may it affect Farrar?

4. **A Broader Perspective •** The title of this story comes from Shakespeare's description of old age as a time when "the heyday in the blood is tame." Grandfather Pendleton, at the time of this story, is eighty-eight. What is the source of his exuberance and energy? Can an adventurous spirit overcome fear? illness? aging? Is it something one must be born with, or can it be cultivated? Is it true that, by will alone, we can become whatever we wish?

The Secret Life of Walter Mitty

JAMES THURBER

"We're going through!" The Commander's voice was like thin ice breaking. He wore his full-dress uniform, with the heavily braided white cap pulled down rakishly over one cold gray eye. "We can't make it, sir. It's spoiling for a hurricane, if you ask me." "I'm not asking you, Lieutenant Berg," said the Commander. "Throw on the power lights! Rev her up to 8,500! We're going through!" The pounding of the cylinders increased: ta-pocketa-pocketa-pocketa-*pocketa-pocketa*. The Commander stared at the ice forming on the pilot window. He walked over and twisted a row of complicated dials. "Switch on No. 8 auxiliary!" he shouted. "Switch on No. 8 auxiliary!" repeated Lieutenant Berg. "Full strength in No. 3 turret!" shouted the Commander. "Full strength in No. 3 turret!" The crew, bending to their various tasks in the huge, hurtling eight-engined Navy hydroplane,[1] looked at each other and grinned. "The Old Man'll get us through," they said to one another. "The Old Man ain't afraid of Hell!" . . .

"Not so fast! You're driving too fast!" said Mrs. Mitty. "What are you driving so fast for?"

"Hmm?" said Walter Mitty. He looked at his wife, in the seat beside him, with shocked astonishment. She seemed grossly unfamiliar, like a strange woman who had yelled at him in a crowd. "You were up to fifty-five," she said. "You know I don't like to go more than forty. You were up to fifty-five." Walter Mitty drove on toward Waterbury in silence, the roaring of the SN202 through the worst storm in twenty years of Navy flying fading in the remote, intimate airways of his mind. "You're tensed up again," said Mrs. Mitty. "It's one of your days. I wish you'd let Dr. Renshaw look you over."

Walter Mitty stopped the car in front of the building where his wife went to have her hair done. "Remember to get those overshoes while I'm having my hair done," she said. "I don't need overshoes," said Mitty. She put her mirror back into her bag. "We've been all through that," she said, getting out of the car. "You're not a young man any longer." He raced the engine a little. "Why don't you wear your gloves? Have you lost your gloves?" Walter Mitty reached in a pocket and brought out the gloves. He put them on, but after she had turned and gone into the building and he had driven on to a red light, he took them off again. "Pick it up, brother!" snapped a cop as the light changed, and Mitty hastily pulled on his gloves and lurched ahead. He drove around the streets aimlessly for a time, and then he drove past the hospital on his way to the parking lot.

. . . "It's the millionaire banker, Wellington McMillan," said the pretty nurse. "Yes?" said Walter Mitty, removing his gloves slowly. "Who has the case?" "Dr. Renshaw and Dr. Benbow, but there are two specialists here, Dr. Remington from New York and Dr. Pritchard-Mitford from London. He flew over." A door opened down a long, cool corridor and Dr. Renshaw came out. He looked distraught and haggard. "Hello, Mitty," he said. "We're having the devil's own time with McMillan, the millionaire banker and close personal friend of Roosevelt.

[1] **hydroplane:** seaplane.

Obstreosis of the ductal tract. Tertiary.[2] Wish you'd take a look at him." "Glad to," said Mitty.

In the operating room there were whispered introductions: "Dr. Remington, Dr. Mitty. Dr. Pritchard-Mitford, Dr. Mitty." "I've read your book on streptothricosis," said Pritchard-Mitford, shaking hands. "A brilliant performance, sir." "Thank you," said Walter Mitty. "Didn't know you were in the States, Mitty," grumbled Remington. "Coals to Newcastle,[3] bringing Mitford and me up here for a tertiary." "You are very kind," said Mitty. A huge, complicated machine, connected to the operating table, with many tubes and wires, began at this moment to go pocketa-pocketa-pocketa. "The new anaesthetizer is giving way!" shouted an interne. "There is no one in the East who knows how to fix it!" "Quiet, man!" said Mitty, in a low, cool voice. He sprang to the machine, which was now going pocketa-pocketa-queep-pocketa-queep. He began fingering delicately a row of glistening dials. "Give me a fountain pen!" he snapped. Someone handed him a fountain pen. He pulled a faulty piston out of the machine and inserted the pen in its place. "That will hold for ten minutes," he said. "Get on with the operation." A nurse hurried over and whispered to Renshaw, and Mitty saw the man turn pale. "Coreopsis[4] has set in," said Renshaw nervously. "If you would take over, Mitty?" Mitty looked at him and at the craven figure of Benbow, who drank, and at the grave, uncertain faces of the two great specialists. "If you wish," he said. They slipped a white gown on him; he adjusted a mask and drew on thin gloves; nurses handed him shining . . .

"Back it up, Mac! Look out for that Buick!" Walter Mitty jammed on the brakes. "Wrong lane, Mac," said the parking-lot attendant, looking at Mitty closely. "Gee. Yeh," muttered Mitty. He began cautiously to back out of the lane marked "Exit Only." "Leave her sit there," said the attendant. "I'll put her away." Mitty got out of the car. "Hey, better leave the key."

[2] **Obstreosis. . . . Tertiary:** This "diagnosis," like the incident itself, is sheer fantasy.

[3] **Coals to Newcastle:** unnecessary effort. Newcastle-on-Tyne is one of the chief coal-producing centers in England.

[4] **Coreopsis:** in reality, a common flower related to the sunflower.

"Oh," said Mitty, handing the man the ignition key. The attendant vaulted into the car, backed it up with insolent skill, and put it where it belonged.

They're so damn cocky, thought Walter Mitty, walking along Main Street; they think they know everything. Once he had tried to take his chains off, outside New Milford, and he had got them wound around the axles. A man had had to come out in a wrecking car and unwind them, a young, grinning garageman. Since then Mrs. Mitty always made him drive to a garage to have the chains taken off. The next time, he thought, I'll wear my right arm in a sling; they won't grin at me then. I'll have my right arm in a sling and they'll see I couldn't possibly take the chains off myself. He kicked at the slush on the sidewalk. "Overshoes," he said to himself, and he began looking for a shoe store.

When he came out into the street again, with the overshoes in a box under his arm, Walter Mitty began to wonder what the other thing was his wife had told him to get. She had told him twice before they set out from their house for Waterbury. In a way he hated these weekly trips to town — he was always getting something wrong. Kleenex, he thought, Squibb's, razor blades? No. Toothpaste, toothbrush, bicarbonate, carborundum, initiative and referendum? He gave it up. But she would remember it. "Where's the what's-its-name?" she would ask. "Don't tell me you forgot the what's-its-name." A newsboy went by shouting something about the Waterbury trial.

. . . "Perhaps this will refresh your memory." The District Attorney suddenly thrust a heavy automatic at the quiet figure on the witness stand. "Have you ever seen this before?" Walter Mitty took the gun and examined it expertly. "This is my Webley-Vickers 50.80," he said calmly. An excited buzz ran around the courtroom. The Judge rapped for order. "You are a crack shot with any sort of firearms, I believe?" said the District Attorney, insinuatingly. "Objection!" shouted Mitty's attorney. "We have shown that the defendant could not have fired the shot. We have shown that he wore his right arm in a sling on the night of the fourteenth of July." Walter Mitty raised his hand briefly and the bickering attorneys were stilled. "With any known make of gun," he said evenly, "I could have killed Gregory Fitzhurst at three hundred feet *with my left hand.*"

Pandemonium broke loose in the courtroom. A woman's scream rose above the bedlam and suddenly a lovely, dark-haired girl was in Walter Mitty's arms. The District Attorney struck at her savagely. Without rising from his chair, Mitty let the man have it on the point of the chin. "You miserable cur!" . . .

"Puppy biscuit," said Walter Mitty. He stopped walking and the buildings of Waterbury rose up out of the misty courtroom and surrounded him again. A woman who was passing laughed. "He said 'Puppy biscuit,'" she said to her companion. "That man said 'Puppy biscuit' to himself." Walter Mitty hurried on. He went into an A. & P., not the first one he came to but a smaller one farther up the street. "I want some biscuit for small, young dogs," he said to the clerk. "Any special brand, sir?" The greatest pistol shot in the world thought a moment. "It says 'Puppies Bark for It' on the box," said Walter Mitty.

His wife would be through at the hairdresser's in fifteen minutes, Mitty saw in looking at his watch, unless they had trouble drying it; sometimes they had trouble drying it. She didn't like to get to the hotel first; she would want him to be there waiting for her as usual. He found a big leather chair in the lobby, facing a window, and he put the overshoes and the puppy biscuit on the floor beside it. He picked up an old copy of *Liberty* and sank down into the chair. "Can Germany Conquer the World Through the Air?" Walter Mitty looked at the pictures of bombing planes and of ruined streets.

. . . "The cannonading has got the wind up in[5] young Raleigh, sir," said the sergeant. Captain Mitty looked up at him through tousled hair. "Get him to bed," he said wearily. "With the others. I'll fly alone." "But you can't, sir," said the sergeant anxiously. "It takes two men to handle that bomber and the Archies[6] are pounding hell out of the air. Von Richtman's circus[7] is between here and Saulier." "Somebody's got to get that ammunition dump," said Mitty. "I'm going over. Spot of brandy?" He poured a drink for the sergeant and one for himself. War thundered and whined around the dugout and battered at the door. There was a rending of wood, and splinters flew through the

[5] **got the wind up in:** frightened.

[6] **Archies:** antiaircraft.

[7] **Von Richtman's circus:** von Richthofen's Flying Circus, a squadron of German fighter planes in World War I.

room. "A bit of a near thing," said Captain Mitty carelessly. "The box barrage is closing in," said the sergeant. "We only live once, Sergeant," said Mitty, with his faint, fleeting smile. "Or do we?" He poured another brandy and tossed it off. "I never see a man could hold his brandy like you, sir," said the sergeant. "Begging your pardon, sir." Captain Mitty stood up and strapped on his huge Webley-Vickers automatic. "It's forty kilometres through hell, sir," said the sergeant. Mitty finished one last brandy. "After all," he said softly, "what isn't?" The pounding of the cannon increased; there was the rat-tat-tatting of machine guns, and from somewhere came the menacing pocketa-pocketa-pocketa of the new flame-throwers. Walter Mitty walked to the door of the dugout humming "Auprès de Ma Blonde."[8] He turned and waved to the sergeant. "Cheerio!" he said. . . .

Something struck his shoulder. "I've been looking all over this hotel for you," said Mrs. Mitty. "Why do you have to hide in this old chair? How did you expect me to find you?" "Things close in," said Walter Mitty vaguely. "What?" Mrs. Mitty said. "Did you get the what's-its-name? The puppy biscuit? What's in that box?" "Overshoes," said Mitty. "Couldn't you have put them on in the store?" "I was thinking," said Walter Mitty. "Does it ever occur to you that I am sometimes thinking?" She looked at him. "I'm going to take your temperature when I get you home," she said.

They went out through the revolving doors that made a faintly derisive whistling sound when you pushed them. It was two blocks to the parking lot. At the drugstore on the corner she said, "Wait here for me. I forgot something. I won't be a minute." She was more than a minute. Walter Mitty lighted a cigarette. It began to rain, rain with sleet in it. He stood up against the wall of the drugstore, smoking. . . . He put his shoulders back and his heels together. "To hell with the handkerchief," said Walter Mitty scornfully. He took one last drag on his cigarette and snapped it away. Then, with that faint, fleeting smile playing about his lips, he faced the firing squad; erect and motionless, proud and disdainful, Walter Mitty the Undefeated, inscrutable to the last.

* * *

[8] **"Auprès de Ma Blonde": a drinking song.**

EXAMINING THE STORY

1. Consider the roles Walter Mitty plays in his daydreams. In them what capabilities and personal qualities does he demonstrate? What impression does he make on others? How do the daydreams contrast with his daily life?
2. Mitty's daydreams grow out of his daily experience. What incident "triggers" each fantasy? Do the dreams help or hinder Mitty's effectiveness as a person? (Notice especially his returns to reality.)
3. What does Mitty reveal about himself when he says, "We only live once, sergeant . . . Or do we?" (Might some people be said never to "live" at all?) How does he show self-understanding when he replies to the sergeant's "It's forty kilometers through hell, sir" — "What isn't?"
4. What gives Mitty satisfaction in his last daydream? Compare the last dream with the first. What trend do you see?
5. **A Broader Perspective** • Daydreams can serve as visions in which a normal person sets goals for future action. For Mitty, however, a timid, bumbling little man with a domineering wife, they serve another purpose. Explain what it is. Walter Mitty may be seen as a symbol of modern man, bored with the safe routines of civilized living and threatened by a technological culture he can neither understand nor control. To this man nothing is left except dreams of perfect competence and magnificent heroism.

   Is Walter Mitty humorous to himself? to other people in the story? to you? Is he helpless, or does he choose to be what he is?

Interpreting from Structure

Structure has to do with the selection and arrangement of events in a story. The order is important. For example, if a friend begins to tell you about a narrow escape he has had, you want him to keep things "straight" — that is, in the order in which they happened. That order, called *chronological,* is the one most often adopted by the live story-teller telling his tale to a listening audience.

When a story is written, however, the author may choose to arrange events in a different order. He may, for example, begin at a dramatic moment near the end of the story, then *flash back* to events leading up to the crisis, and finally return to the ending, for which the reader now has acquired a deepened interest and understanding. Another pattern, popular in modern fiction, is called the *stream of consciousness.* It shows the jumbled succession of sights, sounds, recollections and moods which pass through a character's mind, imitating the structure of consciousness itself; its organizing principle is not time, but association.

Selection, as well as order, is important. Selection is, in large part, determined by the *point of view* from which events in a story are seen or interpreted. Some stories, for example, are told from the viewpoint of one character in them (*first-* or *third-*person narrator); others from a viewpoint above all the characters (*omniscient* narrator).

Each of the various patterns and points of view is closely connected with the story's meaning. The skillful reader learns to interpret such structural devices, finding in them clues to the meaning of particular events as well as signals of the author's general intention.

"Quality" presents chronologically a series of episodes which show the Gesslers' losing fight against economic change. The bootmakers' story is told from the point of view of a patron who visits their shop at regular intervals. How does such a narrator help the author to focus on just those facts which are essential? to cover the necessary time span? to show a broader perspective than the Gesslers' view could have provided? (Would the meaning have been changed if Mr. Gessler had been made the narrator? Would his viewpoint have emphasized as successfully as that of the periodic visitor the changes which take place in the Gesslers' fortunes?)

"The Heyday of the Blood" is built on the rather formal model of a *frame.* The short opening section frames the main narrative; it establishes a situation from which the main episode is launched and to which it returns. Like all well-chosen frames, this one is nicely adjusted to the material it contains: in the frame, Farrar reveals his problem to Professor Mallory; Mallory then tells about a person whose life provides the key to Mallory's problem. What shift in point of view do you notice between the frame section and the main narrative? How does the first-person narration (the *I* point of view) help to tie the whole story together? Has it any other advantage?

"The Secret Life of Walter Mitty" illustrates still another way of arranging materials. Here the structure takes the form of episodes alternating between the inner and outer experiences of one man. Which kind of experience is given the most space in the story? How does this emphasis help the reader to understand Mitty's personality? Does the *direction* of Mitty's fantasies, established by the order of the episodes, also tell us something important? (In the first, he is the dauntless commander who saves a planeful of men; in the last, he is facing the firing squad, comforted only by the pathetic notion that he is "inscrutable.")

The design of a story also sets up expectations in the reader. "Promises" made in the beginning — about action to come, ideas to be examined, or mood to be developed — should be kept. They invite the reader to anticipate what is coming. Thus to the reader's enjoyment of the narrative itself is added the drama of seeing when and how his expectations will be confirmed. In "The Most Dangerous Game" (page 18), curiosity is aroused at the opening of the story about the mystery of the island and is fully answered by the subsequent action; in "Quality," the implied promise of the first words of the story ("I knew him") is made good by the intimate portrait of Mr. Gessler's character that the story provides. In the next story you will read, "Fever Dream," the startling ending is hinted at in the delirious words of a sick boy. As you read that story, try to anticipate the ending.

FOR WRITING

1. **Explain the advantages of the point of view chosen for "The Secret Life of Walter Mitty" or "The Heyday of the Blood." (What would be lost if Mitty's day were narrated by his wife? if Grandfather Pendleton's story were narrated by himself?)**
2. **Explain how the Gesslers' story illustrates some aspects of the Industrial Revolution, or how Walter Mitty illustrates a truth about all human beings.**
3. **Would Grandfather Pendleton's attitudes have helped the Gesslers or Walter Mitty to lead more satisfying lives? Why or why not?**

6 How does fear affect personality?

Fever Dream

RAY BRADBURY

They put him between fresh, clean, laundered sheets and there was always a newly squeezed glass of thick orange juice on the table under the dim pink lamp. All Charles had to do was call and Mom or Dad would stick their heads into his room to see how sick he was. The acoustics of the room were fine; you could hear the toilet gargling its porcelain throat of mornings, you could hear rain tap the roof or sly mice run in the secret walls or the canary singing in its cage downstairs. If you were very alert, sickness wasn't too bad.

He was thirteen, Charles was. It was mid-September, with the land beginning to burn with autumn. He lay in the bed for three days before the terror overcame him.

His hand began to change. His right hand. He looked at it and it was hot and sweating there on the counterpane alone. It fluttered, it moved a bit. Then it lay there, changing color.

That afternoon the doctor came again and tapped his thin chest like a little drum. "How are you?" asked the doctor, smiling. "I know, don't tell me: 'My *cold* is fine, Doctor, but *I* feel awful!' Ha!" He laughed at his own oft-repeated joke.

Charles lay there and for him that terrible and ancient jest was becoming a reality. The joke fixed itself in his mind. His mind touched and drew away from it in a pale terror. The doctor did not know how cruel he was with his jokes! "Doctor," whispered Charles, lying flat and colorless. "My *hand,* it doesn't *belong* to me any more. This morning it *changed* into something else. I want you to change it back, Doctor, Doctor!"

The doctor showed his teeth and patted his hand. "It looks fine to me, son. You just had a little fever dream."

"But it changed, Doctor, oh, Doctor," cried Charles, pitifully holding up his pale wild hand. "It *did!*"

The doctor winked. "I'll give you a pink pill for that." He popped a tablet onto Charles's tongue. "Swallow!"

"Will it make my hand change back and become *me,* again?"

"Yes, yes."

The house was silent when the doctor drove off down the road in his car under the quiet, blue September sky. A clock ticked far below in the kitchen world. Charles lay looking at his hand.

It did not change back. It was still something else.

The wind blew outside. Leaves fell against the cool window.

At four o'clock his other hand changed. It seemed almost to become a fever. It pulsed and shifted, cell by cell. It beat like a warm heart. The fingernails turned blue and then red. It took about an hour for it to change and when it was finished, it looked just like any ordinary hand. But it was not ordinary. It no longer was him any more. He lay in a fascinated horror and then fell into an exhausted sleep.

Mother brought the soup up at six. He wouldn't touch it. "I haven't any hands," he said, eyes shut.

"Your hands are perfectly good," said mother.

"No," he wailed. "My hands are gone. I feel like I have stumps. Oh, Mama, Mama, hold me, hold me, I'm scared!"

She had to feed him herself.

"Mama," he said, "get the doctor, please, again. I'm so sick."

"The doctor'll be here tonight at eight," she said, and went out.

At seven, with night dark and close around the house, Charles was sitting up in bed when he felt the thing happening to first one leg and then the other. "Mama! Come quick!" he screamed.

But when mama came the thing was no longer happening.

When she went downstairs, he simply lay without fighting as his legs beat and beat, grew warm, red-hot, and the room filled with the warmth of his feverish change. The glow crept up from his toes to his ankles and then to his knees.

"May I come in?" The doctor smiled in the doorway.

"Doctor!" cried Charles. "Hurry, take off my blankets!"

The doctor lifted the blankets tolerantly. "There you are. Whole and healthy. Sweating, though. A little fever. I told you not to move around, bad boy." He pinched the moist pink cheek. "Did the pills help? Did your hand change back?"

"No, no, now it's my other hand and my legs!"

"Well, well, I'll have to give you three more pills, one for each limb, eh, my little peach?" laughed the doctor.

"Will they help me? Please, please. What've I *got?*"

"A mild case of scarlet fever, complicated by a slight cold."

"Is it a germ that lives and has more little germs in me?"

"Yes."

"Are you *sure* it's scarlet fever? You haven't taken any tests!"

"I guess I know a certain fever when I see one," said the doctor, checking the boy's pulse with cool authority.

Charles lay there, not speaking until the doctor was crisply packing his black kit. Then in the silent room, the boy's voice made a small, weak pattern, his eyes alight with remembrance. "I read a book once. About petrified trees, wood turning to stone. About how trees fell and rotted and minerals got in and built up and they look just like trees, but they're not, they're stone." He stopped. In the quiet warm room his breathing sounded.

"Well?" asked the doctor.

"I've been thinking," said Charles after a time. "Do germs ever get big? I mean, in biology class they told us about one-celled animals, amoebas and things, and how millions of years ago they got together until there was a bunch and they made the first body. And more and more cells got together and got bigger and then finally maybe there was a fish and finally here *we* are, and all we are is a bunch of cells that decided to get together, to help each other out. Isn't that right?" Charles wet his feverish lips.

"What's all this about?" the doctor bent over him.

"I've got to tell you this. Doctor, oh, I've got to!" he cried. "What would happen, oh just pretend, please pretend, that just like in the old days, a lot of microbes got together and wanted to make a bunch, and reproduced and made *more* ——"

His white hands were on his chest now, crawling toward his throat.

"And they decided to *take over* a person!" cried Charles.

"Take over a person?"

"Yes, *become* a person. *Me,* my hands, my feet! What if a disease somehow knew how to kill a person and yet live after him?"

He screamed.

The hands were on his neck.

The doctor moved forward, shouting.

At nine o'clock the doctor was escorted out to his car by the mother and father, who handed him his bag. They conversed in the cool night wind for a few minutes. "Just be sure his hands are kept strapped to his legs," said the doctor. "I don't want him hurting himself."

"Will he be all right, Doctor?" The mother held to his arm a moment.

He patted her shoulder. "Haven't I been your family physician for thirty years? It's the fever. He imagines things."

"But those bruises on his throat, he almost choked himself."

"Just you keep him strapped; he'll be all right in the morning."

The car moved off down the dark September road.

At three in the morning, Charles was still awake in his small black room. The bed was damp under his head and his back. He was very warm. Now he no longer had any arms or legs, and his body was beginning to change. He did not move on the bed, but looked at the vast blank ceiling space with insane concentration. For a while he had screamed and thrashed, but now he was weak and hoarse from it, and his mother had gotten up a number of times to soothe his brow with a wet towel. Now he was silent, his hands strapped to his legs.

He felt the walls of his body change, the organs shift, the lungs catch fire like burning bellows of pink alcohol. The room was lighted up as with the flickerings of a hearth.

Now he had no body. It was all gone. It was under him, but it was filled with a vast pulse of some burning, lethargic drug. It was as if a guillotine had neatly lopped off his head, and his head lay shining on a midnight pillow while the body, below, still alive, belonged to somebody else. The disease had eaten his body and from the eating had reproduced itself in feverish duplicate. There were the little hand hairs and the fingernails and the scars and the toenails and the tiny mole on his right hip, all done again in perfect fashion.

I am dead, he thought. I've been killed, and yet I live. My body is dead, it is all disease and nobody will know. I will walk around and it will not be me, it will be something else. It will be something all bad, all evil, so big and so evil it's hard to understand or think about. Something that will buy shoes and drink water and get married some day maybe and do more evil in the world than has ever been done.

Now the warmth was stealing up his neck, into his cheeks, like a hot wine. His lips burned, his eyelids, like leaves, caught fire. His nostrils breathed out blue flame, faintly, faintly.

This will be all, he thought. It'll take my head and my brain and fix each eye and every tooth and all the marks in my brain, and every hair and every wrinkle in my ears, and there'll be nothing left of me.

He felt his brain fill with a boiling mercury. He felt his left eye clench in upon itself and, like a snail, withdraw, shift. He was blind in his left eye. It no longer belonged to him. It was enemy territory. His tongue was gone, cut out. His left cheek was numbed, lost. His left ear stopped hearing. It belonged to someone else now. This thing that was being born, this mineral thing replacing the wooden log, this disease replacing healthy animal cell.

He tried to scream and he was able to scream loud and high and sharply in the room, just as his brain flooded down, his right eye and right ear were cut out, he was blind and deaf, all fire, all terror, all panic, all death.

His scream stopped before his mother ran through the door to his side.

It was a good, clear morning, with a brisk wind that helped carry the doctor up the path before the house. In the window above, the boy stood, fully dressed. He did not wave when the doctor waved and called, "What's this? Up? My God!"

The doctor almost ran upstairs. He came gasping into the bedroom.

"What are you doing out of bed?" he demanded of the boy.

He tapped his thin chest, took his pulse and temperature. "Absolutely amazing! Normal. Normal, by God!"

"I shall never be sick again in my life," declared the boy, quietly, standing there, looking out the wide window. "Never."

"I hope not. Why, you're looking fine, Charles."

"Doctor?"

"Yes, Charles?"

"Can I go to school *now?*" asked Charles.

"Tomorrow will be time enough. You sound positively eager."

"I am. I like school. All the kids. I want to play with them and wrestle with them, and spit on them and play with the girls' pig-tails and shake the teacher's hand, and rub my hands on all the cloaks in the cloakroom, and I want to grow up and travel and shake hands with people all over the world, and be married and have lots of children, and go to libraries and handle books and—*all* of that I want to!" said the boy, looking off into the September morning. "What's the name you called me?"

"What?" The doctor puzzled. "I called you nothing but Charles."

"It's better than no name at all, I guess." The boy shrugged.

"I'm glad you want to go back to school," said the doctor.

"I really anticipate it," smiled the boy. "Thank you for your help, Doctor. Shake hands."

"Glad to."

They shook hands gravely, and the clear wind blew through the open window. They shook hands for almost a minute, the boy smiling up at the old man and thanking him.

Then, laughing, the boy raced the doctor downstairs and out to his car. His mother and father followed for the happy farewell.

"Fit as a fiddle!" said the doctor. "Incredible!"

"And strong," said the father. "He got out of his straps himself during the night. Didn't you, Charles?"

"Did I?" said the boy.

"You did! How?"

"Oh," the boy said, "that was a long time ago."

"A long time ago!"

They all laughed, and while they were laughing, the quiet boy moved his bare foot on the sidewalk and merely touched, brushed against a number of red ants that were scurrying about on the sidewalk. Secretly, his eyes shining, while his parents chatted with the old man, he saw the ants hesitate, quiver, and lie still on the cement. He sensed they were cold now.

"Good-by!"

The doctor drove away, waving.

The boy walked ahead of his parents. As he walked he looked away toward the town and began to hum "School Days" under his breath.

"It's good to have him well again," said the father.

"Listen to him. He's so looking forward to school!"

The boy turned quietly. He gave each of his parents a crushing hug. He kissed them both several times.

Then without a word he bounded up the steps into the house.

In the parlor, before the others entered, he quickly opened the bird cage, thrust his hand in, and petted the yellow canary, *once*.

Then he shut the cage door, stood back, and waited.

* * *

EXAMINING THE STORY

1. What changes does Charles observe taking place in his right hand? This pattern is repeated in the other parts of his body. Why is his head the last part to be affected? What does Charles imagine happens to it? How reliable an observer is he of what is taking place? How does the doctor explain Charles's sensations?

2. "The hands were on his neck" (page 147). *Whose* hands were they. really? How does the reader find this out? What wild vision do the hands conjure up in Charles's mind? Charles compares his condition to that of petrifying wood. How reasonable is his idea of being taken over by changed cells?

3. When the fever drops, Charles has changed. Why is he eager now to return to school? to give his parents a "crushing" hug? What does the death of the ants mean? Charles pets the canary — once; why not twice? What is the meaning of the last line of the story? Has Charles's fantasy about himself come true?

4. **A Broader Perspective** • "Fever Dream" is first of all a story about the effects of fever on a boy's mind. But in a deeper sense, the story suggests the struggle between the forces of good (health) and evil (sickness) for a person's soul. The first paragraph shows the powers of joy and health at work in Charles; the ending suggests the triumph

of something "so evil it's hard to understand or think about." What is that evil? Why — and when — does it grow in Charles? (Charles is absorbed within himself. Consider, for example, the use he makes of his intelligence and imagination. How does this self-concern permit the evil in his nature to overwhelm him?)

The Telltale Heart

EDGAR ALLAN POE

True! — nervous — very, very dreadfully nervous I had been and am; but why *will* you say that I am mad? The disease had sharpened my senses — not destroyed, not dulled them. Above all was the sense of hearing acute. I heard all things in the heaven and in the earth. I heard many things in hell. How, then, am I mad? Hearken! and observe how healthily, how calmly I can tell you the whole story.

It is impossible to say how first the idea entered my brain; but once conceived, it haunted me day and night. Object there was none. Passion there was none. I loved the old man. He had never wronged me. He had never given me insult. For his gold I had no desire. I think it was his eye! Yes, it was this! He had the eye of a vulture — a pale blue eye, with a film over it. Whenever it fell upon me, my blood ran cold; and so by degrees — very gradually — I made up my mind to take the life of the old man, and thus rid myself of the eye forever.

Now this is the point. You fancy me mad. Madmen know nothing. But you should have seen *me*. You should have seen how wisely I proceeded — with what caution, with what foresight, with what dissimulation I went to work! I was never kinder to the old man than during the whole week before I killed him. And every night, about midnight, I turned the latch of his door and opened it — oh, so gently! And then, when I had made an opening sufficient for my head, I put in a dark lantern, all closed, closed, so that no light shone out, and then I thrust in my head. Oh, you would have laughed to see how cunningly I thrust it in! I moved it slowly — very, very slowly, so that I might not disturb the old man's sleep. It took me an hour to place my whole head within the opening so far that I could see him as he lay upon his bed. Ha! — would a madman have been so wise as this? And then, when my head was well in the room, I undid the lantern cautiously — oh, so cautiously — cautiously (for the hinges creaked), I undid it just so much that a single thin ray fell upon the vulture eye. And this I did for seven long nights — every night just at midnight — but I found the eye always closed; and so it was impossible to do the work, for it was not the old man who vexed me, but his Evil Eye. And every morning, when the day broke, I went boldly into the chamber, and spoke courageously to him, calling him by name in a hearty tone, and inquiring how he had passed the night. So you see he would have been a very profound old man, indeed, to suspect that every night, just at twelve, I looked in upon him while he slept.

Upon the eighth night I was more than usually cautious in opening the door. A watch's minute hand moves more quickly than did mine. Never before that night had I *felt* the extent of my own powers, of my sagacity. I could scarcely contain my feelings of triumph. To think that there I was, opening the door, little by little, and he not even to dream of my secret deeds or thoughts. I fairly chuckled at the idea; and perhaps he heard me, for he moved on the bed suddenly, as if startled. Now you may think that I drew back — but no. His room was as black as pitch with the thick darkness (for the shutters were close fastened, through fear of robbers), and so I knew that he could not see the opening of the door, and I kept pushing it on steadily, steadily.

I had my head in, and was about to open the lantern, when my thumb slipped upon the tin fastening, and the old man sprang up in bed, crying out, "Who's there?"

I kept quite still and said nothing. For a whole hour I did not move a muscle, and in the meantime I did not hear him lie down.

He was still sitting up in the bed, listening — just as I have done night after night, hearkening to the deathwatches[1] in the wall.

Presently I heard a slight groan, and I knew it was the groan of mortal terror. It was not a groan of pain or of grief — oh no! — it was the low, stifled sound that arises from the bottom of the soul when overcharged with awe. I knew the sound well. Many a night, just at midnight, when all the world slept, it has welled up from my own bosom, deepening with its dreadful echo the terrors that distracted me. I say I knew it well. I knew what the old man felt, and pitied him, although I chuckled at heart. I knew that he had been lying awake ever since the first slight noise, when he had turned in the bed. His fears had been ever since growing upon him. He had been trying to fancy them causeless, but could not. He had been saying to himself, "It is nothing but the wind in the chimney — it is only a mouse crossing the floor," or "It is merely a cricket which has made a single chirp." Yes, he had been trying to comfort himself with these suppositions, but he had found all in vain. *All in vain,* because Death, in approaching him, had stalked with his black shadow before him and enveloped the victim. And it was the mournful influence of the unperceived shadow that caused him to feel — although he neither saw nor heard — to *feel* the presence of my head within the room.

When I had waited a long time, very patiently, without hearing him lie down, I resolved to open a little — a very, very little — crevice in the lantern. So I opened it — you cannot imagine how stealthily, stealthily — until, at length, a single dim ray, like the thread of the spider, shot from out the crevice and fell full upon the vulture eye.

It was open — wide, wide open — and I grew furious as I gazed upon it. I saw it with perfect distinctness — all a dull blue, with a hideous veil over it that chilled the very marrow in my bones; but I could see nothing else of the old man's face or person, for I had directed the ray, as if by instinct, precisely upon the damned spot.

And now — have I not told you that what you mistake for madness is but overacuteness of the senses? — now, I say, there

[1] **deathwatches:** beetles that live in old woodwork. Their ticking was believed to be a warning of death.

came to my ears a low, dull, quick sound, such as a watch makes when enveloped in cotton. I knew *that* sound well, too. It was the beating of the old man's heart. It increased my fury, as the beating of a drum stimulates the soldier into courage.

But even yet I refrained and kept still. I scarcely breathed. I held the lantern motionless. I tried how steadily I could maintain the ray upon the eye. Meantime the hellish tattoo of the heart increased. It grew quicker and quicker, and louder and louder every instant. The old man's terror *must* have been extreme! It grew louder, I say, louder every moment! — Do you mark me well? I have told you that I am nervous; so I am. — And now at the dead hour of the night, amid the dreadful silence of that old house, so strange a noise as this excited me to uncontrollable terror. Yet, for some minutes longer I refrained and stood still. But the beating grew louder, louder! I thought the heart must burst. And now a new anxiety seized me — the sound would be heard by a neighbor! The old man's hour had come! With a loud yell, I threw open the lantern and leaped into the room. He shrieked once — once only. In an instant I dragged him to the floor and pulled the heavy bed over him. I then smiled gaily, to find the deed so far done. But, for many minutes, the heart beat on with a muffled sound. This, however, did not vex me; it would not be heard through the wall. At length it ceased. The old man was dead. I removed the bed and examined the corpse. Yes, he was stone, stone dead. I placed my hand upon the heart and held it there many minutes. There was no pulsation. He was stone dead. His eye would trouble me no more.

If still you think me mad, you will think so no longer when I describe the wise precautions I took for the concealment of the body. The night waned, and I worked hastily but in silence. First of all I dismembered the corpse. I cut off the head and the arms and the legs.

I then took up three planks from the flooring of the chamber and deposited all between the scantlings.[2] I then replaced the boards so cleverly, so cunningly, that no human eye — not even *his* — could have detected anything wrong. There was nothing to wash out — no stain of any kind, no blood spot whatever. I had been too wary for that. A tub had caught all — ha! ha!

[2] **scantlings:** timbers.

When I had made an end of these labors, it was four o'clock — still dark as midnight. As the bell sounded the hour, there came a knocking at the street door. I went down to open it with a light heart — for what had I *now* to fear? There entered three men, who introduced themselves, with perfect suavity, as officers of the police. A shriek had been heard by a neighbor during the night; suspicion of foul play had been aroused; information had been lodged at the police office, and they (the officers) had been deputed to search the premises.

I smiled — for *what* had I to fear? I bade the gentlemen welcome. The shriek, I said, was my own in a dream. The old man, I mentioned, was absent in the country. I took my visitors all over the house. I bade them search — search *well*. I led them, at length, to *his* chamber. I showed them his treasures, secure, undisturbed. In the enthusiasm of my confidence I brought chairs into the room, and desired them *here* to rest from their fatigues, while I myself, in the wild audacity of my perfect triumph, placed my own seat upon the very spot beneath which reposed the corpse of the victim.

The officers were satisfied. My *manner* had convinced them. I was singularly at ease. They sat, and while I answered cheerily, they chatted of familiar things. But ere long I felt myself getting pale and wished them gone. My head ached, and I fancied a ringing in my ears; but still they sat and still chatted. The ringing became more distinct; it continued and became more distinct. I talked more freely to get rid of the feeling, but it continued and gained definitiveness — until at length I found that the noise was *not* within my ears.

No doubt I now grew *very* pale — but I talked more fluently, and with a heightened voice. Yet the sound increased — and what could I do? It was a *low, dull, quick sound — much such a sound as a watch makes when enveloped in cotton.* I gasped for breath — and yet the officers heard it not. I talked more quickly, more vehemently — but the noise steadily increased. I arose and argued about trifles, in a high key and with violent gesticulations, but the noise steadily increased. Why *would* they not be gone? I paced the floor to and fro with heavy strides, as if excited to fury by the observations of the men — but the noise steadily increased. Oh, God! What *could* I do? I foamed — I raved — I swore! I swung the chair upon which I had been sitting, and grated it upon the boards, but the noise arose over all and continually increased. It grew louder — louder — *louder!* And still the men chatted pleasantly, and smiled. Was it possible they heard not? Almighty God! No, no! They heard! — They suspected! — They *knew!* — They were making a mockery of my horror! — This I thought, and this I think. But anything was better than this agony! Anything was more tolerable than this derision! I could bear those hypocritical smiles no longer! I felt that I must scream or die! And now — Again! — Hark! — Louder! Louder! Louder! *Louder!*

"Villains!" I shrieked, "dissemble no more! I admit the deed! Tear up the planks! — here, here! — It is the beating of his hideous heart!"

* * *

EXAMINING THE STORY

1. The narrator insists that he is not mad. Does his conduct — even before the final scene — suggest otherwise? Does his speech? How? At first the narrator is tormented by the eye of the old man, then by a heartbeat. What does this single-minded concentration on certain things suggest about the narrator's mental state?
2. The narrator helps to bring about his own conviction. What has brought the police to the house? Why do they remain? The narrator is afraid the police will hear the beating heart. Whose heartbeat is frightening him? In what way is it "telltale"? How does the narrator's own behavior give him away?
3. Poe says very little about the facts of the murder itself — that is not his main concern. What *is* he interested in? Why is the narrator telling the story? To whom is he telling it?
4. **A Broader Perspective •** "The Telltale Heart" is a study in horror. It shows how the terrors of the mind can distort a person's view of the world until he is driven to madness and violence. For example, when the narrator first imagines he hears the old man's heart beating, he is sure it must be beating in *terror*. Why is he so sure of this? (Does he know the old man that well, or is he projecting his own fear?) What does the old man's eye remind the narrator of? How does it make him feel? Would *any* observing eye have had a similar effect on him? Why? How does the eye act as a symbol in the story?

   The narrator tries to destroy all the things he fears. Can he ever succeed by this means in freeing himself from fear?

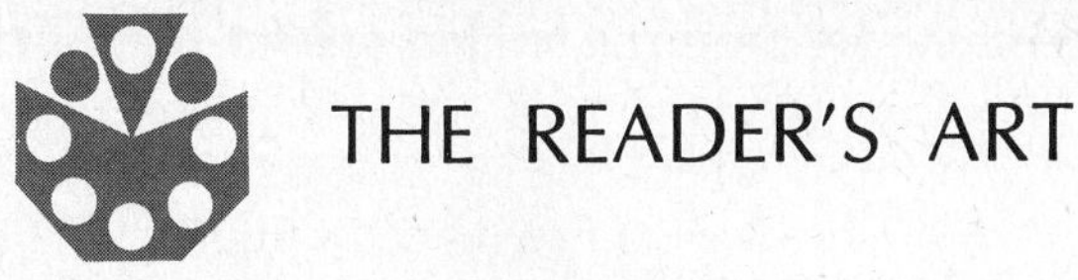

THE READER'S ART

Entering the Story's Mood

Edgar Allan Poe, who helped to create the short story form, once said that the mood of a story should control every detail in it. Every action, every idea, every individual word should help to establish a single emotional effect. In life, an intense emotion can fuse the experience of several incidents into a single memory; so, in a story, coherence depends on the unifying effect of mood. For example, if the beginning of a story leads the reader to expect a horror tale, the story cannot abruptly shift to humor without shattering the illusion of reality it is attempting to create (unless, of course, the writer is using this method to make fun of horror stories).

Notice how precisely detail builds upon detail in "The Telltale Heart": the blackness of the night, the stealth of the murderer, the chuckling at his own triumph, the mention of death-watches in the wall — all of these climaxed by the deafening beat of a human heart. Is the horror intensified by the narrator's insistence that he is normal?

In "Fever Dream" there is little physical action until the end. Does this fact help to explain the powerful effect of the incidents of the ants and the canary? What effect do the words "secretly, his eyes shining" (page 149) have on the reader? Why does the story stop where it does?

Throughout this story, mood is maintained by the vivid *images* (pictures) in Charles's mind — which, like the murderer's in "The Telltale Heart," distorts everything he experiences. These images are communicated to the reader by means of comparisons describing things in the story: metaphors (the September landscape was "beginning to burn with autumn") and similes (his eyelids, "like leaves, caught fire"). They convey Charles's feeling of terror, and at the same time intensify the mood of the story. What fantastic image of himself, born of delirium, is recalled by Charles's behavior to the ants and canary? What is the overall mood of the story? (Is it the same as *Charles's* feeling of terror?)

FOR WRITING

1. Both Charles and the narrator in "The Telltale Heart" have allowed their minds to turn inward. Each lives in a self-created world; each has lost contact with the world around him, particularly with the needs of other people. What do these stories show about the importance of maintaining a fresh interest in other people's rights, feelings, and connection with us? Apply this question to one of the characters in these two stories, to a character in some other story you have read, to some person you know, or to a problem in international relations.
2. Metaphorical language communicates both ideas and mood by means of comparing things within the story to selected things outside of it. Choose a metaphor or simile from one of these stories and explain (1) the feelings it evokes in you, and (2) what it contributes to the story's overall mood.

7 What price is paid for pretense?

The Necklace

GUY DE MAUPASSANT

She was one of those attractive pretty girls, born by a freak of fortune in a lower-middle-class family. She had no dowry, no expectations, no way of getting known, appreciated, loved and married by some wealthy gentleman of good family. And she allowed herself to be married to a junior clerk in the Ministry of Public Instruction.

She dressed plainly, having no money to spend on herself. But she was as unhappy as if she had known better days. Women have no sense of caste or breeding, their beauty, their grace, and their charm taking the place of birth and family. Their natural refinement, their instinctive delicacy and adaptability are their only passport to society, and these qualities enable daughters of the people to compete with ladies of gentle birth.

She always had a sense of frustration, feeling herself born for all the refinements and luxuries of life. She hated the bareness of her flat, the shabbiness of the walls, the worn upholstery of the chairs, and the ugliness of the curtains. All these things, which another woman of her class would not even have noticed, were pain and grief to her. The sight of the little Breton maid doing her simple housework aroused in her passionate regrets and hopeless dreams. She imagined hushed anterooms hung with oriental fabrics and lit by tall bronze candelabra, with two

Guy de Maupassant: pronounced gē də mō′pə· sä^{n}.

"The Necklace," from Guy de Maupassant's *The Mountain Inn and Other Stories,* translated by H. N. P. Sloman, published by Penguin Books 1955. Reprinted by permission of Penguin Books Ltd.

impressive footmen in knee breeches dozing in great armchairs, made drowsy by the heat of radiators. She imagined vast drawing rooms, upholstered in antique silk, splendid pieces of furniture littered with priceless curios, and dainty scented boudoirs, designed for teatime conversation with intimate friends and much sought-after society gentlemen, whose attentions every woman envies and desires.

When she sat down to dinner at the round table covered with a three-days-old cloth opposite her husband, who took the lid off the casserole with the delighted exclamation: "Ah! your hot-pot[1] again! How lovely! It's the best dish in the world!" she was dreaming of luxurious dinners with gleaming silver and tapestries peopling the walls with classical figures and exotic birds in a fairy forest; she dreamed of exquisite dishes served on valuable china and whispered compliments listened to with a sphinxlike smile, while toying with the pink flesh of a trout or the wing of a hazel-hen.

She had no evening clothes, no jewels, nothing. But she wanted only those things; she felt that that was the kind of life for her. She so much longed to please, be envied, be fascinating and sought after.

She had a rich friend who had been with her at a convent school, but she did not like going to see her now, the contrast was so painful when she went home. She spent whole days in tears; misery, regrets, hopeless longings caused her such bitter distress.

One evening her husband came home with a broad smile on his face and a large envelope in his hand: "Look!" he cried. "Here's something for you, dear!"

She tore open the envelope eagerly and pulled out a printed card with the words: "The Minister of Public Instruction and Mme. Georges Ramponneau request the honor of the company of M. and Mme. Loisel[2] at the Ministry on the evening of Monday, January 18th."

Instead of being delighted as her husband had hoped, she threw the invitation pettishly down on the table, murmuring: "What's the good of this to me?"

"But I thought you'd be pleased, dear! You never go out and

[1] **hot-pot:** beef or mutton stew.
[2] **Loisel:** pronounced lwä · zel′.

this is an occasion, a great occasion. I had the greatest difficulty to get the invitation. Everybody wants one; it's very select and junior clerks don't often get asked. The whole official world will be there."

She looked at him crossly and declared impatiently: "What do you think I'm to wear?"

He hadn't thought of that and stuttered: "Why! the frock you wear for the theater. I think it's charming!"

He stopped in astonished bewilderment when he saw his wife was crying. Two great tears were running slowly down from the corners of her eyes to the corners of her mouth; he stammered: "What's the matter? What's the matter?"

But with a great effort she had controlled her disappointment and replied quietly, drying her wet cheeks: "Oh! Nothing! Only not having anything to wear I can't go to the party. Pass on the invitation to some colleague whose wife is better dressed than I."

"Look here, Mathilde! How much would a suitable frock cost, something quite simple that would be useful on other occasions later on?"

She thought for a few seconds, doing a sum and also wondering how much she could ask for without inviting an immediate refusal and an outraged exclamation from the close-fisted clerk. At last with some hesitation she replied: "I don't know exactly but I think I could manage on four hundred francs."[3]

He went slightly pale, for this was just the amount he had put by to get a gun so that he could enjoy some shooting the following summer on the Nanterre plain with some friends who went out lark-shooting on Sundays. But he said: "Right! I'll give you four hundred francs, but try and get a really nice frock."

The date of the party was approaching and Mme. Loisel seemed depressed and worried, though her dress was ready. One evening her husband said to her: "What's the matter? The last three days you've not been yourself."

She replied: "It's rotten not to have a piece of jewelry, not a stone of any kind, to wear. I shall look poverty-stricken. I'd rather not go to the party."

He answered: "But you can wear some real flowers. That's very smart this year. For ten francs you could get two or three magnificent roses."

[3] **four hundred francs:** about $80.

She was not impressed. "No, there's nothing more humiliating than to look poor in a crowd of wealthy women."

But her husband suddenly cried: "What a fool you are! Go to your friend, Mme. Forestier,[4] and ask her to lend you some of her jewelry. You know her well enough to do that."

She uttered a joyful cry: "That's a good idea! I'd never thought of it!"

Next day she went to her friend's house and explained her dilemma.

Mme. Forestier went to a glass-fronted wardrobe, took out a large casket, brought it over, opened it, and said to Mme. Loisel:

"Take what you like, my dear!"

First she looked at bracelets, then a pearl collar, then a Venetian cross in gold and stones, a lovely piece of work. She tried the various ornaments in front of the glass, unable to make up her mind to take them off and put them back; she kept asking: "Haven't you got anything else?"

"Yes, go on looking; I don't know what you would like."

Suddenly she found a black satin case containing a magnificent diamond necklace, and she wanted it so desperately that her heart began to thump. Her hands were shaking as she picked it up. She put it round her throat over her high blouse and stood in ectasy before her reflection in the glass. Then she asked hesitantly, her anxiety showing in her voice: "Could you lend me that, just that, nothing else?"

"But of course!"

She threw her arms round her friend's neck and kissed her wildly, and hurried home with her treasure.

The day of the party arrived. Mme. Loisel had a triumph. She was the prettiest woman in the room, elegant, graceful, smiling, in the seventh heaven of happiness. All the men looked at her, asked who she was, and wanted to be introduced. All the private secretaries wanted to dance with her. The Minister himself noticed her.

She danced with inspired abandon, intoxicated with delight, thinking of nothing in the triumph of her beauty and the glory of her success; she was wrapped in a cloud of happiness, the result of all the compliments, all the admiration, all these awakened desires, that wonderful success so dear to every woman's heart.

[4] **Forestier:** pronounced fō · re · styā'.

She left about four in the morning. Her husband had been dozing since midnight in a small, empty drawing room with three other gentlemen, whose wives were also enjoying themselves.

He threw over her shoulders the wraps he had brought for going home, her simple everyday coat, whose plainness clashed with the smartness of her ball dress. She was conscious of this and wanted to hurry away, so as not to be noticed by the ladies who were putting on expensive fur wraps.

Loisel tried to stop her: "Wait a minute! You'll catch cold outside. I'll call a cab."

But she would not listen and ran down the stairs. When they got into the street they could not find a cab and began to hunt for one, shouting to the drivers they saw passing in the distance. In despair they went down towards the Seine, shivering. At last, on the Embankment they found one of those old carriages that ply by night and are only seen in Paris after dark, as if ashamed of their shabbiness in the daytime. It took them back to their house in the Rue des Martyrs and they went sadly up to their apartment. For her this was the end; and he was remembering that he had got to be at the office at ten o'clock.

She took off the wraps she had put round her shoulders, standing in front of the glass to see herself once more in all her glory. But suddenly she uttered a cry; the diamond necklace was no longer round her neck. Her husband, already half undressed, asked: "What's the matter?"

She turned to him in a panic: "Mme. Forestier's necklace has gone!"

He stood up, dumbfounded: "What? What do you mean? It's impossible!"

They searched in the folds of her dress, in the folds of her cloak, in the pockets, everywhere; they could not find it. He asked: "Are you sure you had it on when you left the ball?"

"Yes, I fingered it in the hall at the Ministry."

"But, if you had lost it in the street, we should have heard it drop. It must be in the cab."

"Yes, it probably is. Did you take the number?"

"No! And you didn't notice it, I suppose?"

"No!"

They looked at each other, utterly crushed. Finally Loisel dressed again: "I'll go back along the way we walked and see if I can find it."

He went out and she remained in her evening dress, without the strength even to go to bed, collapsed on a chair, without a fire, her mind a blank.

Her husband returned about seven, having found nothing. He went to the police station, to the papers to offer a reward, to the cab companies, in fact anywhere that gave a flicker of hope.

She waited all day in the same state of dismay at this appalling catastrophe. Loisel came back in the evening, his face pale and lined; he had discovered nothing.

"You must write to your friend," he said, "and say you have broken the clasp of the necklace and are getting it mended. That will give us time to turn round."

So she wrote at his dictation. After a week they had lost all hope and Loisel, who had aged five years, declared: "We must do something about replacing it."

Next day they took the case which had contained the necklace to the jeweler whose name was in it. He looked up his books: "I did not sell the jewel, Madame; I must only have supplied the case."

They went from jeweler to jeweler, looking for a necklace like the other, trying to remember exactly what it was like, both of them sick with worry and anxiety.

At last in the Palais Royal they found a diamond necklace just like the one lost. Its price was forty thousand francs, but they could have it for thirty-six thousand.

So they asked the jeweler to keep it for three days. They made it a condition that he should take it back for thirty-four thousand if the first was found before the end of February.

Loisel had got eighteen thousand francs which his father had left him; he would borrow the rest.

He borrowed one thousand francs from one, five hundred from another, one hundred here, sixty there. He gave I.O.U.'s and notes of hand on ruinous terms, going to the loan sharks and moneylenders of every kind. He mortgaged the whole of the rest of his life, risked his signature on bills without knowing if he would ever be able to honor it; he was tormented with anxiety about the future, with the thought of the crushing poverty about to descend upon him and the prospect of physical privations and mental agony. Then he went and collected the necklace, putting down the thirty-six thousand francs on the jeweler's counter.

When Mme. Loisel took the necklace back to Mme. Forestier, the latter said rather coldly: "You ought to have brought it back sooner; I might have wanted it."

She did not open the case, as her friend had feared she might. If she had detected the replacement what would she have thought? What would she have said? Would she have considered her a thief?

Now Mme. Loisel learned to know the grim life of the very poor. However, she faced the position with heroic courage. This ghastly debt must be paid and she would pay it. They got rid of the maid; they gave up the apartment and took an attic under the tiles. She did all the heavy work of the house as well as the hateful kitchen jobs. She washed up, ruining her pink nails on the coarse crockery and the bottoms of the saucepans. She washed the dirty linen and shirts and the kitchen cloths and dried them on a line. She carried the rubbish down to the street every morning and brought up the water, stopping on every floor to get her breath. And dressed as a woman of the people, she went to the fruiterer, the grocer and the butcher with her basket on her arm, bargaining in spite of their rudeness and fighting for every penny of her miserable pittance.

Every month some notes of hand had to be paid off and others renewed to gain time. Her husband worked in the evening keeping a tradesman's books and often at night he did copying at twenty-five centimes[5] a page. This life went on for ten years.

After ten years they had paid everything back, including the interest and the accumulated compound interest.

Mme. Loisel now looked an old woman. She had become the strong, tough, coarse woman we find in the homes of the poor. Her hair was neglected, her skirt was askew, her hands were red, and her voice loud; she even scrubbed the floors. But sometimes, when her husband was at the office, she would sit down near the window and dream of that evening long ago, the ball at which she had been such a success.

What would have happened to her if she had not lost the necklace? Who can say? Life is such a strange thing with its changes and chances. Such a little thing can make or mar it!

[5] **twenty-five centimes** (sän′tēm): about 5 cents.

One Sunday, when she had gone for a stroll in the Champs-Élysées[6] as a change from the week's grind, she suddenly saw a lady taking a child for a walk. It was Mme. Forestier, still young, still beautiful, still attractive.

Mme. Loisel felt a wave of emotion. Should she speak to her? Yes, she would. Now that she had paid, she would tell her everything. Why not?

She went up to her: "Good morning, Jeanne!"

The other woman did not recognize her; surprised at being addressed in this familiar fashion by a common woman, she stammered: "But, Madame . . . I don't know you . . . there must be some mistake."

"No! I'm Mathilde Loisel!"

Her friend exclaimed: "Oh! Poor Mathilde, how you've changed!"

"Yes, I've had a pretty grim time since I saw you last, with lots of trouble — and it was all your fault!"

"My fault? What do you mean?"

"You remember that diamond necklace you lent me to go to the party at the Ministry?"

"Yes, what about it?"

"Well! I lost it!"

"What! But you brought it back to me."

"I brought you back another exactly like it; and for ten years we've been paying for it. You'll realize it hasn't been easy, for we had no money of our own. Well, now it's all over and I'm glad of it!"

Mme. Forestier had stopped: "You say you bought a diamond necklace to replace mine?"

"Yes! And you never spotted it, did you? They were as like as two peas."

And she smiled with simple proud pleasure.

Mme. Forestier, deeply moved, took both her hands: "Oh! my poor Mathilde! But mine was only paste,[7] not worth more than five hundred francs at most!"

* * *

[6] **Champs-Élysées** (shäⁿ′zā · lē · zā′): a boulevard in Paris, noted for its beauty.
[7] **paste:** a brilliant glass used to make artificial jewels.

EXAMINING THE STORY

1. What in life does Mathilde value most highly? Why does she nevertheless marry a man of small means? Despite everything her husband does for her, she remains discontented. Why?
2. Mathilde does not realize that the necklace she borrows is paste; what does this reveal about her background and experience? Mme. Forestier does not examine the returned necklace; what does this show about her? What other qualities does she show by her response to Mathilde's confession in the park?
3. Mathilde doesn't tell Mme. Forestier about the lost necklace immediately. Why not? What does she do instead? Can you explain the "simple proud pleasure" she feels in telling everything at the end? Do you think Mme. Forestier appreciated Mathilde's sacrifice? Explain.
4. **A Broader Perspective** • Many of the world's great stories are stories of redemption — that is, a person grows slowly from a vain and useless life into a life of meaning and worth. Is this such a story? Would its theme be different if Mathilde had learned that the lost necklace was of real diamonds? What would have been lost if the story had been written that way?

Cress Delahanty

JESSAMYN WEST

Mrs. Delahanty went to the door of Crescent's room to remind her that it was time to set the table for supper. It was a fine Saturday afternoon in November, and ordinarily Cress would have been outside, up in the hills with friends or helping her father with the irrigation. But this afternoon Cress had spent in her room in spite of the clear, warm weather. Mrs. Delahanty examined her daughter's stubby, somewhat boyish profile outlined against the golden light of the west windows with considerable curiosity.

"What are you writing, Cress?"

Cress looked up from the sheets of paper spread before her on the drop leaf of the rickety bamboo desk she had bought for herself that summer and said, "I'm not exactly writing, Mother. I'm making a list of traits."

"Traits?" Mrs. Delahanty asked.

"Good and bad traits," Cress said, and then explained further. "For school, that is."

"You mean personal traits?" Mrs. Delahanty asked.

"Kind of," Cress replied.

Mrs. Delahanty wondered anew. She had never in her life made a list of any kind except a grocery list, and this only when pushed into it by John. Life was bigger, and better too, she thought, than words. And it was disappointing and restricting to see a picnic summed up in "Remember Citronella, Kleenex, Band Aid"; or a trip to the city drained of half its promise by a list headed "Articles Needed En Route." There were clearly two classes of people in the world: those for whom the world was magnified and enriched in words, and those who could never find the beautiful world of their living and knowing on any sheet of paper. John and Cress belonged to the first class and she, belonging to the second, could only stand apart, as she did now, trying to understand the need they had for their journals and records — for their "Yesterday I rose at 6:30," their "Tomorrow I plan to begin rereading *David Copperfield*," and their I's, II's, and III's.

"Traits like honesty, kindness, cheerfulness?" she asked.

"Well, like them" Cress said, "but they aren't on it. This is a list of traits useful for school."

"Isn't honesty useful for school?"

"Nobody at school I ever heard of was popular for honesty," Cress said. After Mrs. Delahanty had considered this in silence for some seconds, Cress asked, "Did you ever hear anybody say, 'I'm just crazy about her; she's so honest'? Did you?"

"No," Mrs. Delahanty admitted, "I guess I never did."

"Me either," Cress said. "It's all right to be honest," Cress reassured her, "but there's nothing very outstanding about it."

"Oh I don't know," Mrs. Delahanty said, trying to keep a foothold in this conversation, which she felt to be, in spite of its subject matter, pretty slippery. "Look at Diogenes.[1] We've remembered him all these years."

Cress sniffed. "He was hunting for an honest man, not being one. And it was his lantern that was outstanding. That was his trademark. That and his barrel."

"There have been a lot of people with lanterns and barrels we've forgotten, I expect."

Cress agreed. "The trademark's got to stand for something. But if you get a good gag and it stands for something" — for all her conviction of tone Cress looked uncertain — "you're fixed, don't you think?" Before Mrs. Delahanty had answered this — if she could have answered it — Cress asked another question: "Mother, do you think I'm funny?"

"Funny?" Mrs. Delahanty repeated. If Cress was in the midst of some schoolgirl gloom because someone had called her funny, she certainly didn't want to add to it. On the other hand, if by "funny" Cress meant "witty," she could not truthfully say she wasn't.

"I mean amusing," Cress explained forthrightly. "In your opinion can I say and do amusing things? Can I make you laugh?"

Controlling an inclination to laugh right then, Mrs. Delahanty answered, "Yes, Cress. I think you can be very amusing and you have made me laugh many a time."

"Yesterday," Cress said, "I was told very confidentially something Bernadine Deevers said. She said, 'That Crescent Delahanty is deliciously amusing.' It wasn't a trade last[2] or anything like that. I didn't promise Hazel a thing in return for the compliment."

Mrs. Delahanty said, "I don't know about 'deliciously,' but the rest is true enough."

Cress gave her mother a look of awe and unbelieving. "Bernadine Deevers," she said. "Why, I didn't suppose she knew I was alive, let alone amusing."

"Let alone deliciously," Mrs. Delahanty said. Then seeing

[1] **Diogenes** (dī · oj′ə · nēz): an ancient Greek philosopher who lived in a barrel and carried a lantern in daylight, searching for an honest man.

[2] **trade last:** exchange in which a person offers to repeat a compliment he has heard about another person if the other will first tell him one.

her daughter's expression alter, doubt replacing radiance, she hurried to add, "Who is this Bernadine, anyway?"

Cress brightened again at once. "Just about the most popular girl in school, that is all. Just about the most outstanding sophomore, anyway." Cress herself was a freshman.

"What makes Bernadine so outstanding?"

Cress considered for a while. "Well, Bernadine's got practically everything, but her trademark is personality."

"Doesn't everyone have personality? Even fathers and mothers?" Mrs. Delahanty asked, trying to be a little amusing herself.

"Everybody has personality," Cress agreed. "Some people have positive personality and some people have negative personality." Mrs. Delahanty waited rather self-consciously for a further development of this idea, but Cress was interested only in Bernadine. "But glamorous personality is Bernadine's trademark."

"How is a person," Mrs. Delahanty asked with real curiosity, "when a glamorous personality is her trademark?"

Mrs. Delahanty had supposed that this question would take some thinking about, but Cress had evidently thought about it before. "When glamorous personality is your trademark, you are a law unto yourself," she answered promptly.

Mrs. Delahanty whistled. "Thank goodness your trademark isn't personality."

Cress put down her pencil with melancholy finality. "At present," she said, "I don't have a trademark — not of any kind."

That night after supper Mr. Delahanty, who had been up at five, irrigating, and who was put out with a climate so tardy with its rains that irrigating this late in November was necessary, said to his wife, "I think I'll just stay home and read tonight. I have to reset the water at ten anyway and we'd have to rush home. You and Cress go ahead into town if you want to."

"I don't want to go," Cress said. "I'm busy."

"I'm not busy," Mrs. Delahanty admitted, "but I'm not enough interested in what happens when a lady mayor meets a male mayor to drive to the movies alone to find out."

Cress listened to this exchange with an unsmiling face, then went to her room. Mrs. Delahanty heard the lid of the bamboo desk creak open. The evening had cooled, and at eight Mrs. Delahanty lit a fire of eucalyptus chunks, then challenged her husband to a game of Russian bank. Mr. Delahanty accepted the challenge, but he did not care whether he won or lost. Mrs. Delahanty wished for Cress, who followed the fall of each card with the intensity of a player who has the home ranch up at stake. At nine Cress came out, advised her father to his benefit on his play, but refused to play herself. "No, I just came out because of the fire. I've got work to do," she said, and took her papers to the dining-room table.

At nine thirty, after losing his second game, Mr. Delahanty said, "Anybody want to go out and reset the water for me?" When no one answered, he said, "Woman's work is from sun to sun but man's work is never done," and went outside cheerfully whistling "Swanee River."

Mrs. Delahanty went to the kitchen and made a pot of chocolate and a plate of toasted cheese sandwiches. Cress wandered out, watched her whip the chocolate to a foam and put the sandwiches in the oven, refused anything to eat, then picked up a large wedge of cheese, and went off toward her room nibbling gloomily.

Mrs. Delahanty had planned to take the food in by the fire, but Mr. Delahanty said as he pulled off his muddy boots, "Let's have it on the dining-room table where there's room to spread out." He carried the tray in himself and had the chocolate poured by the time Mrs. Delahanty, who had forgotten the napkins, came to the table.

"What's this?" he asked, gesturing with a cheese sandwich toward the sheet of paper beside his chocolate cup.

Mrs. Delahanty, who had an idea, answered only, "What does it say?"

Mr. Delahanty read, stared, drank chocolate, and finally said in a voice in which disbelief and sorrowful understanding mingled, "It says here, *Useful Traits for School. I. Personality, A. Unusual, 1. Witty.*" He put the sheet down. "What's the meaning of this?"

"It's a list," Mrs. Delahanty said. "You ought to understand if anybody would."

Mr. Delahanty ate half a sandwich, then picked up a second sheet. "*My Trademark. 'Isn't She Crazy!'* is the heading here," he said thoughtfully. "'*Isn't She Crazy!*' is in quotes," he explained. "Under it is *Useful Gags for Craziness. I. Clothes, A. Shoes, 1. Unmatched.*"

He put the second sheet face down on the first and covered both with the sandwich plate. He finished his cheese sandwich and then said, "What a dark world."

"You do understand it, then?" Mrs. Delahanty asked.

"Certainly I understand it. I lived there for a year."

"What year?"

"The year I was thirteen."

Mrs. Delahanty had not known her husband until he was fifteen, and these hints of an earlier life always enthralled her. She saw him at thirteen, a big, solemn boy with soft dark hair, inquiring eyes, and a sensitive mouth.

"You don't know who you are, then, or what you can do. You've got to make a hundred false starts. You've got to make your mark, without knowing what your mark is. Are you a coward or a hero? How do you know without involving yourself in dangerous situations? So you walk ridgepoles and visit cemeteries. How do you know you're alive even at that age if you aren't noticed? It's the dark time of life," Mr. Delahanty said again. "It turns my stomach now, but at thirteen I too had a trademark."

"A trademark!"

Mr. Delahanty grimaced. "Spitting. At thirteen I was a professional spitter. I used to give exhibitions. Distance and accuracy. Power and control. I had everything. And I hated it. And I still hate anybody now from grammar school days who calls me 'Spit' Delahanty."

"I don't ever remember seeing you spit."

"At fifteen I was far past that, an ex-spitter. By that time I had taken up—" He stopped in mid-sentence. "Cress," he said.

Cress, in her pink sprigged seersucker pajamas, the cheek that had been against the pillow pinker than the other, stood in the opening between the living room and dining room. "Did we wake you up with our talk?"

Cress sat down in the chair her father pushed out for her. "No," she said, "you didn't wake me up because I hadn't gone to sleep yet."

Mrs. Delahanty had the feeling that Cress had left her lists out on purpose, had given them time to read them, and would now like to have their opinion of craziness as a trademark. But she was loath to speak of them unless Cress did; Cress was silent and John went on as if he had never heard of trademarks — or craziness.

"How's school?" Mr. Delahanty asked his daughter. "Classes, teachers, kids? Edwin? Honor Gallagher? Everything turning out as well as you thought it would?"

"Everything's all right," Cress said, opening a cheese sandwich, then closing it like a book she didn't care to read. "Did I tell you I'm probably going to be freshman editor of the yearbook?"

"No," said Mr. Delahanty, "you didn't. That's fine. Congratulations."

"I'm not editor yet," Cress reminded him.

"But spoken of for the job. Spoken of favorably for the job."

Cress admitted it. "And it's a tradition that the person who is freshman editor is editor in chief his senior year."

"Congratulations," Mr. Delahanty said again. Then, shaking the chocolate pot, "Have some cocoa? Just what you need to put you to sleep."

"I read the other day it wasn't," Cress said. "I read it had every bit as much caffeine in it as coffee."

"Where? Where'd you read that?"

"In the newspaper."

"The newspaper!" scoffed Mr. Delahanty. "You can read anything in the newspapers. Let's consult the authority." He sprang from his chair with the enthusiasm which the search for a fact always gave him and came back to the table bearing Volume IV of the *Britannica,* Bisharin to Calgary. Cress got up and leaned across his shoulder as he flipped the pages. Mrs. Delahanty, while the two of them pursued the word, took the thing itself — caffeine or no caffeine — to the kitchen to reheat for Cress.

The campaign "Craziness as a Trademark" seemed to be going well in spite of Mrs. Delahanty's doubts. Cress, as November wore on, had never seemed more happy. Certainly she had never been more active or engrossed — and her activities engaged Mrs. Delahanty's energies as well as her own.

"Life now," Mrs. Delahanty reported to her husband one gray day at lunch, "is very full for me. It is like being property manager for a vaudeville star. It takes a good deal of equipment and thought to achieve the effect of craziness when actually you're as sober as a judge."

"Cress isn't and never was sober as a judge," Mr. Delahanty said. "That Bernadine had something when she said Cress was amusing. Clowning comes naturally to her."

"Not this clowning," Mrs. Delahanty said. "She memorizes lines. She gathers up equipment. She teaches kids their cues. It's exactly as spontaneous as a vaudeville act, and I think we ought to put a stop to it."

"How?" Mr. Delahanty asked.

"Just tell her it's silly and to stop it."

"And for the rest of her life she'd blame us for keeping her from finding out who she really was."

"Well, there's no use her finding out the hard way when we could tell her that she suits us just as she is."

"Cress is trying out her wings."

"She is trying the wrong wings then, John. Do you know what she did this morning?" Mrs. Delahanty didn't wait for any reply from her husband. "She wore her bedroom slippers to the bus and carried her oxfords. She had to have new bedroom slippers for this, by the way. The old ones wouldn't do for a public appearance. Do you know what the gag is there?"

This time she waited for Mr. Delahanty's answer. "No," he said, "I don't."

"The gag is that she has figured that it takes three minutes' time to put on her oxfords. Time on the bus is waste time. So, if she puts them on there, that three minutes is saved. Three minutes a day is fifteen minutes a week, an hour a month, nine hours in a school year. The whole bus load will have it reported at school ten minutes after they've arrived. 'Hear the latest about Cress Delahanty? That crazy kid. She's figured out how to save nine hours a year: by putting on her shoes in the bus. What a girl! What a card!'"

Mrs. Delahanty's imitation of the high school crowd did not awaken her husband from his musing. "Nine hours," he murmured thoughtfully. "A whole workday. I suppose she can sleep that much longer?"

"John Delahanty," Mrs. Delahanty said, "you surely—" But in the midst of that she changed her tack. "Did you hear her phoning last night?"

"With one ear. I was busy at the time."

Yes, he had been. Mrs. Delahanty felt her lips pursing and unpursed them. He had been working on a three-sheet list: "Articles Needed for Complete Electrification of the Delahanty Ranch."

"It would've paid you to listen."

Mr. Delahanty looked up from his Spanish rice. "Why?" he asked.

"She makes this call every night. Her algebra teacher made the sad mistake of saying in class that he couldn't possibly rest at night for wondering whether the class had done its homework. So Cress calls him."

"What does she say?"

"She says," Mrs. Delahanty said crisply, "'This is Crescent Delahanty reporting, Mr. Holcomb. I have finished my homework. I hope you will sleep well now.'" About this exploit Mrs. Delahanty, feeling that such a lily needed no gilding,[3] made no comment.

Mr. Delahanty appeared to choke a little on his Spanish rice. "More red pepper than usual in this today," he said.

Mrs. Delahanty said, "I have been making that dish for seventeen years, and I put exactly the same amount of red pepper in it now as I did then."

"Maybe my mouth is getting more sensitive with the years."

"Maybe so," Mrs. Delahanty agreed. "But I doubt it."

"I suppose that really was carrying things a little far?"

Mrs. Delahanty waited for a more adequate summing up of the situation.

"I should think Mr. Holcomb would be over any night now to strangle her," Mr. Delahanty said.

This seemed quite a lot more likely to Mrs. Delahanty, and she relaxed somewhat, pleased to find that the family still contained two sane members. Mr. Delahanty's sudden whoop of laughter, however, dispelled this happy supposition.

[3] **such a lily needed no gilding:** "To gild the lily" means to adorn something that is beautiful in itself. Here the expression is used sarcastically.

With that laugh still in her mind's ear, Mrs. Delahanty handed her husband the *Tenant Hi-Lights* at lunch a few days later. "Cress gave this to me this morning before she left for school," she said. "I think maybe she thought we would take some time alone to digest it." The paper was folded to the column called "The Hi-Light's On ——" by I. Marcum. This week's Hi-Light was on "Cress Delahanty, That Crazy Freshman," and there was a drawing of her in the center of the column in her fur-topped bedroom slippers, holding an oxford in each hand. "Read it out loud," Mrs. Delahanty said. "I want to be sure I wasn't seeing things when I read it."

After some preliminary smoothing and folding, which the *Hi-Lights* didn't need, Mr. Delahanty read in an expressionless voice, *"Crazy or Cagy? Freshman girl sole discoverer of way never to be on her uppers, and you are a heel if you suggest that this is not the last word on this soulful subject. Personally, the ice-blonde freshman can vamp us any time she wants to."* Mr. Delahanty stopped reading. "Gertrude, do you really want me to go on with this?"

"Yes," Mrs. Delahanty said, "I do."

Mr. Delahanty took up the *Hi-Lights* again, but before continuing he said, "Ice blonde! Why, Cress is nothing but a mere child."

"A color is a color, I suppose," Mrs. Delahanty answered mildly, "regardless of age."

"Ice blonde is something more than a color," Mr. Delahanty argued. But when Mrs. Delahanty asked him to explain, he could do no more than mention two or three movie stars.

"Go on reading," Mrs. Delahanty urged. "There's a good deal more."

Mr. Delahanty gave the *Hi-Lights* a couple more of the flattening whacks it did not require and continued. *"Personally the ice-blonde freshman can vamp us any time she wants to. We get a boot out of Delahanty. We pumped Cress, and this is her version of what she calls 'Delahanty's Law,' or, to add our own interpretation, 'What You Do on the Bus Doesn't Count.'"*

Mr. Delahanty paused once more and Mrs. Delahanty waited expectantly, but about Delahanty's Law and its interpretation he had nothing to say.

"It goes on, Gertrude, as you doubtless remember, this way," he said. *"No nit-wit she, Cress — and we quote — thus explained her discovery while we listened, tongue hanging out, so to speak, and all unlaced with interest. 'I, in my tireless search for efficiency, discovered that I spent fifteen minutes a week putting on and tying my shoes. Now if I did this on the bus — time ordinarily lost, as all bus riders know, in useless chatter — I would gain one hour a month, or one full working day a year.'*

"Asked what she intended doing with this 'saved' time, Cress answered demurely, 'Study.' Asked what, she replied, 'Algebra. Mr. Holcomb, you know, can't rest nights if the homework for his class isn't done.' (See next week's Hi-Lights *for the Holcomb-Delahanty story. Adv't.) Asked what her ultimate goal was, Cress said, 'Oxford.'*

"Excuse us, please, now while we pull on our own Congressional Gaiters (not on a bus, thus losing, according to Delahanty's Law, three minutes). We're going to hot-foot it over to Cress's. Got a little equation we want help with. Delahanty + I. Marcum = ? (See next week's column for answer. Adv't.)"

Mr. Delahanty folded the *Tenant Hi-Lights* into a compact oblong and threw it toward the fireplace, which he missed. "What have we got for dessert?" he asked.

"It's right there before you," Mrs. Delahanty said, indicating the raisin pie by his plate. Mr. Delahanty grunted and began slowly to eat.

Mrs. Delahanty didn't feel like raisin pie herself. "John," she asked, "what's your opinion of that?"

"My opinion is that I. Marcum will go far."

"What do you really think, John?"

"I think it's a pity and a crying shame."

"You'll speak to Cress then?"

"It wouldn't do any good. What can we say to her? Stop saying and doing funny things?"

"Yes, we can."

"Sure, we can. But in the first place we can't stop her; and in the second place if we could stop her, Cress would hate us for the rest of her life. I tell you she's finding out who she is. At that age the only way to know whether craziness is your trademark is to *be* crazy. It's something you've got to do."

"I didn't have to."

"No, Gertrude, you didn't. You never had to bother trying on attitudes. You were born wearing one that fit beautifully."

Still, and startled, at this sudden turning of the conversation,

Mrs. Delahanty watched her husband eat raisin pie. He paused to ask, "Don't you want to know its name?"

Mrs. Delahanty nodded mutely.

"Radiant loving kindness."

This unexpected and extravagant compliment made Mrs. Delahanty feel shy. It was too extraordinary for her to deal with instantaneously, and she put it aside for later consideration. "Whatever you think about Cress, John, I'm going to speak to her. I think it's my duty and I'm going to warn her at the first opportune minute."

The first opportune minute came that very afternoon, and Cress, after being warned, went in tears to her room. She came out, ate her supper wordlessly, then went again to her room. When Mrs. Delahanty heard the lid of the bamboo desk creak down, she said to her husband, "There is Cress writing out a list of reasons for hating me."

"What now?" Mr. Delahanty asked, and Mrs. Delahanty, with no heart for dishwashing, said, "Come on in by the fire and I'll tell you."

Mr. Delahanty settled himself in the Morris chair which had been his father's, and Mrs. Delahanty stood in front of the fireplace.

"This afternoon," she said, "Cress came skipping and hopping home from the bus, clapping those two horrible bedroom slippers together over her head like castanets."

"Cymbals," said Mr. Delahanty.

"Together, anyway, and happy as a lark. It seems they had an assembly today —"

"Assemblies, assemblies," said Mr. Delahanty. "Bird imitations, football rallies, talent shows. When do the kids go to school?"

"Assemblies," said Mrs. Delahanty, who went to P.T.A., "provide the children opportunity for participation in life situations."

"Is that thought to be a good thing? A life situation, if you ask me, is just about to engulf Cress. If you ask me, a little participation in something unlifelike on the order of ancient history or the ablative case[4] is what Cress has a crying need for. A little

[4] **ablative case:** a grammatical form in Latin.

more life participation and she'll bust apart at the seams. I can hear them —"

"John," Mrs. Delahanty said, "I just want to tell you what Cress told me, and what I told her. I don't give a whit one way or another about assemblies. The point is, they had one. And when Mr. DuMont came out on the stage —"

"Who is this Mr. DuMont? A bird imitator?"

"Mr. DuMont is the vice principal in charge of student activities. He has premature gray hair, a beautiful tan, and sings 'On the Road to Mandalay' so — Cress says — you can feel the waves rising and falling beneath you. He —"

"That's enough about DuMont," Mr. Delahanty said, "unless you've got some Mothersills[5] handy."

"I've seen him," Mrs. Delahanty said, "and he really is nice. He has —"

"He came out on the stage," Mr. Delahanty reminded her.

"On his way out Mr. DuMont stumbled over a pair of tennis shoes somebody had left on the stage. He stooped, picked them up by the strings, swung them back and forth, and then said in what Cress reports as being a perfectly dead-pan, side-splitting way: 'I see Delahanty has been here.' Then when everyone had stopped laughing at that, he said: 'They look like my size, but as a student of Delahanty's Law I intend to wait until I'm on a bus to try them on.'"

"Mr. DuMont's trademark appears to be craziness too," Mr. Delahanty remarked.

"The kids seem to love him."

"Why not?" asked Mr. Delahanty. "The kids are one with Mr. DuMont."

"I thought you approved of craziness. I thought that was what we've been arguing about."

"Gertrude, I haven't been arguing, and what I approve of is not craziness but freedom to find out who and what you are."

"Well, Cress thinks she's found out. She thinks she's a wit . . . or a wag . . . or the school jester. She says that about Delahanty's Law really panicked them and that not an eye in the auditorium but was on her — even though she was sitting in an obscure spot under the balcony in the midst of one hundred and seventy-two other freshmen and practically invisible."

[5] **Mothersills:** pills for seasickness.

"She didn't say anything about standing up or whistling and waving her handkerchief to help them see her, did she?"

"No, John. Anyway when she finished, and I hated to do it because she was as happy as —"

"A prima donna?"[6] suggested Mr. Delahanty.

"Oh no! A baby who's picked its first flower. Well, when she finished, I told her everything I've been thinking. I told her to stop it at once, that it was cheap and silly to play to the grandstand that way, and that she was going to regret getting a reputation as a harebrained clown when she was really a good, sweet, solid, sensible child." Mrs. Delahanty was unable to keep her voice from trembling.

"What did Cress say?"

"She said, 'Good, solid, sensible, sweet,' as if I had — as if I had reviled her. Then she began to cry."

Mr. Delahanty nodded and nodded as if this were all an old story to him.

"Then she stopped crying long enough to say that I didn't understand a thing — not her, not school, not young people in general, not Mr. DuMont, not I. Marcum. And she said her constant prayer was that when she grew up and had children that she would not forget what it was like to be young — the way I have. And she said that for three months at school she *had* been sweet, solid, and sensible. And where had it gotten her? At the end of three months of that, she had been a complete nonentity, and not a soul at school could've told you who Crescent Delahanty was. And now at the end of three weeks of planned living, with craziness for her trademark, she is a great success. And she doubts there is even a custodian at school who has not heard of Crescent Delahanty and Delahanty's Law. 'In fact,' I said, 'you are now a character.' She said yes, she was, and proud of it. Then she went to her room. But before she left, she said, 'Anyway my father understands me.' And now she is in there making a list headed 'What's Wrong with Mother.' But I don't care. I had to tell her."

"I think just what you think, Gertrude, except that I think Cress will have to find it out for herself. She'll wake up pretty soon, and it'll be a painful awakening, but it's bound to come."

"You believe that?"

[6] **prima donna:** leading female singer in an opera company.

"Of course. You don't think our daughter's a fool, do you?"

"No," Mrs. Delahanty said. "No, how could I?"

The "awakening," as Mr. Delahanty had named it, came the first week in December. The rains which had held off through the whole of November arrived the minute the November leaf on the calendar was torn off, and made up by their abundance for their lateness. On Friday afternoon Mr. Delahanty, happily housebound by the downpour, sat before a drowsy fire.

On the other side of the fire Mrs. Delahanty was shelling English walnuts preparatory to sugaring them for annual Christmas gifts to eastern relatives. She listened to the pleasant blend of sounds — fire sighing, pen scratching, nut shells cracking — and behind and giving body to the blend, the fine heavy sound of the constant rain. She was, she thought, reasonably happy. Then, as the pile of walnut kernels rose in the crock on the floor by her side, she decided that there is no such thing as reasonable happiness since happiness, like love, is without reason.

Cress came in from the bus, but she was neither the old Cress, solid and sensible, nor the new one, crazy and show-off. This Cress had been crying. She had on a hooded raincoat. But she had walked up from the bus with the hood hanging down her shoulders, and her hair, soaked to the scalp, was lank and mousey. She was no ice blonde now. I. Marcum would scarcely recognize her. Water dripped from her cheeks and beaded her eyelashes and stood in the corners of her mouth, which she held with unchildlike firmness. She went without a word to the fireplace and stood there with her back to her parents, while occasional drops of water hissed off her raincoat onto the andirons. Then she turned around to face them. It was the first time Mrs. Delahanty had ever heard adult resignation in her daughter's voice, adult acceptance of the fact that the source of one's joy is also often the source of one's sorrow. "I may have forgotten what it's like to be a girl," she thought, "but Cress is learning what it's like to be a parent."

"You have a perfect right to say, 'I told you so' now if you want to, Mother," Cress said. "You told me I was getting to be a character and I was, all right."

"What do you mean, Cress?" her father asked.

"I mean I'm a Character," Cress said bleakly. "I'm 'Irresponsible Delahanty.' I'm that 'Crazy Kid.' If I said I was dying, people would laugh." Water ran out of her hair and across her face and dripped off her chin, but she scorned to wipe it away.

"I made a good speech to the Student Council, and they laughed at every word I said. They laughed and held their sides and rolled in their chairs like loons."

"What speech was this, Cress?"

"The speech everybody who is a candidate for an office has to make to them. Then if they like you, they nominate you. I was a candidate for freshman editor. What they nominated me for was *Josh* editor. *Josh* editor. A two-year-old can be *Josh* editor. All you need to be *Josh* editor is a pair of scissors to cut out jokes with. I wouldn't be *Josh* editor if they shot me for not being. It's a silly job."

"Take off your coat, Cress," Mrs. Delahanty said, and Cress, not ceasing to speak, began also to unbutton.

"I would've been a good editor, and I told them the reasons — like I was responsible, knew the meaning of time, would see that the assignments were in on time, and so forth. They laughed like hyenas," she said, not bitterly but reflectively. "They said, 'This is the richest thing yet. Delahanty is a real character.' So they nominated me for *Josh* editor and I'm branded for life."

She threw her raincoat, which she had finished unbuttoning, onto the floor, said, "I have ruined my life," and walked out of the room, no longer trying to hide the fact that she was crying.

Mr. and Mrs. Delahanty still held the positions they had had when Cress entered — Mr. Delahanty, pen above his list; Mrs. Delahanty, nutcracker in one hand, cracked, unshelled nut in the other. Mr. Delahanty said, "I guess you were right. I guess it would've been better to have forbidden it."

"I did forbid it," Mrs. Delahanty said, "in so far as I could, and you can see what came of that." Mechanically she picked the kernel from the nut she still held, then got up, and threw the pan of shells into the fire. She herself was going to Cress.

John saw her look and let her take his hand. "I told you it was a dark time," he said quietly.

She let go his hand and went toward Cress's room. She didn't know what she would or could say when she got there. Maybe, "Cress, people like you and your father have to try on more than one way of being and doing to see who you are. And you're bound to make mistakes." Maybe she would say, "My sweet, sensible daughter." But she would surely hug her and kiss her. Her arms, as she heard through the closed door those catching sobs, already felt that stocky body grow quiet. She opened the door and said, "Cress, honey."

* * *

EXAMINING THE STORY

1. What traits does Cress select for her list? What traits does she show, in doing this?
2. What is Cress's purpose in making the list? Does she achieve her goal? Do her actions bring her satisfaction and happiness? What does she really need to discover?
3. Why is Mr. Delahanty opposed to speaking to Cress about her behavior? (Do events prove him right?) How does Mrs. Delahanty's belief that "life was bigger . . . than words" equip her to help her daughter in a moment of crisis? Which of her parents' traits might Cress have considered for her list? Why doesn't she?
4. **A Broader Perspective** • When characters do not understand their own emotions and actions, their stories are often adventures in self-discovery — as this story is. Why is the name *Crescent* appropriate for a girl at this stage of life? How do her painful experiences help Cress to grow?

The Unlucky Winner

MAX SHULMAN

My next girl is going to be honest. I don't care if she looks like a doorknob. Just so she's honest.

This determination arises from a late unhappy attachment to one Clothilde Ellingboe. Now, don't misunderstand; I'm not calling Clothilde a crook. Let's say she was irresponsible. Or unethical. Or unprincipled. Or amoral. Let's not go around calling ladies crooks. Watch that stuff.

I met Clothilde at the University of Minnesota's annual Freshman Prom. I was standing in the stag line and I saw her dancing with a fellow halfway across the floor. They were doing the "Airborne Samba," the latest dance craze at the university. In the "Airborne Samba" the girl locks her hands behind the fellow's neck and he carries her all through the dance. She never touches the floor; she just lashes out rhythmically with her feet.

I cut in on them, laughing lightly at the resultant abrasions. I transported Clothilde through the rest of the medley, and then we went out on the terrace for some air. There, in a very short time, I knew I was hers. How vivacious she was! How socially aware she was! You would never believe she was only a freshman, the way she had been everywhere and had done everything and knew everyone. In a very short time I was, as I say, hers.

Then began a social whirl that I would not have thought possible. We were out every night — dancing, movies, sleigh rides, hayrides, wiener roasts, bridge games, community sings. Not a night did we miss.

At first I was a little worried. "Clothilde," I would say, "I'd love to go out tonight, but I've got homework. I've got to translate ten pages of Virgil[1] for Latin tomorrow."

"Dobie, you oaf," she would laugh. "Don't you know *anything?*"

Then she would produce a Virgil pony — a Latin textbook with English translations set in smaller type beneath each line of Latin.

When I said that I had to do some work in political science, she would hand me a syllabus that condensed the whole course into an hour's easy reading. If I was concerned about an English history quiz, she would come up with a card the size of a bookmark on which there was printed the dates of all the kings in the British dynasty, plus thumbnails of all significant events.

"This is all very well," I said one night, "but I don't feel that I'm learning anything."

"To the contrary, Dobie," she replied, taking my hands in

[1] **Virgil:** ancient Roman poet.

hers. "Without all this social life, you could never become a well-rounded-out personality. What's more important, Dobie — to know a lot of old facts and figures or to become a well-rounded-out personality?"

"To become a well-rounded-out personality," I said. "Clearly."

"There you are," she said, spreading her palms. "C'mon, Dobie, let's go down to the Kozy Kampus Kave and hear E-String Eddie and his T.N.T. Trio."

And so it went, night after night. I'll confess that I was a stranger to the Phi Beta Kappa selection board, but nonetheless, my grades were adequate. I got by, and whatever happened in my classes, I had the comfort of knowing that I was becoming a well-rounded-out personality. Some nights I could actually feel my personality rounding out — like a balloon.

But occasionally a doubt would dart through my mind like a lizard across a rock. Then I would say to myself, "This can't go on forever." I found out I was right one morning in my English class.

On that morning at the end of the class hour, our instructor, Mr. Hambrick, announced, "There will be a five-hundred-word theme due next Friday. Write about any subject you want to. No excuses will be accepted for late themes. Class dismissed."

The heart within me sank. I had long been worried about Mr. Hambrick. Mr. Hambrick was one of those college English instructors who had taken a teaching job thirty years before so they could have an income while they worked on their novels. Now they were still teaching English and they were still on the first chapters of their novels. They vented their frustration on their students.

Up to this assignment I had managed to get along in Mr. Hambrick's class. Before this I had had to turn in three or four book reports, all of which Clothilde supplied from the *Book Review Digest*. But a theme was different. You can't go about clipping original themes from other sources.

"Clothilde," I said that evening, "I'm afraid the movies are out for tonight. I've got to turn in a theme for English on Friday and here it is Tuesday and I'd better get to work."

"But, Dobie," wailed Clothilde. "It's Montgomery Clift. He knocks me out. Doesn't he knock you out?"

"No," I said truthfully. "Listen, Clothilde, I'd better do this theme. This isn't the kind of thing I can chisel on. I've got to do it myself, and I'd better get started."

"How long does it have to be?"

"Five hundred words."

"What's the topic?"

"Anything I want."

"Well, then, what's your hurry? It's only Tuesday. You've got Wednesday and Thursday to work on it."

"No, I'd better start it right away. I don't know whether I can finish it all in one night. Don't forget, Clothilde, I'm not very bright."

"Yes, I know," she said, "but even *you* should be able to write a five-hundred-word theme in one night. Especially if you can pick your own subject."

"Look, Clothilde, I don't want to seem stubborn, but I've made up my mind. I'm going to start that theme tonight and that's final."

"Shelley Winters is in the picture too."

"Let's hurry so we can get good seats," I said.

The next night, Wednesday, I was positively going to work on the theme. *Positively*. But Benny Goodman was playing a one-night stand at the Auditorium, and, as Clothilde said, "You can't just not go to hear Benny Goodman. How will you explain it to people?"

And Thursday afternoon there was a Sunlite Dance in the Union with a jitterbug contest for which Clothilde and I had been rehearsing for weeks. Unfortunately, Clothilde threw a shoe and pulled up lame at the end of the second lap and we had to drop out.

Not until six o'clock Thursday evening did I get to the theme. I set two fountain pens, a bottle of ink, an eraser, three pencils, a dictionary, a thesaurus, and a ream of fresh white paper on my desk. I adjusted the goose-neck lamp for minimum eye-strain. I pulled up a straight-backed chair. I opened the window. I filled a pitcher with water. I took my phone off the hook. Then I sat down and drew isosceles triangles for two hours.

Not an idea came to me. Not a fragment of an idea. Not a teensy-weensy glimmer of an idea. I had just about decided to drop out of the university and enroll in a manual-training school when I heard Clothilde calling me outside my window.

I stuck my head out. "How ya doin', Dobie?" she asked.

I grimaced.

"I thought so," she said. "Well, don't worry. I've got it all figured out. Look." She held up two white cards.

"What's that?" I asked.

"Stack permits," she replied.

"What?"

"Come on out and I'll explain the whole thing."

"Listen, Clothilde, I don't know what you're up to, but I don't want any part of it. I'm going to sit here all night if I have to, but I'm going to finish that theme. I don't care what you say; there's no other way to do it."

"Come on out, you jerk. I've never failed you yet, have I? Listen, you'll not only have your theme written tonight, but we'll be able to catch the last feature at the Bijou."

"No."

"You don't really believe you're going to get that theme written, do you?"

She had me there.

"Come on out."

"What's a stack permit?" I asked.

"Come on out."

I came out.

She took my arm. "We'd better hurry, Dobie. It's after eight o'clock and the library closes at nine."

"What's that got to do with anything?"

She was pulling me along, toward the library. "Dobie, you've been to the library, haven't you?"

"I used to go occasionally," I said, "before I met you."

"All right. You know how the library works?"

"Sure," I said. "You go in and look up the book you want in the card catalogue and then you write your name and the card number of the book on a request slip and you give the slip to the librarian and she sends a page boy after your book."

"Ah," said Clothilde, "but do you know where the books come from?"

"They keep them on shelves in the back of the library."

"Stacks," said Clothilde. "Those are called stacks."

"So?"

"Ordinarily," Clothilde continued, "they don't let students go back into the stacks. They're afraid we might get the books mixed up or steal them or something. When you want a book, you turn in a request slip for it and they send a page boy after it."

"This is all very informative, Clothilde, but I wish you had picked another time to tell it to me. I've got a theme to write."

Clothilde's big blue eyes narrowed craftily into little blue eyes. "Some students, Dobie, *are* allowed to go back in the stacks. Some graduate students and a few seniors get permits. If they are doing the kind of work that requires a lot of books at hand, particularly obscure books, they can get stack permits. Then they can go back themselves and find the books they want without tying up the librarian and several page boys. These" — she waved the two white cards — "are stack permits."

"I still don't see ——"

"I borrowed them," said Clothilde, "from a couple of graduate students I know. With these cards we can get into the stacks."

"But how is all this going to get my theme written?"

We were almost at the library now.

"Dobie Gillis, you dope. I swear if you didn't have freckles and a crew haircut, I'd quit going with you in a minute. Don't you understand? We're going back in the stacks and find some old book of essays that nobody has ever heard of and you'll copy one of the essays and that will be your theme."

I stopped dead. "Clothilde," I whispered, "you can't mean it."

"Why not? It's foolproof. There won't be any record of your ever having seen the book. You won't turn in a request slip for it, so nobody will be able to check back through the slips. We're going into the stacks on somebody else's permit, so you can't be checked that way. You're not going to take the book out, so there won't be a withdrawal record on your library card. I've got pencil and paper in my purse. You'll copy the essay out of the book while you're in the stacks. Then you'll put the book back exactly where you found it. Then we'll leave and nobody will ever be the wiser."

I sat down beside a tree in front of the library and pulled her down beside me. "Clothilde," I said, "why don't we just get a couple of revolvers and go hold up a filling station?"

"This is no time to be finicky, Dobie. You know very well you'll never get that theme written."

"True," I said after a short silence.

"Then come on into the library. It's eight-thirty."

"I can't, Clothilde. My conscience would never stop bothering me."

She pulled me to my feet. She's quite a bit stronger than I am.

"Anyway," I protested, "it's not safe. How can we be sure that Mr. Hambrick, my English instructor, hasn't read the book that I'm going to copy the essay out of?"

Clothilde smiled. "I was hoping you'd ask that question. Come along. I'll show you."

She dragged me into the library, up the stairs and to the main desk. "Stop perspiring, Dobie," she whispered. "We don't want anybody to remember us." She showed the two stack permits to the librarian. The librarian nodded us back into the stacks.

The stacks filled me with awe. They consisted of metal bookshelves arranged in banks. Each bank was seven tiers high, and each tier was six feet tall. At the end of each bank was a metal spiral staircase, wide enough for only one person. Narrow catwalks ran along each tier, and the various banks were joined by other catwalks. The whole thing, I thought, looked like the cell blocks you see in prison movies. I shuddered at the significance of the comparison.

"Come along," said Clothilde. "The essay collections are in the seventh tier of the fourth bank. Hurry. We haven't much time."

We raced through the catwalks. Our footsteps echoed metallically, and I expected to hear sirens and see spotlights at any moment. I felt like James Cagney in "White Heat."

When we got to the essay shelves, Clothilde said, "Now, quickly, look for a book with a lot of dust on it. Don't take any clean ones."

We looked for a few seconds, and I found a volume gray with dust. I pulled it off the shelf. "This all right, Clothilde?"

She took it. She opened the book and looked at the record card in the envelope pasted inside the cover — the card that the library files when you take out a book. "This one is no good," said Clothilde. "The card shows that this book was last taken out in 1942. It's not very likely, but there's just a chance that your English instructor was the one who took it out. If so, he might still remember the essays. We don't have to take chances; we can find a book that hasn't been taken out for at least ten years. Then, even if your instructor was the one who checked out the book, there's not much chance that he'll remember it."

"You thought any about becoming a gun moll?" I asked.

"Hurry, Dobie, it's a quarter to nine."

We found a couple more dusty volumes, but their cards showed that they had both been out of the library within the past ten years. At seven minutes to nine, we found the right one.

"This is perfect," said Clothilde, holding up the book, a slim collection called *Thoughts of My Tranquil Hours* by one Elmo Goodhue Pipgrass. Mr. Pipgrass's picture appeared on the frontispiece — a venerable gentleman with side whiskers and a white string tie. The record card in the book was almost lily white. The book had been taken out only once, and that was way back in 1926.

"This is perfect," Clothilde repeated. "The book has only been taken out once. It was published" — she looked at the title page — "in 1919. The picture of Pipgrass on the frontispiece shows that he was a man of at least seventy at that time. He's certainly dead now, so you don't even have to worry about plagiarism."

"Plagiarism!" I exclaimed. "You didn't say anything about that before."

"No use to alarm you, Dobie," she said. "Hurry up now. It's five minutes to nine. Here's pencil and paper."

"Plagiarism," I muttered.

"Hurry, Dobie. For Pete's sake, hurry."

With the greatest reluctance, I took pencil and paper and began to copy the first essay in *Thoughts of My Tranquil Hours*. It started like this:

Who has not sat in the arbor of his country seat, his limbs composed, a basin of cheery russet apples at his side, his meerschaum[2] filled with good shag;[3] and listened to the wholesome bucolic sounds around him: the twitter of chimney swifts, the sweet piping of children at their games, the hale cries of the countryman to his oxen, the comfortable cackling of chickens,

[2] **meerschaum** (mir′shəm): tobacco pipe made of a white, claylike mineral.
[3] **shag:** a coarse tobacco that has been finely shredded.

the braying of honest asses; and felt his nostrils deliciously assailed with aromas from the kitchen: the nourishing saddles of beef, the beneficent gruels, the succulent tarts; and basked in the warmth of sun and earth, full bounty of abundant nature; and thought, "Of what moment is man's travail for gain, his mad impetus toward wealth, his great unsettled yearning for he knows not what, when all about him if he would but perceive are the treasures of the globe, more precious far than any jewel which lies deep beneath virgin earth across unplumbed and perilous seas?"

That was the first sentence, and the shortest one. I scribbled furiously until I had the whole thing down, and we left. We got out of the library at five seconds before nine.

Outside, I turned on Clothilde. "Why did I ever listen to you?" I cried. "Not only do I run the risk of getting kicked out of school in disgrace, but I've got to worry about getting arrested for plagiarism too. And to top it all off, the essay stinks. He'll probably flunk me on it anyway."

"Could *you* have done better?" she asked.

"That's not the point ——"

"Come on," she said impatiently. "We'll miss the last show at the Bijou."

I didn't enjoy the show one bit. I enjoyed even less handing in my theme on Friday morning. As I laid the sheets on Mr. Hambrick's desk, visions of policemen and hanging judges and prison gates sped through my head. My forehead was a Niagara of perspiration.

"You feel all right, Mr. Gillis?" asked Mr. Hambrick.

"Yes, sir," I said. "I feel fine, thank you."

"I was just asking," he said. "I don't really care."

The gaiety of the week end failed to cheer me up. Dressed as a buccaneer on Saturday night, I swashbuckled listlessly through a masquerade party, and on Sunday I sat like a lump all through a hayride, never once joining in the four hundred verses of "Sweet Violets."

In my English class Monday morning I was resigned. I was prepared for the worst. I wasn't even surprised when Mr. Hambrick told me to stay behind at the end of the class.

"I want to talk to you about the theme you turned in Friday,

Mr. Gillis," said Mr. Hambrick when we were alone in the room.

"Yes, sir," I said, my voice hitting high C above middle E.

"Frankly," he continued, "I was amazed at that theme. Until Friday, Mr. Gillis, I had merely thought of you as dull."

"Yes, sir."

"But now I know I was wrong. The trouble with you is that you're archaic."

"Huh?"

"You're archaic. You're way behind the times. You were born one century too late. And," he added, "so was I. I tell you, Mr. Gillis, I have no regard for modern writing. It all seems like gibberish to me — all that clipped prose, that breakneck pacing, that lean objectivity. I don't like it. I think writing should be leisurely and rich. Sentences should be long and graceful, filled with meaning and sensitive perception. Your theme, Mr. Gillis, is a perfect example of the kind of writing I most admire."

"Call me Dobie," I said genially.

"I'm going to give you an 'A' on that theme, and I hope in the future you will write some more like it."

"You bet," I said. "I know just where to get them."

"And if you're ever free on a Sunday afternoon, I'd be pleased if you'd stop at my place for a cup of tea. I'd like to talk to you about a novel I've been toying with. It's a great deal like your stuff."

"Sure, pal. Now if you'll give me my theme, I've got to get on to my next class."

"Ah," he smiled, his neutral-colored eyes twinkling behind tortoise-shelled glasses, "I'm afraid I can't do that. I've got a little surprise for you, Mr. Gillis. I've entered your theme in the Minnesota Colleges Essay Contest."

I just made it to a chair. "Again," I gasped. "Say that again."

"I've entered your theme in the Minnesota Colleges Essay Contest," he repeated. "It's a competition sponsored once a year by the State Board of Education for all the colleges in Minnesota — the university and Hamline and Macalester and St. John's and all the rest. The contest is judged by the four members of the Board of Education and the winner gets a free cruise on the Great Lakes."

"Please!" I screamed. "I don't want to be in any contest.

I don't want to win a Great Lakes cruise. I get seasick. Even in a bathtub I get seasick."

"Come, come, Mr. Gillis. You mustn't be so modest. Let me give you a bit of advice, my boy. I was just like you are. I hid my light beneath a bushel too. Now look at me — teaching English to a bunch of little morons. No, Mr. Gillis, you've got to assert yourself, and I'm going to see that you do."

"Please, Mr. Hambrick," I begged tearfully.

"It's too late anyhow. As soon as I read your theme last Friday night, I put it in the mail immediately. It's already in the hands of the Board of Education. The results of the contest will be announced Thursday. Well, goodbye, Mr. Gillis. I must rush to my next class."

I sat there alone in that classroom for two hours. Twitching. Just twitching. I couldn't even think. I just twitched. Like a horse dislodging flies. Then, skulking behind trees, I walked to my room, crawled into bed, and moaned until sundown.

In the evening I found Clothilde and, with a great deal of bitterness, told her the whole story.

"That's not good," said Clothilde. Sharp, that girl.

"I wish," I said honestly, "that I had never set eyes on you."

"Don't be vile, Dobie. Let's figure something out."

"Oh no you don't. I'm through listening to you. Tomorrow I'm going to Mr. Hambrick and confess everything. There's nothing else to be done, no matter what *you* say."

"Dobie, you really work hard at being stupid, don't you? That's the silliest thing I ever heard. Really, I don't see what you have to worry about. If Mr. Hambrick, a professional English instructor, didn't suspect anything, what makes you think that the members of the State Board of Education are going to get wise?"

"Now you listen to me, Clothilde. Every minute I delay my confession just makes it worse for me. It stands to reason that at least one of those Board of Education members has read Elmo Goodhue Pipgrass's *Thoughts of My Tranquil Hours*."

"Fat chance," sneered Clothilde.

"No, Clothilde. I won't do it. I know I'm going to get caught, and I might just as well get it over with."

"Honestly, I've never met such a yuck. You'll never get caught, you poor goof. They'll read the theme and reject it, and the whole business will be over with. The things you find to worry about."

"Good God, girl. What if I win the contest?"

"With that corn?" she asked. "Ha. Honestly, Dobie."

Then she argued some more, but I was firm as a rock. It took her more than twenty minutes to talk me into it.

For the next three days, as tragedy mounted on tragedy, I was numb with fear. I'll tell you how numb I was: a practical joker in my political science class put a tack on my seat and I sat on it all through the class.

Tuesday Mr. Hambrick said to me, "Good news, Mr. Gillis. Your essay has advanced into the quarter-finals."

I nodded mutely and went out into the hall and twitched some more.

Wednesday Mr. Hambrick said to me, "Great news, Mr. Gillis. Your essay is now in the semi-finals."

I tried to confess everything to him then, but all that came out of my throat were hoarse croaks.

And Thursday the walls came tumbling down.

"Mr. Gillis," said Mr. Hambrick, "something very curious has happened. Your essay won out in the semi-finals and was entered in the finals. Your competition in the finals was an essay by a young man named Walter Bradbury from Macalester College. Mr. Bradbury's essay is a description of iron mining in northern Minnesota. Now, it happens that of the four members of the Board of Education, two are from the Iron Range district. Those two insist on awarding the prize to Mr. Bradbury. But the other two members want to give you the prize. Neither side will yield."

"I'll withdraw," I said hastily.

"That's noble of you," said Mr. Hambrick, "but it won't be necessary. The Board of Education has agreed to call in an impartial judge to pick the winner. You and Mr. Bradbury are to go over to the Board of Education office in the state capital this afternoon for the final judging. I've arranged transportation for you."

"Mr. Hambrick," I pleaded desperately. "Let them give the prize to Bradbury. The sea air will do him good."

"Nonsense." Mr. Hambrick laughed. "You're sure to win. I know the judge they picked is going to favor you. He's a distinguished essayist himself, who used to write much as you do. He's been in retirement for many years at a cottage near Lake Minnetonka. He's very old. Possibly you may have heard of him. His name is Elmo Goodhue Pipgrass."

Click. I heard a distinct click in my head. Then a terrifying calm came over me. I felt drained of emotion, no longer capable of fear or worry. I felt as a man must feel who is finally strapped into the electric chair.

"There will be a car in front of the Administration Building in thirty minutes to take you to the state capital," said Mr. Hambrick.

"Yes, sir," I said. My voice seemed to be coming from far away.

"Good luck — Dobie."

I found Clothilde and told her everything — told it to her evenly, coolly, without rancor.

"I'm going to the state capital with you," she said. "I'll think of something."

I patted her shoulder. "Thank you, Clothilde, but no. It will be better if we break clean — now. I don't want you to be known as the consort of a criminal. Your whole life is ahead of you, Clothilde. I don't want to be a burden to you. Try to forget me, Clothilde, if you can. Find somebody new."

"You're awfully sweet, Dobie."

"And so are you, Clothilde, in an oblique way."

"Then this — this is it?"

"Yes, Clothilde. This," I said, the little muscles in my jaw rippling, "is it."

"What are you going to do with those two tickets to Tommy Dorsey tonight?"

"They're yours, Clothilde." I handed them to her and added with a wry smile, "I won't be needing them."

We shook hands silently, and I went off to the Administration Building and got into the car and was driven to the state capital.

I went into the Board of Education office and was directed to the conference room. This room contained a long mahogany table with five empty chairs behind it. There were two chairs in front of the table, and in one of them sat a young man wearing a sweater with "Macalester" emblazoned across the front.

"You must be Walter Bradbury," I said. "I'm Dobie Gillis."

"Hi," he said. "Sit down. They'll be here in a minute."

I sat down. We heard footsteps in the hall.

"Here they come," said Bradbury. "Good luck, Dobie."

"Oh no, no, no!" I cried. "Good luck to you. I want you to win. With all my heart I do. Nothing would make me happier."

"Why, thanks. That's awfully decent of you."

They came in, and the pit of my stomach was a roaring vastness. The four members of the Board of Education were dressed alike in dark business suits and looked alike — all plumpish, all bespectacled, all balding. With them, carrying a gnarled walking stick, was Elmo Goodhue Pipgrass, the littlest, oldest man I had ever seen. His side whiskers were white and wispy, the top of his head egg-bald. His eyes looked like a pair of bright shoe buttons. He wore a high collar with a black string tie, a vest with white piping, and congress gaiters.[4] He was ninety-five if he was a day.

One of the Board members took Pipgrass's arm to assist him. "Take your big fat hand off my arm," roared Pipgrass. "Think I'm a baby? Chopped half a cord of wood this morning, which is more than you ever chopped in your whole life. Weaklings. The government is full of weaklings. No wonder the country's gone to rack and ruin. Where are the boys?"

"Right over here, Mr. Pipgrass," said a Board member, pointing at Bradbury and me. "See them?"

"Of course I see them. Think I'm blind? Impudence from public servants. What's the world come to? Howdy, boys." He nodded vigorously at a hall tree. "Sit down."

"They are sitting down, Mr. Pipgrass," said a Board member. "Over here."

"Whippersnapper," muttered Pipgrass. "I remember when they built this state capital. Used to come and watch 'em every day. If I'd known they were going to fill it with whippersnappers, I'd have dynamited it."

"Mr. Pipgrass," said a member gently, "let's get to the essays. The boys have to get back to school."

"Essays? What you talking about? I haven't written an essay since 1919."

Suddenly hope was reborn within me. The man was senile. Maybe I'd get away with it. Maybe . . .

[4] **congress gaiters:** high shoes with elastic sides.

"The boys' essays, Mr. Pipgrass. You're to pick the best one, remember?"

"Certainly, I remember. Think I'm an idiot? Who's Bradbury?"

"I, sir," said Bradbury.

"Ah. You're the fool who wrote an essay on iron mining. Iron mining! Why didn't you write one on plumbing? Or garbage disposal?"

I felt a sinking sensation.

"Or roofing?" continued Pipgrass. "Or piano tuning? Iron mining! What kind of subject is that for an essay? And furthermore you split four infinitives. And don't you know that a compound sentence takes a comma between clauses? Great Jehoshaphat, boy, where'd you ever get the idea you could write?"

Bradbury and I trembled, each for his own reason.

"Gillis," said Pipgrass. "Gillis, you pompous, mealy-mouthed little hack. Who told you that you were a writer?" He picked up my essay, held it a half inch before his face, and read, "'Who has not sat in the arbor of his country seat. . . .'" He threw down the essay. "I'll tell you who has not sat in the arbor of his country seat. You haven't. Bradbury hasn't. All of these four fat fellows haven't. Who the devil has got a country seat? What the devil *is* a country seat? Who talks about country seats these days? What kind of writer are you? Who said you were a writer? Can't anybody write in this confounded state?

"It's a sorry choice," said Pipgrass, "that I have to make between these two wights.[5] Neither of 'em can write worth a nickel. But if I must choose, give the prize to Bradbury."

A great weight rolled off my back. A film dropped from my eyes. I smiled a real smile.

Now they were all around Bradbury shaking his hand, but none so heartily as I. I waited until they all left the room and then I got down on my knees and sent off six quick prayers. I mopped my forehead, my cheeks, my chin, my neck, and my palms, and then I went into the hall.

Pipgrass was waiting for me.

"You Gillis?" he asked.

I nodded, holding the doorjamb for support.

[5] **wights:** a poetic word for *people*.

He took my arm. "I was tempted to give you the prize, boy. Mighty flattering to know that people are still reading *Thoughts of My Tranquil Hours* after all these years."

Then he was gone down the corridor, chuckling and running his walking stick across the radiators.

* * *

EXAMINING THE STORY

1. What kind of girl was Clothilde? Dobie suggests, ". . . she was irresponsible. Or unethical. Or unprincipled. Or amoral." Do you agree with these statements? Why? What other traits does she show? When? (Consider, for example, her elaborate plans at the library.) Does her last remark to Dobie support your earlier impressions of Clothilde?
2. What qualities does Mr. Hambrick admire in Dobie's theme? Describe Mr. Hambrick as a teacher; as a person. Give evidence from the story for your analysis of him.
3. What traits of character does Elmo Pipgrass show in his early essay? at the School Board meeting? after the meeting? Why does he keep secret the matter of the essay's authorship?
4. What is the flaw in Clothilde's view of the "well-rounded-out personality"? (Does a person become "well-rounded" partly *by means of* study?)
5. **A Broader Perspective** • Clothilde, whom Dobie first sees doing the "Airborne Samba," is a person who will never be able to get her feet on the ground. It is Dobie's slow recognition of this fact, and what it costs him, that gives meaning, and humor, to this story.

   "In a very short time I knew I was hers," Dobie says, recalling his first whirlwind meeting with Clothilde. What is the effect of this line? What other statements humorously expose Dobie's immaturity? What finally causes him to break with Clothilde? Would the story have been as humorous if told from Clothilde's *point of view* (see Glossary)? Is there *irony* (page 199) in the title? in the events of the story? Explain.

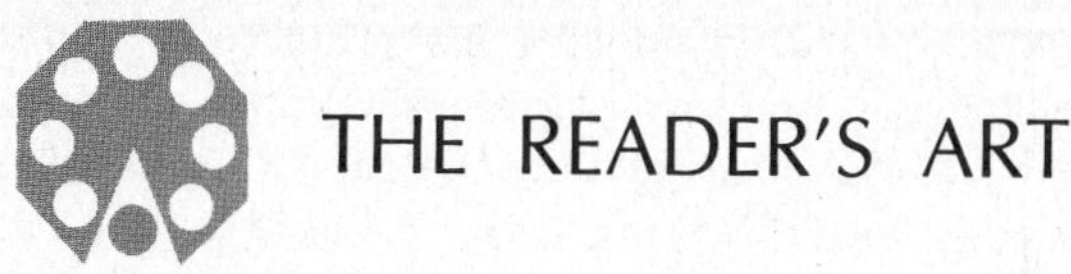

THE READER'S ART

Responding to the Author's Tone

Tone refers to something behind the story — the author's manner toward the reader and his attitude toward the characters and events he is describing. Although tone may reveal an author's unconscious values and attitudes, it more pointedly serves to direct the reader's response to the events of the story.

In speech, we recognize the tone of a statement by the stress and inflection of the speaker's voice. Words like *charming, brilliant,* and *superb,* for example, can each mean different — even opposite — things according to the speaker's tone: "Brilliant!" we moan, when our team fumbles at the goal line. The meaning of spoken words depends on the situation and on how the speaker's tone tells us to think of it.

In literature, we must infer the author's tone from the situation and the printed words on the page. The tone may be somber ("Old Man at the Bridge") or playful ("The Summer of the Beautiful White Horse"); formal ("Quality") or humorous and colloquial ("The Unlucky Winner"). If the author's purpose is to ridicule behavior in order to suggest a better way of living, the tone is called *satirical.* "Antaeus," for example, satirizes the unsympathetic attitude of certain adults toward children's activities. Do any of the other stories you have read adopt the tone of satire?

A tone prevalent in literature is *irony.* Something boomerangs: events turn out in an unexpected, and often painful, manner. "The Necklace" is an ironic story in several ways. The situation is ironic: Mathilde's sacrifice was unnecessary. Separate episodes also are ironic: M. Loisel expects Mathilde to be pleased with her invitation to the ball — she is miserable; she is a success at the ball, but this only increases her despair when the ball is over; she despises middle-class life, but her actions condemn her to an even lower social station. Underlying all is the irony of a character who wants — and gets — something which destroys him. This last irony is emphasized by a detail, the name of Mme. Loisel's street: Rue des Martyrs. From the beginning of the story, Mme. Loisel martyrs herself (destroys her life) through her ironically misplaced faith in the worth of material possessions.

Language itself can be used ironically: the apparent meaning of words is the opposite of that intended. For example, when Mrs. Delahanty says (page 175), ". . . such a lily needed no gilding" — the expression "gilding the lily" means to add unnecessary ornament to something already beautiful — she does not mean that Cress's behavior in telephoning the algebra teacher is beautiful, nor that the comment she, Mrs. Delahanty, refrains from making would have been praise: she means the opposite. She is using *verbal* irony (the irony of *words*).

Can you explain the verbal irony in Zaroff's remark "We try to be civilized" (page 29)? in the fact that the narrator of "The Telltale Heart" claims to tell his story *healthily*? in the description of Mitty, whose inner life is laid open to the reader, as *inscrutable?*

A special form of verbal irony is called *sarcasm:* words used in an opposite sense for the purpose of insulting or hurting another person — as when Mallory calls the nerve specialists "great friends" of Farrar (page 126). Watch for sarcasm in the next story ("Water Never Hurt a Man"), where it spurs a boy to fight.

FOR WRITING

1. Discuss the main character of any one of the stories in this section. What price does he pay for pretense? Are there any situations in life in which a pose is justified?
2. Summarize the action of "Cress Delahanty" in a serious tone; in a playful tone; in a condescending tone.
3. Explain the irony in one of the following stories: "Antaeus," "The Interlopers," "Fever Dream."

8 Is it necessary to suffer in order to grow?

Water Never Hurt a Man

WALTER D. EDMONDS

He trudged with his hands tight fists in his pockets, his head bowed to the wind and rain. Ahead of him in the darkness, so that he could hear the squdge of their hoofs, the towing team bowed their necks against the collars. He could not see them in the darkness. When he lifted his face, the rain cut at his eyes; and when lightning split the darkness, he shut his eyes tight and pulled his head closer into his coat collar, waiting blindly for the thunder. Once in a lull he looked back. He could barely make out the bow-lantern and the arrows of gray rain slanting against it. Between him and the light he caught glimpses of the towrope, dipped slightly between the team's heaves, and the roughened water in the canal. Somewhere behind the light his father stood by the rudder-sweep,[1] his beard curled and wet, his eyes slits, sighting for the bank. John wanted to go back, wanted to tie-by for the night, wanted to be in the bunk with his head buried in the friendly, musty smell of the blanket, where the storm could not reach him. He had gone back once, but his father had reached for his belt, saying, "Go on back. Watter never hurt a man. It keeps his hide from cracking."

[1] **rudder-sweep:** long steering oar.

John had gone back to the team. They did not need his guidance. But it was his place to keep the rope from fouling if a packet boat[2] coming their way signaled to pass. He was afraid of his father at night, afraid of the big belt and strong hands with hair on the fingers over the knuckles. He caught up with the plodding horses and let the rain have its way. At each stroke of lightning his small back stiffened. It was his first year on the canal and he was afraid of storms at night.

He had been proud that spring when his father said, "John's old enough to be a driver-boy; he's coming along with me and the *Bacconola*." He had showed his dollar to his brothers and sisters, first pay in advance, and his father had bought him a pair of cowhide boots from the cobbler when he came to the village. Later, when the frost was out of the mud, John would go barefoot.

He was proud of his father. In Westernville, with other small boys, he had heard the dock loafers talking about his father, George Brace, bully[3] of the Black River Canal. In some strange way they had news of every fight his father fought a day after it happened. "George licked the Amsterdam Bully Wednesday mornin'. Lock fifty-nine. It tuk nineteen minits only." "George is a great hand. Them big ditch bezabors is learning about George." A stranger had said, "Wait till Buffalo Joe meets up with him." There was silence then. Buffalo Joe Buller, he was bully of the western end of the Erie. A pea-souper, a Canadian, he fought the Erie bullies down one by one, and when he licked them he marked them with his boot in the Canadian style. It had a cross of nails to mark the beaten man's face. "You wait," said the stranger.

Little John, listening, felt shivers down his back. But now, with the wind and rain, and the lightning tumbling the clouds apart, he forgot. They were on the long haul westward, to Buffalo, with ploughs aboard, full-drafted in Rome.[4] They had had to leave three hundredweight[5] on the dock.

He felt his muddy boots slip in the towpath. He heard the squelching of the horses. Squelch-squelch, a steady rhythm as

[2] **packet boat:** boat carrying mail, passengers, and cargo.
[3] **bully:** a riverboatman.
[4] **full-drafted in Rome:** fully loaded in Rome, New York, a town on the Erie Canal.
[5] **three hundredweight:** three hundred pounds.

they kept step. Once the lightning caught his eyes; and he had a clear view of trees beyond the canalside meadow, their budded twigs bent down like old women with their backs to the storm, and the flat, sharp wall of a canal house sixty yards behind him. He had not even seen it as he passed. The rain was finding a channel down his neck. It crept farther, bit by bit, with a cold touch. He could feel his fists white in his pockets from clenching them. His legs ached with the slippery going. They had had supper at six, tied up by the bank, and John had eaten his plate of beans. He had felt sleepy afterward, barely noticing his father's big body bent over the dishpan. It was warm in the cabin, with the little stove roaring red-hot, and his small hat hanging beside his father's cap on the door.

He had been almost asleep when his father's hand shook him roughly, then tumbled him from his chair. "Get out, John. Them ploughs we've got has to get west for spring ploughing. We'll pick up Bob in Syracuse, then we'll have a better chance to rest. Get out now," and he had reached for his belt.

What did John care for the old ploughs anyway? But it hadn't then begun to storm, and he had gone, with a tired sense of importance. One had to keep freight moving on the old Erie. The old *Bacconola* always made fast hauls. He had been proud and shouted in a high voice to the tired horses and kicked one with his new boots.

But now he did not care about the ploughs. He wished the crazy old *Bacconola* would spring a leak in her flat bottom, so they would have to stop till the hurry-up boat came along and patched her up. He thought of her now, bitterly, with her scabs of orange paint. "Crummy old blister," he called her to himself and made names for her, which he said aloud to the horses in a shrill voice. He was only twelve, with all the bitterness of twelve, and the world was a hateful thing.

The lightning caught him, and his throat tightened and he wanted to cry out under the thunder.

A water rat went off the towpath with a splash, and a frog squeaked.

He glanced up to see a team on the opposite towpath heading east. "Hey, there!" yelled the driver in a hoarse voice; but John was too tired to answer. He liked to yell back in the daytime and crack his whip. But he had dropped his whip a while back.

He would get a licking for that in the morning. But he didn't care. To hell with the whip and the driver and Pa!

"Hey, there!" shouted the other driver, a voice in the rain. "All right, all right, you dirty pup. Eat rain, if you want to, and go drownd." The rain took the voice, and the boat came by, silently, noiseless as oil, with its bow light a yellow touch against the rain. The steersman gave a toot upon the horn, but the sound bubbled through the water in it, and the steersman swore.

They were still on the long level, alone once more. It must be midnight. If only the lock would show. In Syracuse, Bob would come. He took turns driving and steering and cooking — a little man with a bent shoulder who had dizzy spells once in a while.

At the lock John could sit down and rest and listen to the tender snarling at his sluices while the boat went down, and heaving at his gate-beam, while John's father heaved against the other. He was crazy, the lock-keeper was; all lock-keepers were crazy. John's father always said so. John had seen a lot of them in their week of hauling, but he did not see why they were crazy. They looked no different even if they were. He hoped the lock-keeper would be asleep, so it would take a while to wake him.

Squelch, squelch-squelch, squelch. The horses kept plodding. Suddenly John caught a break in the rhythm. One foot sounded light. He pushed his way up beside them against the wind and laid a wet hand against a side. He could not see, but the side felt hot and wet, and he got a smell of sweat. Yes, he could feel the off[6] horse limping. Hope filled him. He waited till the boat came up where he was, a small figure, shrunk with cold. The boat's bow, round and sullen, slipped along, the bow light hanging over and showing an old mullein[7] stalk in silhouette against the water.

"Pa!"

His voice was thin against the wind.

He saw his father's figure, rain dripping from the visor of his cap, straight and big, almighty almost, breast to the wind.

"Pa!"

The head turned.

"Hey, there! What you doin'? Get on back, or I'll soap you proper!"

[6] **off:** right.
[7] **mullein:** wooly-leaved weed.

"Pa! Prince has got a limp in his front foot. Pa!"

The voice turned hoarse with passion. "Get on back, you little pup! Fifty-nine's just round the next bend. Take your whip and tar him, or I'll tar you proper."

John sobbed aloud. For a bare moment he thought of staying still and letting the boat pass on. He would run away and join the railroad. He would get run over by an engine there, just when things went well, and they would be sorry. He started to draw himself a picture of his body coming home in a black box, and his mother crying, and his father looking ashamed and sorry, and then the lightning made a blue flare and he saw the straight figure of his father ahead, on the *Bacconola,* which seemed struck still, a pill box in the flat country, and he was afraid and went running desperately, hoping he could get back to the team before he was missed.

He caught the horses on the bend and, lifting his face to the storm, saw the lock lanterns dimly ahead. And even then his ears caught, coming up behind him, the harsh blast of a tin horn.

He looked back and saw a light, two rope lengths behind the *Bacconola.* Even while he watched over his shoulder, he saw that it was creeping up.

"John!" His father's voice beat down the sound of rain. "Lay into them brutes and beat into the lock!"

He could imagine his father glaring back. If only he had not dropped his whip. He would have liked to ask his father for the big bull whip that cracked like forty guns, but he knew what would happen if he did. He shrieked at the horses and fumbled for a stone to throw. But they had heard and recognized the note in his father's voice, and they were bending earnestly against the collars. A sudden excitement filled John as his father's horn rang out for the lock. The wind took the sound and carried it back, and the other boat's horn sounded a double toot for passing. John yelled shrilly. The horses seemed to stand still, and there was an odd effect in the rain of the canal sliding under them inch by inch laboriously, as if with his own feet he turned the world backward.

Minutes crept at them out of the rain, and the lights of the lock did not seem to stir. Then John heard the squelching of the team behind his back. Little by little they were coming up, past the *Bacconola,* until he could hear them panting through the rain, and saw them close behind, behind dim puffs of steamy breath. He watched them frantically. Then the lightning came once more, a triple bolt, and the thunder shook him, and when he opened his eyes once more he saw the lock lanterns a hundred yards ahead.

At that instant the driver of the boat behind yelled, "Haw!" and the following team swung across his towrope and they were snarled.

The horses stopped of themselves, shuddering. They were old hands, and knew enough not to move, for fear of being thrown from the towpath. The boats came drifting on, placidly as waterlogged sticks. The light of the following boat showed a dark bow coming up. John heard his father roaring oaths, and saw by the bow light of the other boat a tall, clean-shaven man as big as his father, crouched to jump ashore. Then both boats came in by the towpath, and both men jumped. They made no sound except for the thump of their shoes, but John saw them dim against the lantern light, their fists coming at each other in slow, heavy swings.

The strange team was panting close beside him, and he did not hear the blows landing. There was a pushing upward in his chest, which hurt, and his fists made small balls in the pockets of his trousers. The other boater and his father were standing breast to breast, their faces still, cut, stonelike things in the yellow light, and the rain walling them in. He saw his father lift his hand, and the other man slip, and he would have yelled, for all his cold, if the lightning had not come again, so blue that his eyes smarted. He doubled up, hiding his face, and wept. . . .

A hand caught him by the shoulder.

"A little puny girly boy," said a voice. "I wouldn't lick you proper! Not a little girly baby like you. But I'll spank you just to learn you to let us come by!"

John opened his eyes to see a boy, about his own height, but broader built, squinting at him through the rain.

"Take off your pants, dearie," said the boy in a mock voice, digging in his fingers till John winched.[8] "Joe Buller can handle your captain smart enough. Me, I'll just paddle you to learn you."

John, looking up, was afraid. He did not know what to do, but without warning his hands acted for him, and he struck at the

[8] **winched:** winced.

square face with all his might. A pain shot up his arm, making his elbow tingle, and the boy fell back. John could feel the surprise in that body stock-still in the rain, and had an instant of astonished pride.

Then panic laid hold of him and he tried to run. But the other boy jumped on his back. They went down flat in the mud, the older boy on John's shoulders, pummeling him till his head sang, and forcing his face into the track, and crying, "Eat it, you lousy little skunk! Eat it, eat it, eat it, eat it!"

John could taste the mud in his mouth, with a salty taste, and he began to squirm, twisting his head to escape the brown suffocation. He heaved himself behind, throwing the boy unexpectedly forward, twisted round, and kicked with all his might. The boy yelled and jumped back on him. And again they went down; this time the boy bent seriously to business. And this time John realized how it was to be hurt. At the third blow something burst loose in his inside and he screamed. He was crying madly. The other boy was heavier, but John squirmed over on his back, and as the brown hand came down in his face he caught it in both his own and bit with all the strength of his jaws. The hand had a slippery, muddy taste, but in a second it was warm in his mouth, and there was a sick, salt wetness on his tongue. The boy struck him once in the eyes and once on the nose, but John held on and bit. Then the boy howled and tore loose and ran back. There was another stroke of lightning, and John saw him doubled up, holding his hand to his mouth; and he got stiffly up, turned his back to the thunder, and saw his father bent over the other boater, taking off his shoe.

John walked up to them. His father's face was bleeding a trickle of blood from the right eye into his beard, but he was grinning.

"I'll take his boot for a souvenir," he said. "How'd you come out, Johnny?"

"Oh, pretty good. I guess that other feller won't bother us no more," said John, examining the fallen man. He lay half-stunned, by the water's edge, a smooth, big man, with frightened, pale eyes. And one crumpled arm was in the water. John's father looked at the man and then at the boot he had in his hand.

"I'd ought to mark him by the rights of it; but he ain't worth the work, the way he laid down. Who'd ever know his name was Buller?"

Buller. . . . John gazed up admiringly at his big father and studied how the blood ran from the outer corner of the eye and lost its way in the black beard, which the rain had curled. His father had licked the western bully proper.

"Hey, there!"

The hail came in a thin, cracking voice. Turning, they saw the lock-keeper, white-bearded, peering at them from under the battered umbrella he held with both hands against the wind. The tails of his nightshirt whipped round the tops of his boots.

"Hey, there, you. There'll be some down-boats by pretty quick, so you want to hurry along now, while the level's right."

John was aware of his father standing looking down at him.

"Shall we tie-by where we be?" asked his father.

John felt pains coming into the back of his neck where he had been pummeled, and his knuckles ached.

"We can stay here a spell," said his father. "The storm's comin' on again. There'll be bad lightnin', I make no doubt."

As he spoke there came a flash, and John whirled to see if the other driver-boy was still visible. He was proud to see him sitting by the towpath, nursing his hurt hand. John did not notice the thunder. He was elaborating a sentence in his mind.

He made a hole in the mud with the toe of his boot, spat into it, and covered it, the way he had seen his father do at home on a Sunday.

"Why," he said, in his high voice, eying the old *Bacconola,* "I guess them poor bezabor farmers will be wantin' them ploughs for the spring ploughing, I guess."

"Me, I'm kind of tuckered," said his father, raising his shoulders to loose the wet shirt off his back. "And the rain's commencing, too."

John said importantly, "Watter never hurt a man; it keeps his hide from cracking."

His father jumped aboard. He took his horn and tooted it for the lock. John ran ahead and put back the other boat's team and cried to their own horses to go on. They took up the slack wearily, and presently little ripples showed on the *Bacconola's* bow, and the lantern showed the shore slipping back. On the stern, George Brace blew a blast for the lock. The old lock-keeper was standing by the sluices, drops of water from his beard falling between his feet.

The boat went down, and the horses took it out. Ahead, the team and the boy left the lantern light and entered once more the darkness. The rope followed. And once more the *Bacconola* was alone with its own lantern.

Presently, though, in a stroke of light, George saw his son beside the boat.

"What's the matter? Hey, there!" he asked.

"Say, Pa! Will you chuck me your bull whip here ashore? Them horses is getting kind of dozy. They need soaping proper."

"Where's your whip?"

"I guess I left it a while back. I guess it was in that kind of scrummage we had. I guess it needs a heavier whip anyhow. I guess a man couldn't spare the time going back for it."

"Sure," said George.

He reached down and took it from its peg, recoiled it, and tossed it ashore. The boat went ahead, slowly, with a sound of water, and of rain falling, and of wind.

* * *

EXAMINING THE STORY

1. How do details about the weather, the father's physical strength, and lore about canal "bullies" help the reader to understand John's boyish fear? At the beginning of the story, what keeps John going in the face of the storm? Who controls the situation then?
2. Why does each boat try to beat the other to the lock? Why is time important to them? Is anything more than time at stake? When the tow-ropes snarl, why do John's father and the other boatman jump ashore and begin to fight?
3. What change has come over John at the end of the story? What has caused the change? How is it reflected in his words to his father: "Watter never hurt a man"? In what other statements does John assert his new role? Have John and his father reversed positions? Explain.
4. **A Broader Perspective •** A ceremony initiating a boy into manhood is a common practice in many societies, though the exact form of this ordeal varies greatly with time and place. According to this story, what tests did a canaller's son have to undergo in order to prove his manhood? What personal qualities did he have to demonstrate? How did a sarcastic remark finally goad John into proving himself?

   What is it, according to the story, that never hurts a man?

A Visit to Grandmother

WILLIAM MELVIN KELLEY

Chig knew something was wrong the instant his father kissed her. He had always known his father to be the warmest of men, a man so kind that when people ventured timidly into his office, it took only a few words from him to make them relax, and even laugh. Doctor Charles Dunford cared about people.

But when he had bent to kiss the old lady's black face, something new and almost ugly had come into his eyes: fear, uncertainty, sadness, and perhaps even hatred.

Ten days before in New York, Chig's father had decided suddenly he wanted to go to Nashville to attend his college class reunion, twenty years out. Both Chig's brother and sister, Peter and Connie, were packing for camp and besides were too young for such an affair. But Chig was seventeen, had nothing to do that summer, and his father asked if he would like to go along. His father had given him additional reasons: "All my running buddies got their diplomas and were snapped up by them crafty young gals, and had kids within a year — now all those kids, some of them gals, are your age."

The reunion had lasted a week. As they packed for home, his father, in a far too offhand way, had suggested they visit Chig's grandmother. "We this close. We might as well drop in on her and my brothers."

So, instead of going north, they had gone farther south, had just entered her house. And Chig had a suspicion now that the reunion had been only an excuse to drive south, that his father had been heading to this house all the time.

His father had never talked much about his family, with the exception of his brother, GL, who seemed part con man,[1] part

[1] **con man:** confidence man, swindler; one who uses personal charm to defraud people.

practical joker and part Don Juan;[2] he had spoken of GL with the kind of indulgence he would have shown a cute, but ill-behaved and potentially dangerous, five-year-old.

Chig's father had left home when he was fifteen. When asked why, he would answer: "I wanted to go to school. They didn't have a Negro high school at home, so I went up to Knoxville and lived with a cousin and went to school."

They had been met at the door by Aunt Rose, GL's wife, and ushered into the living room. The old lady had looked up from her seat by the window. Aunt Rose stood between the visitors.

The old lady eyed his father. "Rose, who that? Rose?" She squinted. She looked like a doll, made of black straw, the wrinkles in her face running in one direction like the head of a broom. Her hair was white and coarse and grew out straight from her head. Her eyes were brown — the whites, too, seemed light brown — and were hidden behind thick glasses, which remained somehow on a tiny nose. "That Hiram?" That was another of his father's brothers. "No, it ain't Hiram; too big for Hiram." She turned then to Chig. "Now that man, he look like Eleanor, Charles's wife, but Charles wouldn't never send my grandson to see me. I never even hear from Charles." She stopped again.

"It Charles, Mama. That who it is." Aunt Rose, between them, led them closer. "It Charles come all the way from New York to see you, and brung little Charles with him."

The old lady stared up at them. "Charles? Rose, that really Charles?" She turned away, and reached for a handkerchief in the pocket of her clean, ironed, flowered housecoat, and wiped her eyes. "God have mercy. Charles." She spread her arms up to him, and he bent down and kissed her cheek. That was when Chig saw his face, grimacing. She hugged him; Chig watched the muscles in her arms as they tightened around his father's neck. She half rose out of her chair. "How are you, son?"

Chig could not hear his father's answer.

She let him go, and fell back into her chair, grabbing the arms. Her hands were as dark as the wood, and seemed to become part of it. "Now, who that standing there? Who that man?"

"That's one of your grandsons, Mama." His father's voice

[2] **Don Juan:** the "great lover" of Spanish legend.

cracked. "Charles Dunford, junior. You saw him once, when he was a baby, in Chicago. He's grown now."

"I can see that, boy!" She looked at Chig squarely. "Come here, son, and kiss me once." He did. "What they call you? Charles too?"

"No, ma'am, they call me Chig."

She smiled. She had all her teeth, but they were too perfect to be her own. "That's good. Can't have two boys answering to Charles in the same house. Won't nobody at all come. So you that little boy. You don't remember me, do you. I used to take you to church in Chicago, and you'd get up and hop in time to the music. You studying to be a preacher?"

"No, ma'am. I don't think so. I might be a lawyer."

"You'll be an honest one, won't you?"

"I'll try."

"Trying ain't enough! You be honest, you hear? Promise me. You be honest like your daddy."

"All right. I promise."

"Good. Rose, where's GL at? Where's that thief? He gone again?"

"I don't know, Mama." Aunt Rose looked embarrassed. "He say he was going by his liquor store. He'll be back."

"Well, then where's Hiram? You call up those boys, and get them over here — now! You got enough to eat? Let me go see." She started to get up. Chig reached out his hand. She shook him off. "What they tell you about me, Chig? They tell you I'm all laid up? Don't believe it. They don't know nothing about old ladies. When I want help, I'll let you know. Only time I'll need help getting anywheres is when I dies and they lift me into the ground."

She was standing now, her back and shoulders straight. She came only to Chig's chest. She squinted up at him. "You eat much? Your daddy ate like two men."

"Yes, ma'am."

"That's good. That means you ain't nervous. Your mama, she ain't nervous. I remember that. In Chicago, she'd set down by a window all afternoon and never say nothing, just knit." She smiled. "Let me see what we got to eat."

"I'll do that, Mama." Aunt Rose spoke softly. "You haven't seen Charles in a long time. You sit and talk."

The old lady squinted at her. "You can do the cooking if you promise it ain't because you think I can't."

Aunt Rose chuckled. "I know you can do it, Mama."

"All right. I'll just sit and talk a spell." She sat again and arranged her skirt around her short legs.

Chig did most of the talking, told all about himself before she asked. His father only spoke when he was spoken to, and then, only one word at a time, as if by coming back home, he had become a small boy again, sitting in the parlor while his mother spoke with her guests.

When Uncle Hiram and Mae, his wife, came they sat down to eat. Chig did not have to ask about Uncle GL's absence; Aunt Rose volunteered an explanation: "Can't never tell where the man is at. One Thursday morning he left here and next thing we knew, he was calling from Chicago, saying he went up to see Joe Louis fight. He'll be here though; he ain't as young and foot-loose as he used to be." Chig's father had mentioned driving down that GL was about five years older than he was, nearly fifty.

Uncle Hiram was somewhat smaller than Chig's father; his short-cropped kinky hair was half gray, half black. One spot, just off his forehead, was totally white. Later, Chig found out it had been that way since he was twenty. Mae (Chig could not bring himself to call her Aunt) was a good deal younger than Hiram, pretty enough so that Chig would have looked at her twice on the street. She was a honey-colored woman, with long eyelashes. She was wearing a white sheath.

At dinner, Chig and his father sat on one side, opposite Uncle Hiram and Mae; his grandmother and Aunt Rose sat at the ends. The food was good; there was a lot and Chig ate a lot. All through the meal, they talked about the family as it had been thirty years before, and particularly about the young GL. Mae and Chig asked questions; the old lady answered; Aunt Rose directed the discussion, steering the old lady onto the best stories; Chig's father laughed from time to time; Uncle Hiram ate.

"Why don't you tell them about the horse, Mama?" Aunt Rose, over Chig's weak protest, was spooning mashed potatoes onto his plate. "There now, Chig."

"I'm trying to think." The old lady was holding her fork halfway to her mouth, looking at them over her glasses. "Oh, you talking about that crazy horse GL brung home that time."

"That's right, Mama." Aunt Rose nodded and slid another slice of white meat on Chig's plate.

Mae started to giggle. "Oh, I've heard this. This is funny, Chig."

The old lady put down her fork and began: Well, GL went out of the house one day with an old, no-good chair I wanted him to take over to the church for a bazaar, and he met up with this man who'd just brung in some horses from out West. Now, I reckon you can expect one swindler to be in every town, but you don't rightly think there'll be two, and God forbid they should ever meet — but they did, GL and his chair, this man and his horses. Well, I wished I'd-a been there; there must-a been some mighty high-powered talking going on. That man with his horses, he told GL them horses was half-Arab, half-Indian, and GL told that man the chair was an antique he'd stole from some rich white folks. So they swapped. Well, I was a-looking out the window and seen GL dragging this animal to the house. It looked pretty gentle and its eyes was most closed and its feet was shuffling.

"GL, where'd you get that thing?" I says.

"I swapped him for that old chair, Mama," he says. "And made myself a bargain. This is even better than Papa's horse."

Well, I'm a-looking at this horse and noticing how he be looking more and more wide awake every minute, sort of warming up like a teakettle until, I swears to you, that horse is blowing steam out its nose.

"Come on, Mama," GL says, "come on and I'll take you for a ride." Now George, my husband, God rest his tired soul, he'd brung home this white folks' buggy which had a busted wheel and fixed it and was to take it back that day and GL says: "Come on, Mama, we'll use this fine buggy and take us a ride."

"GL," I says, "no, we ain't. Them white folks'll burn us alive if we use their buggy. You just take that horse right on back." You see, I was sure that boy'd come by that animal ungainly.[3]

"Mama, I can't take him back," GL says.

[3] **ungainly:** here, dishonestly.

"Why not?" I says.

"Because I don't rightly know where that man is at," GL says.

"Oh," I says. "Well, then I reckon we stuck with it." And I turned around to go back into the house because it was getting late, near dinner time, and I was cooking for ten.

"Mama," GL says to my back. "Mama, ain't you coming for a ride with me?"

"Go on, boy. You ain't getting me inside kicking range of that animal." I was eying that beast and it was boiling hotter all the time. I reckon maybe that man had drugged it. "That horse is wild, GL," I says.

"No, he ain't. He ain't. That man say he is buggy and saddle broke and as sweet as the inside of a apple."

My oldest girl, Essie, had-a come out on the porch and she says: "Go on, Mama. I'll cook. You ain't been out the house in weeks."

"Sure, come on, Mama," GL says. "There ain't nothing to be fidgety about. This horse is gentle as a rose petal." And just then that animal snorts so hard it sets up a little dust storm around its feet.

"Yes, Mama," Essie says, "you can see he gentle." Well, I looked at Essie and then at that horse because I didn't think we could be looking at the same animal. I should-a figured how Essie's eyes ain't never been so good.

"Come on, Mama," GL says.

"All right," I says. So I stood on the porch and watched GL hitching that horse up to the white folks' buggy. For a while there, the animal was pretty quiet, pawing a little, but not much. And I was feeling a little better about riding with GL behind that crazy-looking horse. I could see how GL was happy I was going with him. He was scurrying around that animal buckling buckles and strapping straps, all the time smiling, and that made me feel good.

Then he was finished, and I must say, that horse looked mighty fine hitched to that buggy and I knew anybody what climbed up there would look pretty good too. GL came around and stood at the bottom of the steps, and took off his hat and bowed and said: "Madam," and reached out his hand to me and I was feeling real elegant like a fine lady. He helped me up to the seat and then got up beside me and we moved out down our alley. And I remember how colored folks come out on their porches and shook their heads, saying: "Lord now, will you look at Eva Dunford, the fine lady! Don't she look good sitting up there!" And I pretended not to hear and sat up straight and proud.

We rode on through the center of town, up Market Street, and all the way out where Hiram is living now, which in them days was all woods, there not being even a farm in sight and that's when that horse must-a first realized he weren't at all broke or tame or maybe thought he was back out West again, and started to gallop.

"GL," I says, "now you ain't joking with your mama, is you? Because if you is, I'll strap you purple if I live through this."

Well, GL was pulling on the reins with all his meager strength, and yelling, "Whoa, you. Say now, whoa!" He turned to me just long enough to say, "I ain't fooling with you, Mama. Honest!"

I reckon that animal weren't too satisfied with the road, because it made a sharp right turn just then, down into a gulley and struck out across a hilly meadow. "Mama," GL yells. "Mama, do something!"

I didn't know what to do, but I figured I had to do something so I stood up, hopped down onto the horse's back and pulled it to a stop. Don't ask me how I did that; I reckon it was that I was a mother and my baby asked me to do something, is all.

"Well, we walked that animal all the way home; sometimes I had to club it over the nose with my fist to make it come, but we made it, GL and me. You remember how tired we was, Charles?"

"I wasn't here at the time." Chig turned to his father and found his face completely blank, without even a trace of a smile or a laugh.

"Well, of course you was, son. That happened in . . . in . . . it was a hot summer that year and —"

"I left here in June of that year. You wrote me about it."

The old lady stared past Chig at him. They all turned to him; Uncle Hiram looked up from his plate.

"Then you don't remember how we all laughed?"

"No, I don't, Mama. And I probably wouldn't have laughed. I don't think it was funny." They were staring into each other's eyes.

"Why not, Charles?"

"Because in the first place, the horse was gained by fraud. And in the second place, both of you might have been seriously injured or even killed." He broke off their stare and spoke to himself more than to any of them: "And if I'd done it, you would've beaten me good for it."

"Pardon?" The old lady had not heard him; only Chig had heard.

Chig's father sat up straight as if preparing to debate. "I said that if I had done it, if I had done just exactly what GL did, you would have beaten me good for it, Mama." He was looking at her again.

"Why you say that, son?" She was leaning toward him.

"Don't you know? Tell the truth. It can't hurt me now." His voice cracked, but only once. "If GL and I did something wrong, you'd beat me first and then be too tired to beat him. At dinner, he'd always get seconds and I wouldn't. You'd do things with him, like ride in that buggy, but if I wanted you to do something with me, you were always too busy." He paused and considered whether to say what he finally did say: "I cried when I left here. Nobody loved me, Mama. I cried all the way up to Knoxville. That was the last time I ever cried in my life."

"Oh, Charles." She started to get up, to come around the table to him.

He stopped her. "It's too late."

"But you don't understand."

"What don't I understand? I understood then; I understand now."

Tears now traveled down the lines in her face, but when she spoke, her voice was clear. "I thought you knew. I had ten children. I had to give all of them what they needed most." She nodded. "I paid more mind to GL. I had to. GL could-a ended up swinging if I hadn't. But you was smarter. You was more growed up than GL when you was five and he was ten, and I tried to show you that by letting you do what you wanted to do."

"That's not true, Mama. You know it. GL was light-skinned and had good hair and looked almost white and you loved him for that."

"Charles, no. No, son. I didn't love any one of you more than any other."

"That can't be true." His father was standing now, his fists clenched tight. "Admit it, Mama . . . please!" Chig looked at him, shocked; the man was actually crying.

"It may not-a been right what I done, but I ain't no liar." Chig knew she did not really understand what had happened, what he wanted of her. "I'm not lying to you, Charles."

Chig's father had gone pale. He spoke very softly. "You're about thirty years too late, Mama." He bolted from the table. Silverware and dishes rang and jumped. Chig heard him hurrying up to their room.

They sat in silence for awhile and then heard a key in the front door. A man with a new, lacquered straw hat came in. He was wearing brown and white two-tone shoes with very pointed toes and a white summer suit. "Say now! Man! I heard my brother was in town. Where he at? Where that rascal?"

He stood in the doorway, smiling broadly, an engaging, open, friendly smile, the innocent smile of a five-year-old.

* * *

EXAMINING THE STORY

1. Why does Charles need the pretense of a college reunion in order to visit his old home? What draws him back there after his long absence? Why is there "fear, uncertainty, sadness, and perhaps even hatred" in Charles's eyes when he greets his mother?
2. Mama says, "I had ten children. I had to give all of them what they needed most." How does she demonstrate that attitude when GL brings home the horse? When he asks her to ride in the buggy? Does she apply the same principle to Charles when she greets him without reproach after his prolonged absence?
3. How did Mama try to show Charles, as a child, that he was advanced for his age? Why didn't he understand her? At the dinner table, he doesn't see the humor of his mother's story. Why? What does he want her to admit? Why can she not admit that?
4. At the end of the story, Charles rushes from the room. Why? Why does he say, "You're about thirty years too late, Mama"?
5. **A Broader Perspective** • This story shows how a misunderstanding can wound a person for life. What is ironic (see Glossary) about Charles's long suffering? Is there any reason to believe, by the end

of the story, that he has recognized his mistake in judgment? (The answer to this question might have been clearer if Charles had been made the narrator of the story. Instead, the author chose to tell it from Chig's point of view. What do you think was his reason?)

The Gift

JOHN STEINBECK

At daybreak Billy Buck emerged from the bunkhouse and stood for a moment on the porch looking up at the sky. He was a broad, bandy-legged little man with a walrus mustache, with square hands, puffed and muscled on the palms. His eyes were a contemplative, watery gray and the hair which protruded from under his Stetson hat was spiky and weathered. Billy was still stuffing his shirt into his blue jeans as he stood on the porch. He unbuckled his belt and tightened it again. The belt showed, by the worn shiny places opposite each hole, the gradual increase of Billy's middle over a period of years. When he had seen to the weather, Billy cleared each nostril by holding its mate closed with his forefinger and blowing fiercely. Then he walked down to the barn, rubbing his hands together. He curried and brushed two saddle horses in the stalls, talking quietly to them all the time; and he had hardly finished when the iron triangle started ringing at the ranch house. Billy stuck the brush and currycomb together and laid them on the rail, and went up to breakfast. His action had been so deliberate and yet so wasteless of time that he came to the house while Mrs. Tiflin was still ringing the triangle. She nodded her gray head to him and withdrew into the kitchen. Billy Buck sat down on the steps, because he was a cow-hand, and it wouldn't be fitting that he should go first into the dining-room. He heard Mr. Tiflin in the house, stamping his feet into his boots.

The high jangling note of the triangle put the boy Jody in motion. He was only a little boy, ten years old, with hair like dusty yellow grass and with shy polite gray eyes, and with a mouth that worked when he thought. The triangle picked him up out of sleep. It didn't occur to him to disobey the harsh note. He never had: no one he knew ever had. He brushed the tangled hair out of his eyes and skinned his nightgown off. In a moment he was dressed — blue chambray shirt and overalls. It was late in the summer, so of course there were no shoes to bother with. In the kitchen he waited until his mother got from in front of the sink and went back to the stove. Then he washed himself and brushed back his wet hair with his fingers. His mother turned sharply on him as he left the sink. Jody looked shyly away.

"I've got to cut your hair before long," his mother said. "Breakfast's on the table. Go on in, so Billy can come."

Jody sat at the long table which was covered with white oilcloth washed through to the fabric in some places. The fried eggs lay in rows on their platter. Jody took three eggs on his plate and followed with three thick slices of crisp bacon. He carefully scraped a spot of blood from one of the egg yolks.

Billy Buck clumped in. "That won't hurt you," Billy explained. "That's only a sign the rooster leaves."

Jody's tall stern father came in then and Jody knew from the noise on the floor that he was wearing boots, but he looked under the table anyway, to make sure. His father turned off the oil lamp over the table, for plenty of morning light now came through the windows.

Jody did not ask where his father and Billy Buck were riding that day, but he wished he might go along. His father was a disciplinarian. Jody obeyed him in everything without questions of any kind. Now, Carl Tiflin sat down and reached for the egg platter.

"Got the cows ready to go, Billy?" he asked.

"In the lower corral," Billy said. "I could just as well take them in alone."

"Sure you could. But a man needs company. Besides your throat gets pretty dry." Carl Tiflin was jovial this morning.

Jody's mother put her head in the door. "What time do you think to be back, Carl?"

"I can't tell. I've got to see some men in Salinas.[1] Might be gone till dark."

The eggs and coffee and big biscuits disappeared rapidly. Jody followed the two men out of the house. He watched them mount their horses and drive six old milk cows out of the corral and start over the hill toward Salinas. They were going to sell the old cows to the butcher.

When they had disappeared over the crown of the ridge Jody walked up the hill in back of the house. The dogs trotted around the house corner hunching their shoulders and grinning horribly with pleasure. Jody patted their heads — Doubletree Mutt with the big thick tail and yellow eyes, and Smasher, the shepherd, who had killed a coyote and lost an ear in doing it. Smasher's one good ear stood up higher than a collie's ear should. Billy Buck said that always happened. After the frenzied greeting the dogs lowered their noses to the ground in a businesslike way and went ahead, looking back now and then to make sure that the boy was coming. They walked up through the chicken yard and saw the quail eating with the chickens. Smasher chased the chickens a little to keep in practice in case there should ever be sheep to herd. Jody continued on through the large vegetable patch where the green corn was higher than his head. The cow-pumpkins were green and small yet. He went on to the sage-brush line where the cold spring ran out of its pipe and fell into a round wooden tub. He leaned over and drank close to the green mossy wood where the water tasted best. Then he turned and looked back on the ranch, on the low, whitewashed house girded with red geraniums, and on the long bunkhouse by the cypress tree where Billy Buck lived alone. Jody could see the great black kettle under the cypress tree. That was where the pigs were scalded. The sun was coming over the ridge now, glaring on the whitewash of the houses and barns, making the wet grass blaze softly. Behind him, in the tall sagebrush, the birds were scampering on the ground, making a great noise

[1] **Salinas** (sə · lē′nəs): town in central California.

among the dry leaves; the squirrels piped shrilly on the side-hills. Jody looked along at the farm buildings. He felt an uncertainty in the air, a feeling of change and of loss and of the gain of new and unfamiliar things. Over the hillside two big black buzzards sailed low to the ground and their shadows slipped smoothly and quickly ahead of them. Some animal had died in the vicinity. Jody knew it. It might be a cow or it might be the remains of a rabbit. The buzzards overlooked nothing. Jody hated them as all decent things hate them, but they could not be hurt because they made away with carrion.[2]

After a while the boy sauntered down hill again. The dogs had long ago given him up and gone into the brush to do things in their own way. Back through the vegetable garden he went, and he paused for a moment to smash a green muskmelon with his heel, but he was not happy about it. It was a bad thing to do, he knew perfectly well. He kicked dirt over the ruined melon to conceal it.

Back at the house his mother bent over his rough hands, inspecting his fingers and nails. It did little good to start him clean to school for too many things could happen on the way. She sighed over the black cracks on his fingers, and then gave him his books and his lunch and started him on the mile walk to school. She noticed that his mouth was working a good deal this morning.

Jody started his journey. He filled his pockets with little pieces of white quartz that lay in the road, and every so often he took a shot at a bird or at some rabbit that had stayed sunning itself in the road too long. At the crossroads over the bridge he met two friends and the three of them walked to school together, making ridiculous strides and being rather silly. School had just opened two weeks before. There was still a spirit of revolt among the pupils.

It was four o'clock in the afternoon when Jody topped the hill and looked down on the ranch again. He looked for the saddle horses, but the corral was empty. His father was not back yet. He went slowly, then, toward the afternoon chores. At the ranch house, he found his mother sitting on the porch, mending socks.

[2] **carrion:** dead, rotting flesh.

"There's two doughnuts in the kitchen for you," she said. Jody slid to the kitchen, and returned with half of one of the doughnuts already eaten and his mouth full. His mother asked him what he had learned in school that day, but she didn't listen to his doughnut-muffled answer. She interrupted, "Jody, tonight see you fill the wood-box clear full. Last night you crossed the sticks and it wasn't only about half full. Lay the sticks flat tonight. And Jody, some of the hens are hiding eggs, or else the dogs are eating them. Look about in the grass and see if you can find any nests."

Jody, still eating, went out and did his chores. He saw the quail come down to eat with the chickens when he threw out the grain. For some reason his father was proud to have them come. He never allowed any shooting near the house for fear the quail might go away.

When the wood-box was full, Jody took his twenty-two rifle up to the cold spring at the brush line. He drank again and then aimed the gun at all manner of things, at rocks, at birds on the wing, at the big black pig kettle under the cypress tree, but he didn't shoot for he had no cartridges and wouldn't have until he was twelve. If his father had seen him aim the rifle in the direction of the house he would have put the cartridges off another year. Jody remembered this and did not point the rifle down the hill again. Two years was enough to wait for cartridges. Nearly all of his father's presents were given with reservations which hampered their value somewhat. It was good discipline.

The supper waited until dark for his father to return. When at last he came in with Billy Buck, Jody could smell the delicious brandy on their breaths. Inwardly he rejoiced, for his father sometimes talked to him when he smelled of brandy, sometimes even told things he had done in the wild days when he was a boy.

After supper, Jody sat by the fireplace and his shy polite eyes sought the room corners, and he waited for his father to tell what it was he contained, for Jody knew he had news of some sort. But he was disappointed. His father pointed a stern finger at him.

"You'd better go to bed, Jody. I'm going to need you in the morning."

That wasn't so bad. Jody liked to do the things he had to do as long as they weren't routine things. He looked at the floor and his mouth worked out a question before he spoke it. "What are we going to do in the morning, kill a pig?" he asked softly.

"Never you mind. You better get to bed."

When the door was closed behind him, Jody heard his father and Billy Buck chuckling and he knew it was a joke of some kind. And later, when he lay in bed, trying to make words out of the murmurs in the other room, he heard his father protest, "But, Ruth, I didn't give much for him."

Jody heard the hoot-owls hunting mice down by the barn, and he heard a fruit tree limb tap-tapping against the house. A cow was lowing when he went to sleep.

When the triangle sounded in the morning, Jody dressed more quickly even than usual. In the kitchen, while he washed his face and combed back his hair, his mother addressed him irritably. "Don't you go out until you get a good breakfast in you."

He went into the dining-room and sat at the long white table. He took a steaming hotcake from the platter, arranged two fried eggs on it, covered them with another hotcake and squashed the whole thing with his fork.

His father and Billy Buck came in. Jody knew from the sound on the floor that both of them were wearing flat-heeled shoes, but he peered under the table to make sure. His father turned off the oil lamp, for the day had arrived, and he looked stern and disciplinary, but Billy Buck didn't look at Jody at all. He avoided the shy questioning eyes of the boy and soaked a whole piece of toast in his coffee.

Carl Tiflin said crossly, "You come with us after breakfast!"

Jody had trouble with his food then, for he felt a kind of doom in the air. After Billy had tilted his saucer and drained the coffee which had slopped into it, and had wiped his hands on his jeans, the two men stood up from the table and went out into the morning light together, and Jody respectfully followed a little behind them. He tried to keep his mind from running ahead, tried to keep it absolutely motionless.

His mother called, "Carl! Don't you let it keep him from school."

They marched past the cypress, where a singletree[3] hung from a limb to butcher the pigs on, and past the black iron kettle, so it was not a pig killing. The sun shone over the hill and threw long, dark shadows of the trees and buildings. They crossed a stubble-field to shortcut to the barn. Jody's father unhooked the door and they went in. They had been walking toward the sun on the way down. The barn was black as night in contrast and warm from the hay and from the beasts. Jody's father moved over toward the one box stall. "Come here!" he ordered. Jody could begin to see things now. He looked into the box stall and then stepped back quickly.

A red pony colt was looking at him out of the stall. Its tense ears were forward and a light of disobedience was in its eyes. Its coat was rough and thick as an airedale's fur and its mane was long and tangled. Jody's throat collapsed in on itself and cut his breath short.

"He needs a good currying," his father said, "and if I ever hear of you not feeding him or leaving his stall dirty, I'll sell him off in a minute."

Jody couldn't bear to look at the pony's eyes any more. He gazed down at his hands for a moment, and he asked very shyly, "Mine?" No one answered him. He put his hand out toward the pony. Its gray nose came close, sniffing loudly, and then the lips drew back and the strong teeth closed on Jody's fingers. The pony shook its head up and down and seemed to laugh with amusement. Jody regarded his bruised fingers. "Well," he said with pride — "Well, I guess he can bite all right." The two men laughed, somewhat in relief. Carl Tiflin went out of the barn and walked up a side-hill to be by himself, for he was embarrassed, but Billy Buck stayed. It was easier to talk to Billy Buck. Jody asked again — "Mine?"

Billy became professional in tone. "Sure! That is, if you look out for him and break him right. I'll show you how. He's just a colt. You can't ride him for some time."

Jody put out his bruised hand again, and this time the red pony let his nose be rubbed. "I ought to have a carrot," Jody said. "Where'd we get him, Billy?"

"Bought him at a sheriff's auction," Billy explained. "A show

[3] **singletree:** swinging bar.

went broke in Salinas and had debts. The sheriff was selling off their stuff."

The pony stretched out his nose and shook the forelock from his wild eyes. Jody stroked the nose a little. He said softly, "There isn't a — saddle?"

Billy Buck laughed. "I'd forgot. Come along."

In the harness room he lifted down a little saddle of red morocco leather. "It's just a show saddle," Billy Buck said disparagingly. "It isn't practical for the brush, but it was cheap at the sale."

Jody couldn't trust himself to look at the saddle either, and he couldn't speak at all. He brushed the shining red leather with his fingertips, and after a long time he said, "It'll look pretty on him though." He thought of the grandest and prettiest things he knew. "If he hasn't a name already, I think I'll call him Gabilan Mountains," he said.

Billy Buck knew how he felt. "It's a pretty long name. Why don't you just call him Gabilan? That means hawk. That would be a fine name for him." Billy felt glad. "If you will collect tail hair, I might be able to make a hair rope for you sometime. You could use it for a hackamore."[4]

Jody wanted to go back to the box stall. "Could I lead him to school, do you think — to show the kids?"

But Billy shook his head. "He's not even halter-broke yet. We had a time getting him here. Had to almost drag him. You better be starting for school though."

"I'll bring the kids to see him here this afternoon," Jody said.

Six boys came over the hill half an hour early that afternoon, running hard, their heads down, their forearms working, their breath whistling. They swept by the house and cut across the stubble-field to the barn. And then they stood self-consciously before the pony, and then they looked at Jody with eyes in which there was a new admiration and a new respect. Before today Jody had been a boy, dressed in overalls and a blue shirt — quieter than most, even suspected of being a little cowardly. And now he was different. Out of a thousand centuries they drew the ancient admiration of the footman for the horseman. They knew instinctively that a man on a horse is spiritually

[4] **hackamore:** a kind of halter used in breaking horses.

as well as physically bigger than a man on foot. They knew that Jody had been miraculously lifted out of equality with them, and had been placed over them. Gabilan put his head out of the stall and sniffed them.

"Why'n't you ride him?" the boys cried. "Why'n't you braid his tail with ribbons like in the fair?" "When you going to ride him?"

Jody's courage was up. He too felt the superiority of the horseman. "He's not old enough. Nobody can ride him for a long time. I'm going to train him on the long halter. Billy Buck is going to show me how."

"Well, can't we even lead him around a little?"

"He isn't even halter-broke," Jody said. He wanted to be completely alone when he took the pony out the first time. "Come and see the saddle."

They were speechless at the red morocco saddle, completely shocked out of comment. "It isn't much use in the brush," Jody explained. "It'll look pretty on him though. Maybe I'll ride bareback when I go into the brush."

"How you going to rope a cow without a saddle horn?"

"Maybe I'll get another saddle for every day. My father might want me to help him with the stock." He let them feel the red saddle, and showed them the brass chain throat-latch on the bridle and the big brass buttons at each temple where the headstall and brow band crossed. The whole thing was too wonderful. They had to go away after a little while, and each boy, in his mind, searched among his possessions for a bribe worthy of offering in return for a ride on the red pony when the time should come.

Jody was glad when they had gone. He took brush and curry-comb from the wall, took down the barrier of the box stall and stepped cautiously in. The pony's eyes glittered, and he edged around into kicking position. But Jody touched him on the shoulder and rubbed his high arched neck as he had always seen Billy Buck do, and he crooned, "So-o-o, boy," in a deep voice. The pony gradually relaxed his tenseness. Jody curried and brushed until a pile of dead hair lay in the stall and until the pony's coat had taken on a deep red shine. Each time he finished he thought it might have been done better. He braided the mane into a dozen little pigtails, and he braided the forelock, and then he undid them and brushed the hair out straight again.

Jody did not hear his mother enter the barn. She was angry when she came, but when she looked in at the pony and at Jody working over him, she felt a curious pride rise up in her. "Have you forgot the wood-box?" she asked gently. "It's not far off from dark and there's not a stick of wood in the house, and the chickens aren't fed."

Jody quickly put up his tools. "I forgot, ma'am."

"Well, after this do your chores first. Then you won't forget. I expect you'll forget lots of things now if I don't keep an eye on you."

"Can I have carrots from the garden for him, ma'am?"

She had to think about that. "Oh — I guess so, if you only take the big tough ones."

"Carrots keep the coat good," he said, and again she felt the curious rush of pride.

Jody never waited for the triangle to get him out of bed after the coming of the pony. It became his habit to creep out of bed even before his mother was awake, to slip into his clothes and to go quietly down to the barn to see Gabilan. In the gray quiet mornings when the land and the brush and the houses and the trees were silver-gray and black like a photograph negative, he stole toward the barn, past the sleeping stones and the sleeping cypress tree. The turkeys, roosting in the tree out of coyotes' reach, clicked drowsily. The fields glowed with a gray frost-like light and in the dew the tracks of rabbits and of field mice stood out sharply. The good dogs came stiffly out of their little houses, hackles up and deep growls in their throats. Then they caught Jody's scent, and their stiff tails rose up and waved a greeting — Doubletree Mutt with the big thick tail, and Smasher, the incipient shepherd — then went lazily back to their warm beds.

It was a strange time and a mysterious journey, to Jody — an extension of a dream. When he first had the pony he liked to torture himself during the trip by thinking Gabilan would not be in his stall, and worse, would never have been there. And he had other delicious little self-induced pains. He thought how the rats had gnawed ragged holes in the red saddle, and how the mice had nibbled Gabilan's tail until it was stringy and thin. He usually ran the last little way to the barn. He unlatched the rusty hasp of the barn door and stepped in, and no matter how quietly he opened the door, Gabilan was always looking at him over the barrier of the box stall and Gabilan whinnied softly and stamped his front foot, and his eyes had big sparks of red fire in them like oakwood embers.

Sometimes, if the work horses were to be used that day, Jody found Billy Buck in the barn harnessing and currying. Billy stood with him and looked long at Gabilan and he told Jody a great many things about horses. He explained that they were terribly afraid for their feet, so that one must make a practice of lifting the legs and patting the hoofs and ankles to remove their terror. He told Jody how horses love conversation. He must talk to the pony all the time, and tell him the reasons for everything. Billy wasn't sure a horse could understand everything that was said to him, but it was impossible to say how much was understood. A horse never kicked up a fuss if someone he liked explained things to him. Billy could give examples, too. He had known, for instance, a horse nearly dead beat with fatigue to perk up when told it was only a little farther to his destination. And he had known a horse paralyzed with fright to come out of it when his rider told him what it was that was frightening him. While he talked in the mornings, Billy Buck cut twenty or thirty straws into neat three-inch lengths and stuck them into his hatband. Then during the whole day, if he wanted to pick his teeth or merely to chew on something, he had only to reach up for one of them.

Jody listened carefully, for he knew and the whole country knew that Billy Buck was a fine hand with horses. Billy's own horse was a stringy cayuse[5] with a hammer head, but he nearly always won the first prizes at the stock trials. Billy could rope a steer, take a double half-hitch about the horn with his riata,[6] and dismount, and his horse would play the steer as an angler plays a fish, keeping a tight rope until the steer was down or beaten.

Every morning, after Jody had curried and brushed the pony, he let down the barrier of the stall, and Gabilan thrust past him

[5] **cayuse:** contemptuous term for an inferior horse.
[6] **riata** (rē · ät′ə): lariat.

and raced down the barn and into the corral. Around and around he galloped, and sometimes he jumped forward and landed on stiff legs. He stood quivering, stiff ears forward, eyes rolling so that the whites showed, pretending to be frightened. At last he walked snorting to the water-trough and buried his nose in the water up to the nostrils. Jody was proud then, for he knew that was the way to judge a horse. Poor horses only touched their lips to the water, but a fine spirited beast put his whole nose and mouth under, and only left room to breathe.

Then Jody stood and watched the pony, and he saw things he had never noticed about any other horse, the sleek, sliding flank muscles and the cords of the buttocks, which flexed like a closing fist, and the shine the sun put on the red coat. Having seen horses all his life, Jody had never looked at them very closely before. But now he noticed the moving ears which gave expression and even inflection of expression to the face. The pony talked with his ears. You could tell exactly how he felt about everything by the way his ears pointed. Sometimes they were stiff and upright and sometimes lax and sagging. They went back when he was angry or fearful, and forward when he was anxious and curious and pleased; and their exact position indicated which emotion he had.

Billy Buck kept his word. In the early fall the training began. First there was the halter-breaking, and that was the hardest because it was the first thing. Jody held a carrot and coaxed and promised and pulled on the rope. The pony set his feet like a burro when he felt the strain. But before long he learned. Jody walked all over the ranch leading him. Gradually he took to dropping the rope until the pony followed him unled wherever he went.

And then came the training on the long halter. That was slower work. Jody stood in the middle of a circle, holding the long halter. He clucked with his tongue and the pony started to walk in a big circle, held in by the long rope. He clucked again to make the pony trot, and again to make him gallop. Around and around Gabilan went thundering and enjoying it immensely. Then he called, "Whoa," and the pony stopped. It was not long until Gabilan was perfect at it. But in many ways he was a bad pony. He bit Jody in the pants and stomped on Jody's feet.

Now and then his ears went back and he aimed a tremendous kick at the boy. Every time he did one of these bad things, Gabilan settled back and seemed to laugh to himself.

Billy Buck worked at the hair rope in the evenings before the fireplace. Jody collected tail hair in a bag, and he sat and watched Billy slowly constructing the rope, twisting a few hairs to make a string and rolling two strings together for a cord, and then braiding a number of cords to make the rope. Billy rolled the finished rope on the floor under his foot to make it round and hard.

The long halter work rapidly approached perfection. Jody's father, watching the pony stop and start and trot and gallop, was a little bothered by it.

"He's getting to be almost a trick pony," he complained. "I don't like trick horses. It takes all the — dignity out of a horse to make him do tricks. Why, a trick horse is kind of like an actor — no dignity, no character of his own." And his father said, "I guess you better be getting him used to the saddle pretty soon."

Jody rushed for the harness-room. For some time he had been riding the saddle on a sawhorse. He changed the stirrup length over and over, and could never get it just right. Sometimes, mounted on the sawhorse in the harness-room, with collars and hames and tugs[7] hung all about him, Jody rode out beyond the room. He carried his rifle across the pommel. He saw the fields go flying by, and he heard the beat of the galloping hoofs.

It was a ticklish job, saddling the pony the first time. Gabilan hunched and reared and threw the saddle off before the cinch could be tightened. It had to be replaced again and again until at last the pony let it stay. And the cinching was difficult, too. Day by day Jody tightened the girth a little more until at last the pony didn't mind the saddle at all.

Then there was the bridle. Billy explained how to use a stick of licorice for a bit until Gabilan was used to having something in his mouth. Billy explained, "Of course we could force-break

[7] **hames and tugs:** Hames are the curved pieces of metal or wood on a horse's collar to which the tugs, or straps, of a vehicle are attached.

him to everything, but he wouldn't be as good a horse if we did. He'd always be a little bit afraid, and he wouldn't mind because he wanted to."

The first time the pony wore the bridle he whipped his head about and worked his tongue against the bit until the blood oozed from the corners of his mouth. He tried to rub the head-stall off on the manger. His ears pivoted about and his eyes turned red with fear and with general rambunctiousness. Jody rejoiced, for he knew that only a mean-souled horse does not resent training.

And Jody trembled when he thought of the time when he would first sit in the saddle. The pony would probably throw him off. There was no disgrace in that. The disgrace would come if he did not get right up and mount again. Sometimes he dreamed that he lay in the dirt and cried and couldn't make himself mount again. The shame of the dream lasted until the middle of the day.

Gabilan was growing fast. Already he had lost the long-leggedness of the colt; his mane was getting longer and blacker. Under the constant currying and brushing his coat lay as smooth and gleaming as orange-red lacquer. Jody oiled the hoofs and kept them carefully trimmed so they would not crack.

The hair rope was nearly finished. Jody's father gave him an old pair of spurs and bent in the side bars and cut down the strap and took up the chainlets until they fitted. And then one day Carl Tiflin said:

"The pony's growing faster than I thought. I guess you can ride him by Thanksgiving. Think you can stick on?"

"I don't know," Jody said shyly. Thanksgiving was only three weeks off. He hoped it wouldn't rain, for rain would spot the red saddle.

Gabilan knew and liked Jody by now. He nickered when Jody came across the stubble-field, and in the pasture he came running when his master whistled for him. There was always a carrot for him every time.

Billy Buck gave him riding instructions over and over. "Now when you get up there, just grab tight with your knees and keep your hands away from the saddle, and if you get throwed, don't let that stop you. No matter how good a man is, there's always some horse can pitch him. You just climb up again before he

gets to feeling smart about it. Pretty soon, he won't throw you no more, and pretty soon he *can't* throw you no more. That's the way to do it."

"I hope it don't rain before," Jody said.

"Why not? Don't want to get throwed in the mud?"

That was partly it, and also he was afraid that in the flurry of bucking Gabilan might slip and fall on him and break his leg or his hip. He had seen that happen to men before, had seen how they writhed on the ground like squashed bugs, and he was afraid of it.

He practiced on the sawhorse how he would hold the reins in his left hand and a hat in his right hand. If he kept his hands thus busy, he couldn't grab the horn if he felt himself going off. He didn't like to think of what would happen if he did grab the horn. Perhaps his father and Billy Buck would never speak to him again, they would be so ashamed. The news would get about and his mother would be ashamed too. And in the schoolyard — it was too awful to contemplate.

He began putting his weight in a stirrup when Gabilan was saddled, but he didn't throw his leg over the pony's back. That was forbidden until Thanksgiving.

Every afternoon he put the red saddle on the pony and cinched it tight. The pony was learning already to fill his stomach out unnaturally large while the cinching was going on, and then to let it down when the straps were fixed. Sometimes Jody led him up to the brush line and let him drink from the round green tub, and sometimes he led him up through the stubble-field to the hilltop from which it was possible to see the white town of Salinas and the geometric fields of the great valley, and the oak trees clipped by the sheep. Now and then they broke through the brush and came to little cleared circles so hedged in that the world was gone and only the sky and the circle of brush were left from the old life. Gabilan liked these trips and showed it by keeping his head very high and by quivering his nostrils with interest. When the two came back from an expedition they smelled of the sweet sage they had forced through.

Time dragged on toward Thanksgiving, but winter came fast. The clouds swept down and hung all day over the land and brushed the hilltops, and the winds blew shrilly at night. All day the dry oak leaves drifted down from the trees until they covered the ground, and yet the trees were unchanged.

Jody had wished it might not rain before Thanksgiving, but it did. The brown earth turned dark and the trees glistened. The cut ends of the stubble turned black with mildew; the haystacks grayed from exposure to the damp, and on the roofs the moss, which had been all summer as gray as lizards, turned a brilliant yellow-green. During the week of rain, Jody kept the pony in the box stall out of the dampness, except for a little time after school when he took him out for exercise and to drink at the water-trough in the upper corral. Not once did Gabilan get wet.

The wet weather continued until little new grass appeared. Jody walked to school dressed in a slicker and short rubber boots. At length one morning the sun came out brightly. Jody, at his work in the box stall, said to Billy Buck, "Maybe I'll leave Gabilan in the corral when I go to school today."

"Be good for him to be out in the sun," Billy assured him. "No animal likes to be cooped up too long. Your father and me are going back on the hill to clean the leaves out of the spring." Billy nodded and picked his teeth with one of his little straws.

"If the rain comes, though —" Jody suggested.

"Not likely to rain today. She's rained herself out." Billy pulled up his sleeves and snapped his arm bands. "If it comes on to rain — why a little rain don't hurt a horse."

"Well, if it does come to rain, you put him in, will you, Billy? I'm scared he might get cold so I couldn't ride him when the time comes."

"Oh sure! I'll watch out for him if we get back in time. But it won't rain today."

And so Jody, when he went to school, left Gabilan standing out in the corral.

Billy Buck wasn't wrong about many things. He couldn't be. But he was wrong about the weather that day, for a little after noon the clouds pushed over the hills and the rain began to pour down. Jody heard it start on the schoolhouse roof. He considered holding up one finger for permission to go to the outhouse and, once outside, running for home to put the pony in. Punishment would be prompt both at school and at home. He gave it up and took ease from Billy's assurance that rain couldn't hurt a horse. When school was finally out, he hurried home through the dark rain. The banks at the sides of the road spouted little jets of muddy water. The rain slanted and swirled under a cold and gusty wind. Jody dog-trotted home, slopping through the gravelly mud of the road.

From the top of the ridge he could see Gabilan standing miserably in the corral. The red coat was almost black, and streaked with water. He stood head down with his rump to the rain and wind. Jody arrived running and threw open the barn door and led the wet pony in by his forelock. Then he found a gunny sack and rubbed the soaked hair and rubbed the legs and ankles. Gabilan stood patiently, but he trembled in gusts like the wind.

When he had dried the pony as well as he could, Jody went up to the house and brought hot water down to the barn and soaked the grain in it. Gabilan was not very hungry. He nibbled at the hot mash, but he was not very much interested in it, and he still shivered now and then. A little steam rose from his damp back.

It was almost dark when Billy Buck and Carl Tiflin came home. "When the rain started we put up at Ben Herche's place, and the rain never let up all afternoon," Carl Tiflin explained. Jody looked reproachfully at Billy Buck and Billy felt guilty.

"You said it wouldn't rain," Jody accused him.

Billy looked away. "It's hard to tell, this time of year," he said, but his excuse was lame. He had no right to be fallible, and he knew it.

"The pony got wet, got soaked through."

"Did you dry him off?"

"I rubbed him with a sack and I gave him hot grain."

Billy nodded in agreement.

"Do you think he'll take cold, Billy?"

"A little rain never hurt anything," Billy assured him.

Jody's father joined the conversation then and lectured the boy a little. "A horse," he said, "isn't any lap-dog kind of thing." Carl Tiflin hated weakness and sickness, and he held a violent contempt for helplessness.

Jody's mother put a platter of steaks on the table and boiled potatoes and boiled squash, which clouded the room with their steam. They sat down to eat. Carl Tiflin still grumbled about weakness put into animals and men by too much coddling.

Billy Buck felt bad about his mistake. "Did you blanket him?" he asked.

"No. I couldn't find any blanket. I laid some sacks over his back."

"We'll go down and cover him up after we eat, then." Billy felt better about it then. When Jody's father had gone in to the fire and his mother was washing dishes, Billy found and lighted a lantern. He and Jody walked through the mud to the barn. The barn was dark and warm and sweet. The horses still munched their evening hay. "You hold the lantern!" Billy ordered. And he felt the pony's legs and tested the heat of the flanks. He put his cheek against the pony's gray muzzle and then he rolled up the eyelids to look at the eyeballs and he lifted the lips to see the gums, and he put his fingers inside his ears. "He don't seem so chipper," Billy said. "I'll give him a rubdown."

Then Billy found a sack and rubbed the pony's legs violently and he rubbed the chest and the withers.[8] Gabilan was strangely spiritless. He submitted patiently to the rubbing. At last Billy brought an old cotton comforter from the saddle-room, and threw it over the pony's back and tied it at neck and chest with string.

"Now he'll be all right in the morning," Billy said.

Jody's mother looked up when he got back to the house. "You're late up from bed," she said. She held his chin in her hard hand and brushed the tangled hair out of his eyes and she said, "Don't worry about the pony. He'll be all right. Billy's as good as any horse doctor in the country."

Jody hadn't known she could see his worry. He pulled gently away from her and knelt down in front of the fireplace until it burned his stomach. He scorched himself through and then went in to bed, but it was a hard thing to go to sleep. He awakened after what seemed a long time. The room was dark but there was a grayness in the window like that which precedes the dawn. He got up and found his overalls and searched for the legs, and then the clock in the other room struck two. He laid his clothes down and got back into bed. It was broad daylight when he awakened again. For the first time he had slept through the ringing of the triangle. He leaped up, flung on his clothes and

[8] **withers:** the ridge between a horse's shoulders.

went out of the door still buttoning his shirt. His mother looked after him for a moment and then went quietly back to her work. Her eyes were brooding and kind. Now and then her mouth smiled a little but without changing her eyes at all.

Jody ran on toward the barn. Halfway there he heard the sound he dreaded, the hollow rasping cough of a horse. He broke into a sprint then. In the barn he found Billy Buck with the pony. Billy was rubbing its legs with his strong thick hands. He looked up and smiled gaily. "He just took a little cold," Billy said. "We'll have him out of it in a couple of days."

Jody looked at the pony's face. The eyes were half closed and the lids thick and dry. In the eye corners a crust of hard mucus stuck. Gabilan's ears hung loosely sideways and his head was low. Jody put out his hand, but the pony did not move close to it. He coughed again and his whole body constricted with the effort. A little stream of thin fluid ran from his nostrils.

Jody looked back at Billy Buck. "He's awful sick, Billy."

"Just a little cold, like I said," Billy insisted. "You go get some breakfast and then go back to school. I'll take care of him."

"But you might have to do something else. You might leave him."

"No, I won't. I won't leave him at all. Tomorrow's Saturday. Then you can stay with him all day." Billy had failed again, and he felt badly about it. He had to cure the pony now.

Jody walked up to the house and took his place listlessly at the table. The eggs and bacon were cold and greasy, but he didn't notice it. He ate his usual amount. He didn't even ask to stay home from school. His mother pushed his hair back when she took his plate. "Billy'll take care of the pony," she assured him.

He moped through the whole day at school. He couldn't answer any questions nor read any words. He couldn't even tell anyone the pony was sick, for that might make him sicker. And when school was finally out he started home in dread. He walked slowly and let the other boys leave him. He wished he might continue walking and never arrive at the ranch.

Billy was in the barn, as he had promised, and the pony was worse. His eyes were almost closed now, and his breath whistled shrilly past an obstruction in his nose. A film covered that part of the eyes that was visible at all. It was doubtful whether the pony could see any more. Now and then he snorted, to clear his nose, and by the action seemed to plug it tighter. Jody looked dispiritedly at the pony's coat. The hair lay rough and unkempt and seemed to have lost all of its old luster. Billy stood quietly beside the stall. Jody hated to ask, but he had to know.

"Billy, is he — is he going to get well?"

Billy put his fingers between the bars under the pony's jaw and felt about. "Feel here," he said and he guided Jody's fingers to a large lump under the jaw. "When that gets bigger, I'll open it up and then he'll get better."

Jody looked quickly away, for he had heard about that lump. "What is it the matter with him?"

Billy didn't want to answer, but he had to. He couldn't be wrong three times. "Strangles," he said shortly, "but don't you worry about that. I'll pull him out of it. I've seen them get well when they were worse than Gabilan is. I'm going to steam him now. You can help."

"Yes," Jody said miserably. He followed Billy into the grain room and watched him make the steaming bag ready. It was a long canvas nose bag with straps to go over a horse's ears. Billy filled it one-third full of bran and then he added a couple of handfuls of dried hops. On top of the dry substance he poured a little carbolic acid and a little turpentine. "I'll be mixing it all up while you run to the house for a kettle of boiling water," Billy said.

When Jody came back with the steaming kettle, Billy buckled the straps over Gabilan's head and fitted the bag tightly around his nose. Then through a little hole in the side of the bag he poured the boiling water on the mixture. The pony started away as a cloud of strong steam rose up, but then the soothing fumes crept through his nose and into his lungs, and the sharp steam began to clear out the nasal passages. He breathed loudly. His legs trembled in an ague, and his eyes closed against the biting cloud. Billy poured in more water and kept the steam rising for fifteen minutes. At last he set down the kettle and took the bag from Gabilan's nose. The pony looked better. He breathed freely, and his eyes were open wider than they had been.

"See how good it makes him feel," Billy said. "Now we'll wrap him up in the blanket again. Maybe he'll be nearly well by morning."

"I'll stay with him tonight," Jody suggested.

"No. Don't you do it. I'll bring my blankets down here and

put them in the hay. You can stay tomorrow and steam him if he needs it."

The evening was falling when they went to the house for their supper. Jody didn't even realize that someone else had fed the chickens and filled the wood-box. He walked up past the house to the dark brush line and took a drink of water from the tub. The spring water was so cold that it stung his mouth and drove a shiver through him. The sky above the hills was still light. He saw a hawk flying so high that it caught the sun on its breast and shone like a spark. Two blackbirds were driving him down the sky, glittering as they attacked their enemy. In the west, the clouds were moving in to rain again.

Jody's father didn't speak at all while the family ate supper, but after Billy Buck had taken his blankets and gone to sleep in the barn, Carl Tiflin built a high fire in the fireplace and told stories. He told about the wild man who ran naked through the country and had a tail and ears like a horse, and he told about the rabbit-cats of Moro Cojo that hopped into the trees for birds. He revived the famous Maxwell brothers who found a vein of gold and hid the traces of it so carefully that they could never find it again.

Jody sat with his chin in his hands; his mouth worked nervously, and his father gradually became aware that he wasn't listening very carefully. "Isn't that funny?" he asked.

Jody laughed politely and said, "Yes, sir." His father was angry and hurt, then. He didn't tell any more stories. After a while, Jody took a lantern and went down to the barn. Billy Buck was asleep in the hay, and, except that his breath rasped a little in his lungs, the pony seemed to be much better. Jody stayed a little while, running his fingers over the red rough coat, and then he took up the lantern and went back to the house. When he was in bed, his mother came into the room.

"Have you enough covers on? It's getting winter."

"Yes, ma'am."

"Well, get some rest tonight." She hesitated to go out, stood uncertainly. "The pony will be all right," she said.

Jody was tired. He went to sleep quickly and didn't awaken until dawn. The triangle sounded, and Billy Buck came up from the barn before Jody could get out of the house.

"How is he?" Jody demanded.

Billy always wolfed his breakfast. "Pretty good. I'm going to open that lump this morning. Then he'll be better maybe."

After breakfast, Billy got out his best knife, one with a needle point. He whetted the shining blade a long time on a little carborundum stone. He tried the point and the blade again and again on his calloused thumb-ball, and at last he tried it on his upper lip.

On the way to the barn, Jody noticed how the young grass was up and how the stubble was melting day by day into the new green crop of volunteer.[9] It was a cold sunny morning.

As soon as he saw the pony, Jody knew he was worse. His eyes were closed and sealed shut with dried mucus. His head hung so low that his nose almost touched the straw of his bed. There was a little groan in each breath, a deep-seated, patient groan.

Billy lifted the weak head and made a quick slash with the knife. Jody saw the yellow pus run out. He held up the head while Billy swabbed out the wound with weak carbolic acid salve.

"Now he'll feel better," Billy assured him. "That yellow poison is what makes him sick."

Jody looked unbelieving at Billy Buck. "He's awful sick."

Billy thought a long time what to say. He nearly tossed off a careless assurance, but he saved himself in time. "Yes, he's pretty sick," he said at last. "I've seen worse ones get well. If he doesn't get pneumonia, we'll pull him through. You stay with him. If he gets worse, you can come and get me."

For a long time after Billy went away, Jody stood beside the pony, stroking him behind the ears. The pony didn't flip his head the way he had done when he was well. The groaning in his breathing was becoming more hollow.

Doubletree Mutt looked into the barn, his big tail waving provocatively, and Jody was so incensed at his health that he found a hard black clod on the floor and deliberately threw it. Doubletree Mutt went yelping away to nurse a bruised paw.

In the middle of the morning, Billy Buck came back and made another steam bag. Jody watched to see whether the pony improved this time as he had before. His breathing eased a little, but he did not raise his head.

[9] **volunteer:** plants growing from self-sown seeds.

The Saturday dragged on. Late in the afternoon Jody went to the house and brought his bedding down and made up a place to sleep in the hay. He didn't ask permission. He knew from the way his mother looked at him that she would let him do almost anything. That night he left a lantern burning on a wire over the box stall. Billy had told him to rub the pony's legs every little while.

At nine o'clock the wind sprang up and howled around the barn. And in spite of his worry, Jody grew sleepy. He got into his blankets and went to sleep, but the breathy groans of the pony sounded in his dreams. And in his sleep he heard a crashing noise which went on and on until it awakened him. The wind was rushing through the barn. He sprang up and looked down the lane of stalls. The barn door had blown open, and the pony was gone.

He caught the lantern and ran outside into the gale, and he saw Gabilan weakly shambling away into the darkness, head down, legs working slowly and mechanically. When Jody ran up and caught him by the forelock, he allowed himself to be led back and put into his stall. His groans were louder, and a fierce whistling came from his nose. Jody didn't sleep any more then. The hissing of the pony's breath grew louder and sharper.

He was glad when Billy Buck came in at dawn. Billy looked for a time at the pony as though he had never seen him before. He felt the ears and flanks. "Jody," he said, "I've got to do something you won't want to see. You run up to the house for a while."

Jody grabbed him fiercely by the forearm. "You're not going to shoot him?"

Billy patted his hand. "No. I'm going to open a little hole in his windpipe so he can breathe. His nose is filled up. When he gets well, we'll put a little brass button in the hole for him to breathe through."

Jody couldn't have gone away if he had wanted to. It was awful to see the red hide cut, but infinitely more terrible to know it was being cut and not to see it. "I'll stay right here," he said bitterly. "You sure you got to?"

"Yes, I'm sure. If you stay, you can hold his head. If it doesn't make you sick, that is."

The fine knife came out again and was whetted again just as carefully as it had been the first time. Jody held the pony's head up and the throat taut, while Billy felt up and down for the right place. Jody sobbed once as the bright knife point disappeared into the throat. The pony plunged weakly away and then stood still, trembling violently. The blood ran thickly out and up the knife and across Billy's hand and into his shirtsleeve. The sure square hand sawed out a round hole in the flesh, and the breath came bursting out of the hole, throwing a fine spray of blood. With the rush of oxygen, the pony took a sudden strength. He lashed out with his hind feet and tried to rear, but Jody held his head down while Billy mopped the new wound with carbolic salve. It was a good job. The blood stopped flowing and the air puffed out the hole and sucked it in regularly with a little bubbling noise.

The rain brought in by the night wind began to fall on the barn roof. Then the triangle rang for breakfast. "You go up and eat while I wait," Billy said. "We've got to keep this hole from plugging up."

Jody walked slowly out of the barn. He was too dispirited to tell Billy how the barn door had blown open and let the pony out. He emerged into the wet gray morning and sloshed up to the house, taking a perverse pleasure in splashing through all the puddles. His mother fed him and put dry clothes on. She didn't question him. She seemed to know he couldn't answer questions. But when he was ready to go back to the barn she brought him a pan of steaming meal. "Give him this," she said.

But Jody did not take the pan. He said, "He won't eat anything," and ran out of the house. At the barn, Billy showed him how to fix a ball of cotton on a stick, with which to swab out the breathing hole when it became clogged with mucus.

Jody's father walked into the barn and stood with them in front of the stall. At length he turned to the boy. "Hadn't you better come with me? I'm going to drive over the hill." Jody shook his head. "You better come on, out of this," his father insisted.

Billy turned on him angrily. "Let him alone. It's his pony, isn't it?"

Carl Tiflin walked away without saying another word. His feelings were badly hurt.

All morning Jody kept the wound open and the air passing in and out freely. At noon the pony lay wearily down on his side and stretched his nose out.

Billy came back. "If you're going to stay with him tonight, you better take a little nap," he said. Jody went absently out of the barn. The sky had cleared to a hard thin blue. Everywhere the birds were busy with worms that had come to the damp surface of the ground.

Jody walked to the brush line and sat on the edge of the mossy tub. He looked down at the house and at the old bunkhouse and at the dark cypress tree. The place was familiar, but curiously changed. It wasn't itself any more, but a frame for things that were happening. A cold wind blew out of the east now, signifying that the rain was over for a little while. At his feet Jody could see the little arms of new weeds spreading out over the ground. In the mud about the spring were thousands of quail tracks.

Doubletree Mutt came sideways and embarrassed up through the vegetable patch, and Jody, remembering how he had thrown the clod, put his arm about the dog's neck and kissed him on his wide black nose. Doubletree Mutt sat still, as though he knew some solemn thing was happening. His big tail slapped the ground gravely. Jody pulled a swollen tick out of Mutt's neck and popped it dead between his thumb-nails. It was a nasty thing. He washed his hands in the cold spring water.

Except for the steady swish of the wind, the farm was very quiet. Jody knew his mother wouldn't mind if he didn't go in to eat his lunch. After a little while he went slowly back to the barn. Mutt crept into his own little house and whined softly to himself for a long time.

Billy Buck stood up from the box and surrendered the cotton swab. The pony still lay on his side and the wound in his throat bellowsed in and out. When Jody saw how dry and dead the hair looked, he knew at last that there was no hope for the pony. He had seen the dead hair before on dogs and on cows, and it was a sure sign. He sat heavily on the box and let down the barrier of the box stall. For a long time he kept his eyes on the moving wound, and at last he dozed, and the afternoon passed quickly. Just before dark his mother brought a deep dish of stew and left it for him and went away. Jody ate a little of it, and, when it was dark, he set the lantern on the floor by the pony's head so he could watch the wound and keep it open. And he dozed again until the night chill awakened him. The wind was blowing fiercely, bringing the north cold with it. Jody brought a blanket from his bed in the hay and wrapped himself in it. Gabilan's breathing was quiet at last; the hole in his throat moved gently. The owls flew through the hayloft, shrieking and looking for mice. Jody put his hands down on his head and slept. In his sleep he was aware that the wind had increased. He heard it slamming about the barn.

It was daylight when he awakened. The barn door had swung open. The pony was gone. He sprang up and ran out into the morning light.

The pony's tracks were plain enough, dragging through the frostlike dew on the young grass, tired tracks with little lines between them where the hoofs had dragged. They headed for the brush line halfway up the ridge. Jody broke into a run and followed them. The sun shone on the sharp white quartz that stuck through the ground here and there. As he followed the plain trail, a shadow cut across in front of him. He looked up and saw a high circle of black buzzards, and the slowly revolving circle dropped lower and lower. The solemn birds soon disappeared over the ridge. Jody ran faster then, forced on by panic and rage. The trail entered the brush at last and followed a winding route among the tall sagebrushes.

At the top of the ridge Jody was winded. He paused, puffing noisily. The blood pounded in his ears. Then he saw what he was looking for. Below, in one of the little clearings in the brush, lay the red pony. In the distance, Jody could see the legs moving slowly and convulsively. And in a circle around him stood the buzzards, waiting for the moment of death they know so well.

Jody leaped forward and plunged down the hill. The wet ground muffled his steps and the brush hid him. When he arrived, it was all over. The first buzzard sat on the pony's head and its beak had just risen dripping with dark eye fluid. Jody plunged into the circle like a cat. The black brotherhood arose in a cloud, but the big one on the pony's head was too late. As it hopped along to take off, Jody caught its wing tip and pulled it down. It was nearly as big as he was. The free wing crashed into his face with the force of a club, but he hung on. The claws fastened on his leg and the wing elbows battered his head on either side. Jody groped blindly with his free hand. His fingers found the neck of the struggling bird. The red eyes looked into his face, calm and fearless and fierce; the naked head turned from side to side. Then the beak opened and vomited a stream of putrefied fluid. Jody brought up his knee and fell on the great bird. He held the neck to the ground with one hand while his other found a piece of sharp white quartz. The first blow broke the beak sideways and black blood spurted from the twisted, leathery mouth corners. He struck again and missed. The red fearless eyes still looked at him, impersonal and unafraid and detached. He struck again and again, until the buzzard lay dead, until its head was a red pulp. He was still beating the dead bird when Billy Buck pulled him off and held him tightly to calm his shaking.

Carl Tiflin wiped the blood from the boy's face with a red bandana. Jody was limp and quiet now. His father moved the buzzard with his toe. "Jody," he explained, "the buzzard didn't kill the pony. Don't you know that?"

"I know it," Jody said wearily.

It was Billy Buck who was angry. He had lifted Jody in his arms, and had turned to carry him home. But he turned back on Carl Tiflin. "'Course he knows it," Billy said furiously. "Jesus Christ! man, can't you see how he'd feel about it?"

* * *

EXAMINING THE STORY

1. Who is to blame, and in what ways, for the death of the pony? Can you find the seeds of the pony's death in Billy Buck's status (he waits to enter the dining room until Jody has entered) and in Carl Tiflin's attitude (shown by his greeting when he comes in to breakfast)?
2. Carl Tiflin does not want Gabilan to be a trick pony. Why? In what ways does he demonstrate his belief that "coddling" causes weakness? Yet Carl tells stories to Jody on the night Billy Buck nurses the pony and, while the pony lies dying, tries to get Jody to leave the barn. Why? Why do all Carl's efforts fail with Jody?
3. How does Billy Buck's approach to boys and horses contrast with Carl Tiflin's? Explain why Billy becomes more and more open with Jody as the pony's condition grows worse. What does Billy give to Jody throughout the story? Is this gift — like those of Jody's father — given "with reservations"?
4. During the story Jody crushes a muskmelon, stones Doubletree Mutt, and kills a buzzard. What idea does each of these represent

to him? Which is most important to him? What does he hope to accomplish by attacking these things? Do his attacks serve any purpose?

5. **A Broader Perspective** • On the morning the story begins, Jody feels "an uncertainty in the air, a feeling of change and of loss and of gain." These words define something in autumn itself. Do they, in addition, anticipate the events of the story? What does Jody lose? Does he gain anything? The pony crystallizes Jody's awareness of many of life's elements — good and bad. What different meanings, therefore, are suggested by the words of the title?

THE READER'S ART

Judging the Story as a Whole

It is possible to judge stories in terms of readers' rights. The reader has the right to expect understandable characters in action which is purposeful and believably motivated. He has the right to know why things happen and, on looking back, to find that they could not have happened otherwise. He has the right to expect that the promises, especially of mood and tone, made at the beginning of the story will be kept. He has the right to a story which moves quickly enough to be interesting, moves honestly — without blind alleys or loose ends or waste — and is long enough to be satisfying. He has the right to language which is clear and adequate, conveying experience without calling attention to itself. In all, he has the right to a literary work in which the elements fuse to create a new reality in his imagination — one that will extend his awareness and enlarge his understanding.

These rights of the reader imply, of course, certain responsibilities. First is the responsibility to read attentively. Another is to read with an open mind and willing heart about people and ideas which may be unfamiliar. The reader has the responsibility to learn the skills of the reading game: how to discover theme, how to interpret structure and symbol, how to recognize mood and tone. Finally, he has the responsibility to think over the story as a whole, both in its inner relationships and in its relation to life. How well do the parts combine to make the story? Does the story say something significant about the way life has been, or may be, lived?

Not until these questions have been carefully answered is the reader ready to ask the ultimate questions of taste and judgment: Do I like this story? and, Is this worthwhile as literature? Experienced readers know that the answers they give to these two questions are not always the same; such readers are careful to distinguish between taste and judgment.

FOR WRITING

1. In each of the stories in this group, a boy suffers — and learns something important. Compare the experiences of these boys and the new understandings they achieve. Is it necessary to suffer in order to grow? Use these stories, or other illustrations, to defend your answer.

2. Examine any of the stories in this book in the light of the following standards:
   (a) Is the story well paced? (That is, do the description and explanation make the action clear, without delaying it unnecessarily?)
   (b) Is all the action relevant to the theme? (Could any part of the story be omitted without significant loss?)
   (c) Are the characters understandable? self-consistent? worth writing about?
   (d) Are the elements so well fused that any change affects them all? (Or could one element — for example, setting — be changed without affecting the other elements — for example, characters or action?)
   (e) Does the language of the story contribute to the meaning? (Does language serve, for example, to characterize the narrator, heighten the mood, or establish the author's tone?)
   (f) Is the theme of the story universal — that is, does it apply, when stated in general terms, to other people and other circumstances? Could another story be written to illustrate the same theme?

   Write an original story which provides an answer to one of the thematic questions preceding each group of stories.

GLOSSARY OF LITERARY TERMS

action: the series of events of which a story is composed. The term may refer to the characters' thoughts, feelings, and words as well as to their physical movements.

allegory: a narrative in which all the characters, actions, objects, and settings stand for religious or political ideas.

anticlimax: an abrupt shift in a story from the important to the insignificant, with a disappointing or amusing effect.

atmosphere: the air, or mood, which prevails at any moment in a story. (See *mood, effect.*)

character: a person in a story. (An animal or thing may also be thought of as a character.)

A *consistent* character is one whose continuing actions conform to what the author has already revealed about him.

A *static* character does not change in the course of a story.

A *dynamic* character changes; he is affected by the events in a story.

A *flat* character is one who is represented as having only a single "side" or trait, and whose behavior is therefore predictable and possibly allegorical.

A *round* character seems as many-sided, and therefore believable, as a person in real life.

characterization: the revelation and development of character. In fiction, a person is characterized chiefly by his own words and actions and by other people's responses to him.

climax: the moment of highest interest and tension in a story.

conflict: the underlying struggle which the action of a story expresses. A character may be opposed by other persons, or by a force such as nature or fate; or he may be troubled by his own divided purposes.

denouement: the unraveling of the complications of a story; the ending.

description: In the form of setting, description establishes the time and place in which the characters act. Description also serves to delineate character and action.

dialogue: spoken words exchanged between two or more characters in a story.

effect: the final impression produced in the reader by the story. The effect may be such an emotion as horror, awareness of irony, or a delight in beauty. Every detail of a well-written story contributes to its total effect.

elements of fiction: the basic ingredients of a story, including character, motivation, action, setting, and implements used to carry out the action. Distinct from the treatment of these elements (see *tone, mood, structure, theme,* and *moral*).

episode: an incident — usually one of a series — in a story.

expectation and **fulfillment:** Details mentioned early in a story may create in the reader expectations of things to come. In the well-written story, the reader's legitimate expectations will be fulfilled.

fantasy: a kind of fiction in which the author's imagination is freed from the restrictions of physical reality. Despite improbable settings and situations, fantasy can convey serious ideas.

flashback: a narrative technique in which the chronological order of events is interrupted in order to relate an earlier event.

frame: a story that contains another story or series of stories. The opening section of the story — the "frame" — establishes a situation from which the main episode is launched and to which it returns.

image: a sight, sound, or other sensory impression conveyed by the words of the author. Metaphorical language makes use of images.

irony: a contradiction between the anticipated and the actual outcome of a situation (dramatic irony) or between the literal and the intended meanings of words (verbal irony).

locale: the place in which the action of a story occurs.

mood (atmosphere): the predominant emotion that a story arouses in the reader. The mood is established by all the other elements of the story in combination.

moral: the implied judgment of behavior made by a story. Distinct from theme.

motivation: the wants or drives which determine a character's behavior.

narrative: an action, related; a story.

parable: a short allegory told to explain or illustrate an idea.

plot: the sequence in which the events of a story take place.

point of view: the position, or viewpoint, from which the events of a story are seen and told.

First-person narration ("I") is by a character who is taking a part or is a bystander in the story.

third-person narration ("he") records events as observed by the eyes and mind of one character in the story.

Omniscient ("all-knowing") narration places the storyteller above all the characters so that he can reveal what any of them may be thinking or doing.

realism: the objective and materialistic portrayal of reality. A realistic story is usually concerned with ordinary people, events, and places. Among the techniques of realism are detailed physical descriptions, references to actual events, and the use of letters and other documents.

romanticism: an attitude, especially in literature, which pictures man as he would like to be, rather than as he is. Contrasted with realism.

satire: a literary work that ridicules behavior in order to correct it.

scene: an episode in a story, presented in a dramatic way — that is, with dialogue and detail that create immediacy, like a play.

setting: the time and place in which the action of a story occurs.

stream-of-consciousness: a fictional attempt to imitate the structure of consciousness by recording the sights, sounds, recollections, and moods that pass through a character's mind.

structure: the plan or framework of a story, created by the author's selection and arrangement of events.

style: the manner in which a writer uses words to relate his story. Style consists of word choice, syntax and sentence structure, and use of metaphorical language. Style is also determined by the form and materials of the work, the author's attitude toward it, and the audience for which it is intended.

symbol: in a general sense, an object that suggests something beyond itself. In fiction, a character, thing, setting, or action may suggest a larger meaning or an idea.

theme: the statement about life in general implied by the central action of a story; the point. The observation may be of cause and effect, conditions, or situations in human life; it is distinct from the *moral*.

tone: the author's attitude toward the reader and toward the characters and events he is describing. In fiction, tone must be inferred from the situation and the author's choice of words.

VWXYZ-A-93210/89